Electrical installation and workshop technology

Volume two
(Fourth Edition)

F. G. Thompson, I.Eng.FIElecIE, LCG
Senior Lecturer, Department of Technology
Lews Castle College, Stornoway

Illustrations by
H. E. MacDonnell

Longman Scientific & Technical,
Longman Group UK Limited,
Longman House, Burnt Mill, Harlow,
Essex CM20 2JE, England
and Associated Companies throughout the world.

First published 1969
Second edition Metric 1975
Third edition 1983
Second impression published by Longman Scientific & Technical 1987
Third impression 1991
Fourth edition 1992

British Library Cataloguing in Publication Data
A catalogue record for this book is available from the British Library.

ISBN 0–582–08559–4

Set in Compugraphic Times 10/12 pt
Printed in Malaysia by CL

In memoriam

James H. Smith, R.I.P.

Late, Inverness Technical College

Contents

List of illustrations

Preface

This textbook is intended mainly for students who are studying the City and Guilds Course 236, Part II, leading to the award of the Electrician's Certificate. The possessor of this certificate is now being designated in industry as an Approved Electrician, indicating a degree of background knowledge of the field of activity known as electrical installation engineering. This field is now emerging from obscurity and is being recognised as an important branch of electrical engineering and of the construction industry.

The engineering content of the book is aimed at those students whose work lies more in the field of electrical maintenance, who will find the material of this book generally useful for the wider appreciation of the installation engineering elements in their chosen specialist fields.

The book has been designed as a follow-on to more advanced material than is contained in the author's Volume I on the same subject. But the book can be used on its own for that part of the Course 236, Part II examination dealing with the subject of Electrical Installation Technology and Practice.

Although much of the material of this book has been presented in a non-technical manner, it is recommended that for a full appreciation of the material, the student obtain a good book on electrical science. Only with a sound background of theory can the student and trainee electrical installation engineer ever hope to progress in his career.

The author wishes to record his thanks to those who helped in one way or another the progress of the book to its completion. Thanks are also due to the following for permission to include some of their illustrative and other matter in this book:

City and Guilds of London Institute
Institution of Electrical Engineers
Association of Supervisory and Executive Engineers
British Standards Institution
British Insulated Callenders Cables Limited
Davis Sheet-metal Engineering Co. Limited
Messrs Ecko-Ensign Limited
J.A. Crabtree & Co. Limited
Walsall Conduits Limited
Evershed & Vignoles Limited
Messrs Klockner-Möeller
Thorn Lighting Limited

Part A

Electrical installation technology

1 Installation regulations

The rules and regulations which govern the practice of electrical installation engineering are essential to ensure that all electrical installations provide an adequate degree of safety from fire and shock risks to those who operate the installations and their associated apparatus, equipment and machines. The general requirement of every electrician is that he be familiar with the principal set of regulations which is issued by the Institution of Electrical Engineers: 'Regulations for Electrical Installations'. The electrician is also required to be familiar with the main requirements of other regulations, some of which are statutory, which means that they form an integral part of the industrial law of the country and must be observed. The essence of these statutory regulations is embodied in the IEE Regulations. Guidance on specific points of installation, choice of electrical equipment, and the maintenance of electrical apparatus, is the subject of many of the codes of practice issued by the British Standards Institution.

IEE Regulations

These Regulations, which are designed to supplement statutory regulations relating to electrical work, have been evolved over the past century to ensure a minimum degree of safety from fire, shock and burns, when electricity is used in and about buildings. Though the Regulations are principally concerned with all aspects of electrical installations, they also touch on certain requirements relating to the selection of electrical equipment used in installations.

Since the advent of the European Common Market there has been international co-operation on the subject of the harmonisation of the electrical regulations used in Britain and the member states of the EEC. The 16th edition of the IEE Wiring Regulations, issued in 1991, now articulate with European electrical standards which will enable electrical contractors to 'cross frontiers' and carry out installation work in any member state. To enhance the status of the IEE Wiring Regulations, they are now included in the documents issued by the British Standards Institution to take effect from January 1993.

Though the 16th edition of the Wiring Regulations is not part of the corpus of statutory regulations (issued by Parliament), they contain the essential elements in these regulations and thus any installation which complies with the requirements of the 16th edition is deemed also to comply with the statutory regulations. The 16th edition can be given a civil legal status by their being cited in their entirety in a contract, thus giving the installation work to be done a technical description of the minimum standard for safety for the persons using the installation.

The 16th edition of the IEE Wiring Regulations is supported by a series of 'Guidance Notes' covering:

Inspection and Testing
Isolation and Switching
Selection and Erection of Equipment
Protection against Fire
Protection against Electric Shock
Protection against Overcurrents
Special Installations and Locations

In addition to the 'Guidance Notes' an 'On-site Guide' is available to serve as a ready source of reference for those electricians engaged on smaller installations in domestic, commercial and industrial premises. This Guide contains relevant information and data such as current ratings for cables, capacities of conduit and trunking and thus allows experienced installers (electricians) to produce satisfactory installations without the need for detailed calculations to verify the design parameters used by estimators, consulting engineers and architects.

The 16th edition is divided into seven parts, each of which contains a number of chapters. These are then subdivided to give groups of regulation numbers, for example:

Part 4: Protection for Safety
Chapter 41: Protection against Electric Shock
Section 411-02: Protection by SELV
Regulation 411-02-01: Requirements for Protection by SELV

The seven parts of the regulations are:

Part 1: Scope, Object and Fundamental Requirements for Safety
Part 2: Definitions
Part 3: Assessment of General Characteristics
Part 4: Protection for Safety
Part 5: Selection and Erection of Equipment
Part 6: Special Installations or Locations
Part 7: Inspection and Testing

Seven appendices are included, covering British Standards relating to electrical installations, statutory regulations, time/current characteristics of overcurrent devices, current-carrying capacities and voltage drop for cables, classification of external influences and forms for the completion and inspection certificates. Much of the detailed information contained in the appendices of the phased-out 15th edition of the Wiring Regulations is not now included in the 16th edition.

Part 1 details the fundamental requirements for safety in electrical installations and contains the essential requirements of the statutory regulations covering installations. It is stated that the object of the Wiring Regulations is to protect persons, property and livestock from any hazards arising from installations and to protect against the possibility of electric shock, fire and burns. The fundamental requirements for safety include the requirement: 'Good workmanship and proper materials shall be used.' This requires that not only must the installer (the electrician) be competent in his or her work in installing wiring systems, accessories and equipment, but the materials used must comply with the relevant specifications produced by the British Standards Institution. Thus, conduit must be used which meets with the standard of BS 31 and 13A fused plugs and socket-outlets should comply with BS 1363.

Part 2 contains a long list of definitions of terminology used in electrical work. Thus there are the meanings of such terms as 'bunched', 'circuit', 'direct contact', 'exposed conductive part', 'protective conductor' and 'wiring system'. The intention of the definitions is to clear away any misunderstanding of terminology used in specifications for electrical installations so that if, say, an 'instructed person' is identified for restricted electrical work, that person is 'A person adequately advised or supervised by skilled persons to enable him to avoid dangers which electricity may create'.

Part 3 deals with the assessment of the general characteristics of the proposed installation and is concerned with the type and nature of the supply, the methods used to provide the installation's earthing and the arrangements of circuits in the installation. External influences which might affect the performance of wiring systems and equipment include environmental conditions, the type of premises and the materials used in the construction of the building. The maintenance of the installation, once commissioned, is important as a 'built-in' feature to ensure that the installation continues to be safe to use during its intended life. An important consideration is 'compatibility': the need to ensure that equipment is not affected by other electrical equipment or services. This takes in motors (whose starting currents tend to cause fluctuations in voltage) and electromagnetic equipment.

Part 4 deals with the requirements to ensure that the installation is safe to use and this takes in protection against electric shock, against thermal effects and against overcurrent. As might be expected, this part of the Wiring Regulations is very detailed but it is essential if any installation is to meet at least the minimum standards required for safety. Those who are familiar with the requirements of the previous 15th edition of the Regulations will recognise that the new edition has taken on board much of the advice offered by practising electrical electricians and contractors. The heading of Part 4 'Protection for Safety' takes in the need for isolation and switching, the latter including emergency switching provisions and switching off equipment to carry out maintenance.

Part 5 'Selection and Erection of Equipment' lays down the requirements for the installation of electrical equipment and wiring systems in buildings. It also includes basic earthing arrangements and the selection of conductors to carry the designed load current of final circuits, taking into account the volt drop which occurs in current-carrying cables. A new section (527) deals with the risk of the spread of fire by way of the wiring system. Recent tragedies in which life has been lost due to smoke inhalation should stress the importance of ensuring that walls and floors through which wiring systems pass should be sealed with incombustible material to prevent the spread of fire and smoke into otherwise reasonably safe areas of a building.

Part 6 deals with special installations or locations and includes:

Locations containing a bath or shower basin
Swimming pools
Locations containing a hot air sauna
Construction site installations
Agricultural and horticultural installations
Caravans and caravan sites

The regulations in Part 6 supplement or modify the information given in the main parts of the Wiring Regulations. The situations in which baths or shower basins are involved have requirements which are little changed from the 15th edition. The section on swimming pools is new and is based on European harmonisation practice.

The section on construction sites deals with requirements intended to enhance the safety provisions in these situations and specifies the use of 'Commando' type plugs (BS 4343) and the use of 110V systems for portable equipment. Emergency switching is now specified with a disconnection time of 0.2 seconds for faulty circuits.

Agricultural and horticultural premises are now required to have special supplementary bonding to be installed and the provision of a 500mA residual current device (RCD), a new feature of these types of installations.

The section on caravan installations is of specific interest because it will herald some changes in previous practice in Britain for these types of situations. Fuses as a means of overcurrent protection are given over in favour of double-pole miniature circuit-breakers (MCBs) since the requirement is that final circuit protective devices must disconnect all live conductors. Other requirements insist on the use of non-metallic conduit.

A new section deals with highway power and street furniture and such lighting columns as are found in locations such as hotel car parks and leisure stadia. There are also requirements relating to the provision of temporary connections, such as those needed for Christmas illuminations on the high street.

Part 7 is concerned with inspection and testing. In general, the requirements will be familiar to practising electricians, though more details are given in the testing of extra-low voltage circuits. The certification documentation has undergone significant changes both in its requirements and in the layout.

Non-statutory regulations

In addition to the IEE Regulations, there are a number of other widely recognised regulations which deal with specific aspects of installation work and equipment in certain conditions and situations. The following are brief notes on some of the most important regulations.

1. The Institute of Petroleum Electrical Code, 1963. This code details the special safety requirements for the petroleum industry. In particular are mentioned the aspects of protection against lightning and static. The code is regarded as being supplementary to the IEE Regulations, where the latter deals only briefly with protection against fire and explosion.
2. Memorandum on the Factories Act, 1961. This memorandum deals with installations in factories and is compiled by the Senior Electrical Inspector of Factories. It clarifies many points which are written in the rather legal jargon of the Act.
3. Explanatory Notes on the Electricity Supply Regulations, 1937. These notes explain the main requirements governing the supply and use of electricity.

4. Hospital Technical Memoranda, No. 7. This memorandum indicates the special requirements associated with electricity supply and distribution in hospitals and the provision of electrical services within hospital buildings.

In addition to the above, there are many valid recommendations issued by responsible professional bodies which may, at some time or other, affect the work of the electrical contractor. Included in this category are:

Safety Regulations of the Institution of Gas Engineers.
Lighting in Corrosive, Flammable and Explosive Situations, issued by the Illuminating Engineering Society.
Handbooks of British Coal, e.g. *The Maintenance of Flameproof Apparatus and The Maintenance of Intrinsically-safe Apparatus*.
Safety Rules for Use in Chemical Works, issued by the Association of British Chemical Manufacturers.
Rules for Automatic Fire Alarms, issued by the Fire Offices' Committee.

Local authority bye-laws

Many local authorities issue bye-laws which have a legal standing within the area administered by the authorities. Those which may affect the electrical contractor are mostly concerned with the degree of protection offered in an installation against the possibility of fire risk. In general, the administration of these laws is the responsibility of the local Firemaster, whose job it is to see that installations conform to the bye-laws, which are usually supplementary to the IEE and statutory regulations. One instance in which a Firemaster may be involved in the planning of an installation is the position of 'fireman's' switches which control high-voltage electric discharge lighting on buildings.

Statutory regulations

These regulations are part of the industrial law of this country and must be complied with on penalty of either fine or imprisonment or both. The main regulations are general in content, being clarified and amplified in special regulations which deal with specific types of installations and installation conditions. The law relating to the supply of electricity is contained in a number of Acts, dating from 1882 to 1963. The Electricity Supply Regulations, 1937, are regulations 'for securing the safety of the public and for ensuring a proper and sufficient supply of electrical energy'. Later, in 1954, it was added that the regulations were 'for the purpose of securing that any supply . . . is regular and efficient, and that the public is, so far as practicable, protected from any personal injury, fire or other dangers arising from the use of electricity'. The bulk of the regulations is in two parts: (*a*) overhead lines, which are the concern of the supply companies and do not come into the work of electrical contractors, and (*b*) the supply to premises of consumers–consumers' installations. The latter group is the concern of contractors, who are contracted to provide service lines and installations. Official recognition is given to the IEE Regulations, by providing that an installation which complies with these regulations shall be deemed to comply with the statutory requirements. It is mentioned that if an installation does not comply with the IEE Regulations, yet still satisfies the statutory regulations, the installation may be connected to the supply.

Under the Factory and Workshop Act of 1901, power was given to the Home Secretary to certify that any machinery, plant or process used in factories or workshops was dangerous, and make regulations for their control. In the early years of electricity utilisation, it was considered that the generation, transformation, distribution and use of electrical energy was dangerous and accordingly, in 1908, the Home Secretary issued the Electricity (Factories Act) Special Regulations, which were augmented in 1944. These regulations lay down the requirements for all electrical installations and apparatus in factories and workshops.

Special statutory regulations apply to such activities as quarries, mines, cinemas and other installation situations where there is an enhanced risk of danger from fire or shock through the use of electrical energy. These include:

1. Metalliferous mine installations, covered by the Miscellaneous Mines (Electricity) Regulations, 1956.
2. Quarry installations, covered by the Quarries (Electricity) Regulations, 1956.
3. Coal mine installations (including stratified ironstone, shale or fireclay), covered by the Coal and other Mines (Electricity) Regulations, 1956.
4. Cinematograph installations, covered by the Cinematograph Regulations made under the Cinematograph Act, 1909 and/or the Cinematograph Act, 1952.

Recent years have seen the appearance of a number of important statutory regulations and requirements which affect the work of the electrical installation contractor. The Health and Safety at Work Act (1974) covers standards of health, safety and welfare of employees in work places and an equal responsibility for safe working practices is placed on both employers and employees. The enforcing agency for the Act is the Health and Safety Executive (HSE) whose inspectors are empowered to visit work premises and ensure that all safety requirements are being satisfied. The HSE also publishes various 'Guidance Notes' (e.g. *The Safe Use of Portable Electrical Apparatus (Electrical Safety)*) which provide useful advice on electrical matters.

In 1990 the Electricity at Work Act came into force and applies to all situations where electricity is used and covers such aspects of installations and equipment such as maintenance and testing, live working, and specifies the persons who should carry out electrical work on premises. Of some interest to the electrical industry is the Electricity Act (1989) which changed the electricity supply industry from a nationalised service to a number of private supply companies.

British Standards specifications

The British Standards Institution (BSI) was formed in 1901 as the Engineering Standards Committee. It was established to formulate national standards for the engineering industry. There are now well over 4,000 standards and codes of practice covering every major industry in the country. The BSI prepares, through its various committees, technical specifications for testing the quality of materials, their performances and their dimensions. The BSI also draws up definitions of technical terms to ensure precise and agreed descriptions. Appendix 1 of the IEE Regulations lists a considerable number of the standards which affect electrical work. The general electrical standards fall into the following groups: batteries and cells; cables, conductors and wires; cable accessories; fans; heating, cooking and domestic appliances; illumination; installation methods, materials and accessories; fuses and circuit-breakers; electrical apparatus for use in explosive gas atmospheres; motors and generators; switchgear; and transformers.

Codes of practice

These codes are drawn up and issued by the BSI. They indicate standards of good practice and take the form of recommendations. So far as electrical installation practice is concerned, the codes generally adopt the same degree of safety as is indicated by the IEE Regulations. In some instances, they go further by selecting one of a number of methods approved by the regulations and recommend it as a preferred practice. The following are the main Codes of Practice which affect the work of the electrician:

BS 6651 *Protection of Structures against Lightning*
BS 6701 *Telecommunication Facilities in Buildings*
BS 4363 *Electricity on Construction Sites*
BS 5345 *Electrical Apparatus in Explosive Atmospheres*
BS 4444 *Earth Monitoring and Protective Conductor Proving*
BS 5839 *Fire Detection and Alarm Systems in Buildings*
BS 5266 *Emergency Lighting*

2 Supply distribution and control

Supply distribution

With few exceptions, the types of electricity supply normally available throughout Britain are alternating current single-phase two-wire, and three-phase four-wire. In large factories involved in certain kinds of processes (e.g. steel mills), the internal works supplies for much of the rotating plant is dc. Direct current supplies outside industry are rarely available from a supply company, although they are, of course, in wide use for emergency lighting, battery-charging and similar applications where the power requirement involved is small. Where the amount of power is large (as in metal-refining), the voltage is small (e.g. 10V) and the current is correspondingly large (e.g. 10,000A). The dc system in general use until the gradual changeover to ac supplies was the three-wire system. This consisted of a dc generator supplying a voltage of 500V between two outer conductors known respectively as the 'positive outer' and the 'negative outer'. A middle wire, generally of smaller cross-sectional area, was earthed and thus provided a voltage of 250V between any of the outer conductors and the neutral or mid-wire. Thus, a 500V motor could be supplied across the outers, while a domestic requirement of 250V was met by connecting the mid-wire and the positive or negative outers. This two-voltage facility was developed from the older single-voltage systems evolved before the turn of this century.

The ac systems came into their own because it was found possible to transmit large amounts of ac electrical power over long distances provided a high voltage was used. AC is generated in the power station usually at 25,000V. This generated voltage is transformed by generator-transformers to transmission-line voltages of 132, 275 and 400kV. The transmission lines form part of what is known as the National Grid, which is an interconnected system of conductors (overhead lines and underground cables) which carry electrical power to points of use. At these points, the transmission voltage is reduced by transformers to 33kV and 11kV for large consumers. The voltage is further reduced to 415/240V for small consumers.

The single-phase, 240V, 50 Hz system is the normal supply for small dwellings, and other single-occupier premises where the load demand is relatively small. The Electricity Supply Regulation 28a, 1937, says that energy for use at low voltage must not be introduced by more than one pair of conductors of a three-phase or multi-phase system unless the connected load exceeds 8kW and it is necessary to do so in order to avoid voltage drop or variation on the distribution system in the area.

The three-phase system is derived from a star-connected winding of a transformer, the star point being earthed. From this point a fourth conductor, the neutral, is taken to form a three-phase, four-wire system. The voltage between any two phase conductors is 415V (Figure 2.1). The voltage between any phase conductor and the neutral conductor is 240V. This system is the normal supply for commercial and industrial premises of medium size: schools, hotels, blocks of flats, hospitals and the like. The lighting and heating circuits of individual tenements in blocks of flats are normally supplied from low-voltage circuits derived from this system, the load across the three phases being balanced as far as practicable. High-voltage, three-phase supplies are fed to very large consumers where the total electrical load exceeds 100kW. The voltages are either 11 or 33kV. The consumer is offered a cheaper tariff if he takes a higher voltage. A balanced load on a three-phase system is usually available only where three-phase motors are used. Heating loads, in most instances, can be connected across three phases and the neutral conductor omitted unless required for control purposes.

Cable sizes are dictated by the amount of elec-

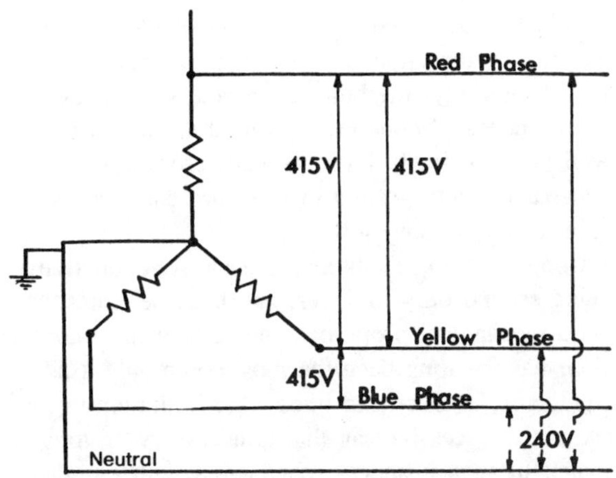

Figure 2.1. Three-phase, four-wire ac supply system.

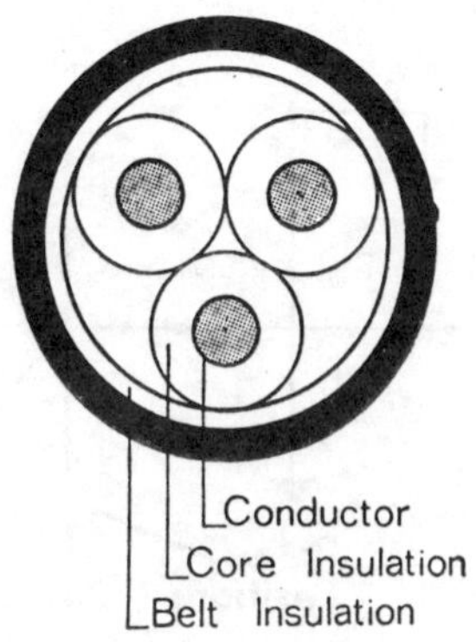

Figure 2.2. Typical belted-type cable: three-core.

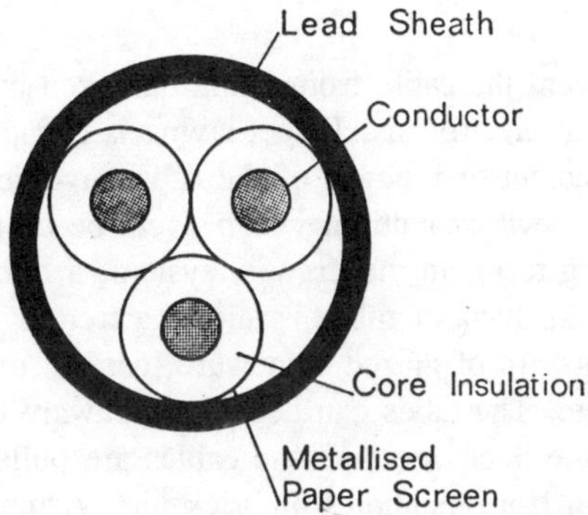

Figure 2.3. Typical screen-type cable: three-core.

trical power to be carried. If a large amount of power is to be taken to a consumer, a high-voltage cable is used, to reduce the current and so the cross-sectional area (csa) of the cable conductors. Because of the high voltage, however, the cable must of necessity cost more to insulate. Despite this, there are sound economic reasons for carrying as much power as possible at a high voltage, leaving the larger csa cables to carry larger currents associated with individual circuits in an installation at low and medium voltages. The main economic reason is to minimise the I^2R watts loss in a conductor. There is also the important aspect of the loss in voltage along the length of the conductor as it carries the load current.

Underground cables are used where there is a visual objection to overhead lines or where it would not be convenient to use lines. Both paper- and PVC-insulated cables are used, with copper and aluminium conductors. The latter material has now come into favour because it costs less than copper and because its light weight requires a smaller cable-laying labour force. Copper conductors are stranded. Aluminium conductors are found in both stranded and solid forms. Belted cables (having an additional outer layer of insulation) are cheaper than screened types (having a metallic screen round each core) and are used for systems up to 11kV (Figures 2.2 and 2.3).

Protection of underground cables from mechanical damage is provided for by steel-wire or steel-tape armouring. Steel-tape armoured cables are cheaper in first cost than the wire-armoured types, but the bending radius is less and they cannot be left 'bright', that is, with the jute serving removed to present a clean appearance in surface work. Also, tape-armouring cannot be taken over a plumbed (wiped) or cone gland to the armour clamp as in wire-armoured cables.

There are three methods of laying underground cables: direct-laying, draw-in and solid. The direct-laying method involves the cable being placed in a trench and then covered with soil. In most instances, the cable is protected by wood planks, bricks, tiles or concrete slabs. Such cables should be armoured, though if the risk of mechanical damage is small, bare-sheath cables can be used. Subsidence of the soil is an important factor in the installation of buried cables. And if the soil contains harmful chemicals, precautions must be taken

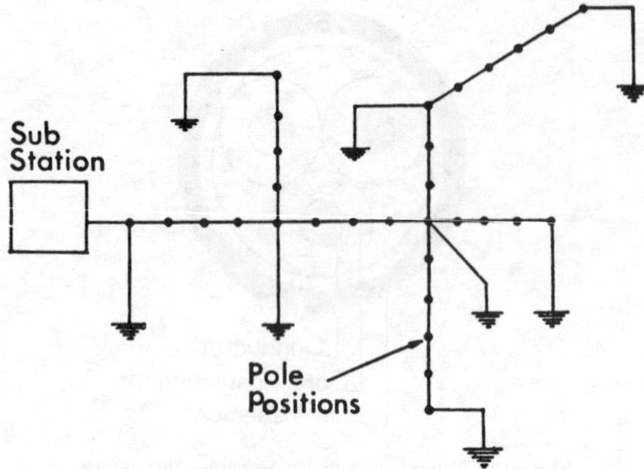

Figure 2.4. Typical arrangement of overhead-line rural distribution. Note earthing at regular intervals.

to prevent the cable from being damaged by corrosion and electrolysis. Direct-laying is cheap, but replacement or renewal of the cable involves completely new excavation, which could be costly in the long term. In the draw-in system, a line of conduits, ducts or tubes is laid in a trench. The conduits are of glazed stoneware, cement or concrete. The tubes can be of earthenware or iron. After the ducts are laid, the cables are pulled into position from manholes or brick pits. Armouring is not necessary, but the cables are usually given a covering of hessian tape or jute to protect them while drawing in. Ducts are usually multi-compartmented. In the solid system, the cable is laid in troughing in an open trench. The troughing is then covered with a bituminous compound, and the trench filled in.

Overhead lines

The cheapest method of carrying power is by overhead line, particularly where light loads are concerned, as might be the case in a farm installation. Overhead line poles for low- and medium-voltage services are of wood, generally 8 m in length with some 7 m out of the ground. There are regulations which govern the minimum lengths of span and minimum heights above ground for consumers' overhead wiring between buildings. In ordinary ground, the erection of poles presents no difficulty. The pole hole should be dug as narrow as possible in the direction of the line. The pole should be positioned in one corner of the hole, so that in two directions it bears against undisturbed soil. Preferably, the butt of the pole should rest on a few inches of concrete or a hard core, and be well rammed in. In loose ground, cross-braces are necessary below ground level to present a larger area to the yielding soil.

Copper, owing to its high electrical conductivity, being second only to silver, and because it has good mechanical properties and resistance to corrosion, has for long been the most commonly used conductor for overhead lines. One limitation to its use is the excessive sag that is necessary on long spans. In such instances, conductors with a higher tensile strength are used, e.g. a composite conductor employing copper or aluminium strands round a steel wire; or a conductor of cadmium-copper alloy. Overhead lines are subject to the requirements of the Overhead Lines Regulations, where a public supply is being carried. A conductor (other than that on a service to a consumer) must have a breaking load of at least 560 kg. Thus, the minimum size for a copper conductor is 8 swg. The minimum permissible size of service line must be such as to have an actual breaking load of not less than 370 kg.

Conductors may be bare, or insulated PBJ, VR or PVC. Line conductors are attached to insulators carried on supports of wood, iron, steel or reinforced concrete. All wooden supports other than oak or hardwood cross-arms must be impregnated with creosote. Two forms of insulator are used; the pin-type and the disc insulator for tension positions (Figures 2.5–2.11).

Supply control

It is a requirement of the Wiring Regulations that every consumer's installation shall be adequately controlled by switchgear which is readily accessible to the consumer and which shall incorporate:

1. Protection against electric shock.
2. Protection against overcurrent.
3. Isolation and switching.

The size and type of main switchgear to be installed depends on the type of premises and anticipated load. For the average domestic

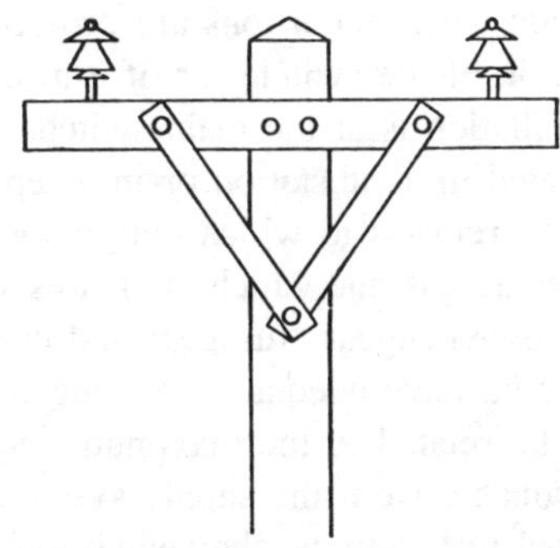
Figure 2.5. Typical cross-arm arrangement for a wood pole.

Figure 2.8. Anti-fog type insulator of the suspension or tension type.

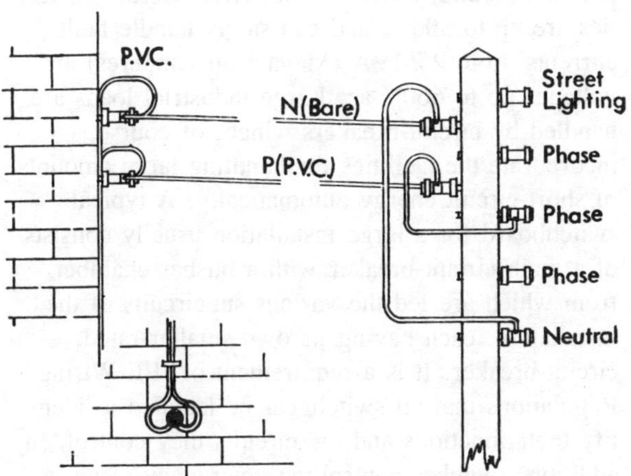

Figure 2.6. Details of conductor make-offs at pole and house terminations, and method of conductor lead-in to building. The drip-loop prevents the ingress of rain and moisture to the building.

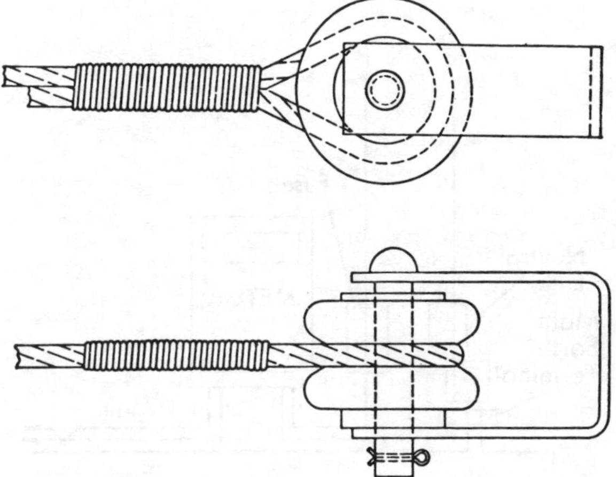
Figure 2.9. Conductor termination (make-off) at a D-iron insulator.

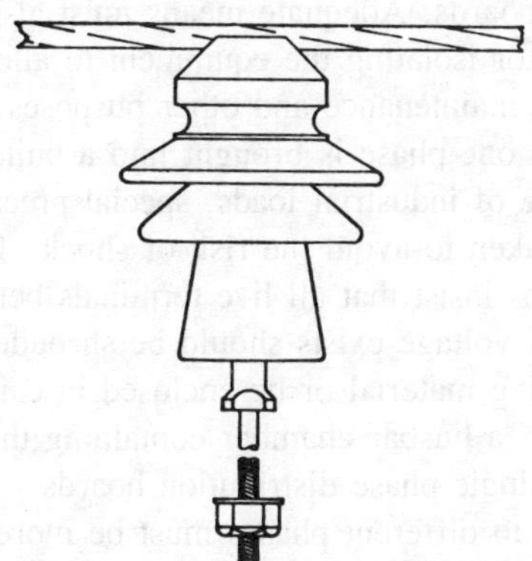
Figure 2.7. Pin-type insulator (dry flashover).

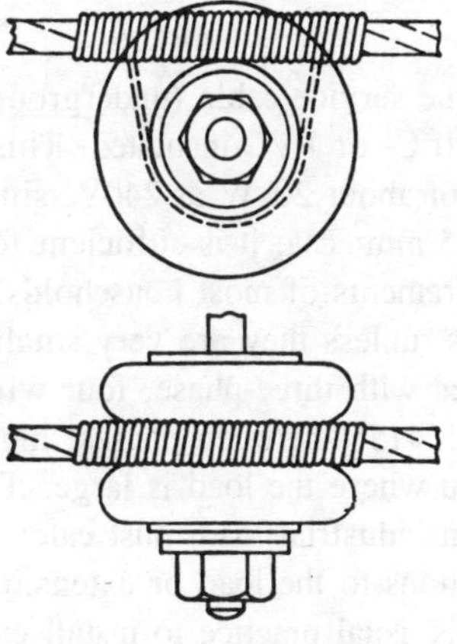
Figure 2.10. A through overhead-line conductor bound to a reel insulator.

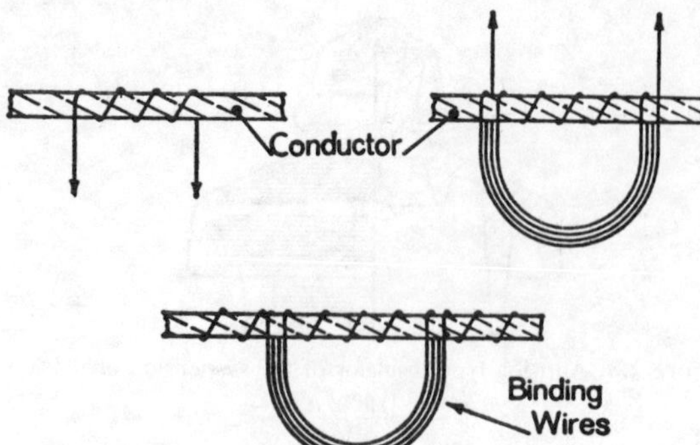

Figure 2.11. Detail of binding through conductor to reel insulator.

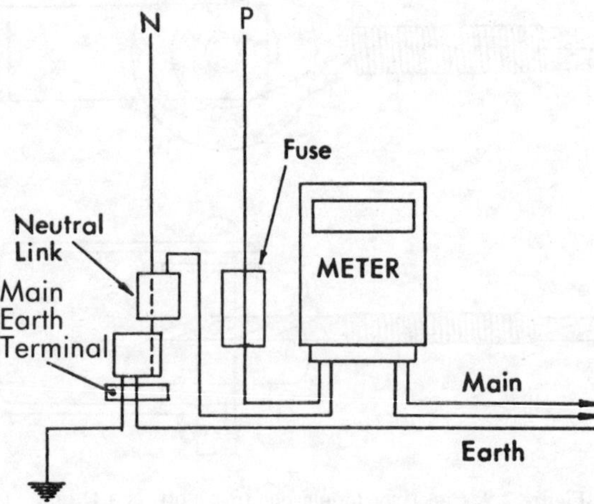

Figure 2.12. Typical supply-intake position for domestic consumers. This illustration shows a PME (protective multiple earthing) TNCS arrangement.

premises, the service cable (underground) is two-core and PILC- or PVC-insulated. This is suitable for a load of about 20kW at 240V, single-phase and is of 25 mm^2 csa; it is sufficient for the electrical requirements of most households. Industrial installations, unless they are very small workshops, are provided with three-phase, four-wire services, usually with 415V between phases; higher voltages are supplied where the load is large. The size of cable for an industrial load must cater for any future additions to the load or extensions to the factory. It is usual practice to install cables of sufficient capacity with appropriate switchgear, to save additional installation expense and outage time at a later date when extensions are projected.

The location of the switchgear of a medium-voltage installation is at the main switchboard. This is situated in a substation or in a separate room on the premises to which only authorised persons have access and which is always kept clean and dry. The switchgear, fusegear and circuit-breakers should have adequate breaking capacity and should be related to the maximum short-circuit current obtainable from the supply system. For medium-sized installations, the switchgear is in the form of manually operated switchfuses. These units are available as metalclad, double- or triple-pole and neutral switches with HRC fuses. Capacities are up to 300A, and can safely handle fault currents up to 25MVA (Mega Volt Amperes) at voltages up to 660V ac. Large industrial loads are handled by circuit-breakers which, of course, incorporate the facilities for handling large amounts of short-circuit energy automatically. A typical switchboard for a large installation usually consists of a main circuit-breaker with a busbar chamber from which are fed the various subcircuits of the installation, each having its own smaller-rated circuit-breaker. It is a requirement of IEE Wiring Regulations that all switchgear be labelled to identify their functions and the circuits they control. In addition, switches controlling emergency services such as fire alarms, firemens' lifts and sprinkler systems should be distinctively marked, for example, by painting them red.

The memorandum by the Senior Inspector of Factories (Form 928) indicates that adequate passageways should be allowed to give access to all switchboards. Adequate means must also be provided for isolating the equipment to allow access for maintenance and other purposes. Where more than one phase is brought into a building, as in the case of industrial loads, special precautions must be taken to avoid the risk of shock. The Regulations insist that all live terminals between which low voltage exists should be shrouded with an insulating material or be enclosed in earthed metal (e.g. a busbar chamber containing three phases). Single-phase distribution boards which are connected to different phases must be more than 2 m apart from each other.

The position of distribution fuseboards (or distri-

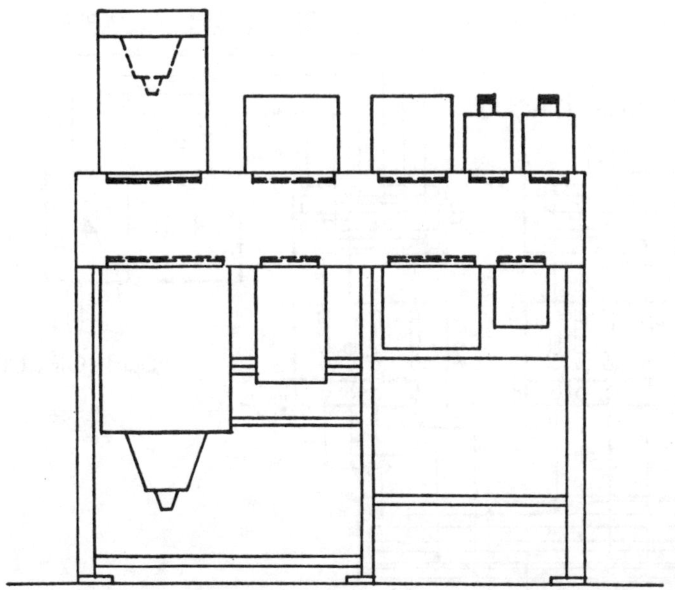

Figure 2.13. (*a*) Typical arrangement of a supply-intake position in an industrial premises.

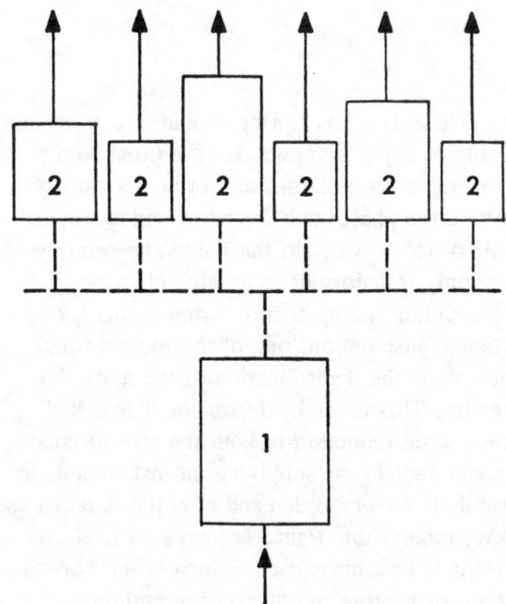

Figure 2.13. (*b*) Schematic diagram of arrangement of main switches (1) and switch fuses (2).

bution circuit-breaker boards where MCBs are used) is important, and should be near the electrical centre of the load they are intended to serve. This reduces of the cost of circuit cables, though the length between the supply-intake position and any particular distribution board should be taken into consideration so that the volt drop does not exceed the permitted maximum of 4 per cent of the nominal voltage of the supply (IEE Regulation 525-01-02).

Sub-main distribution in industrial premises is generally by cables (metal-sheathed, bedded and armoured and served) or by busbar trunking systems. For machine shops and other parts of a factory where alterations in machine layout may occur frequently, the plug-in tap-off system is recommended. Separate sub-mains should be installed for special electrical services such as passenger and goods lifts and ventilating systems. Sub-main circuits should not be run within lift shafts. In small domestic and commercial installations, the distribution board is at the meter position. With the usual two-part tariff, one meter records the energy used for lighting, heating and cooking, and only one main control switch or switchfuse is necessary. If a different tariff is applied, for example, for off-peak loads, a separate meter and switch must be provided. These off-peak loads are controlled by time-switches and contactors.

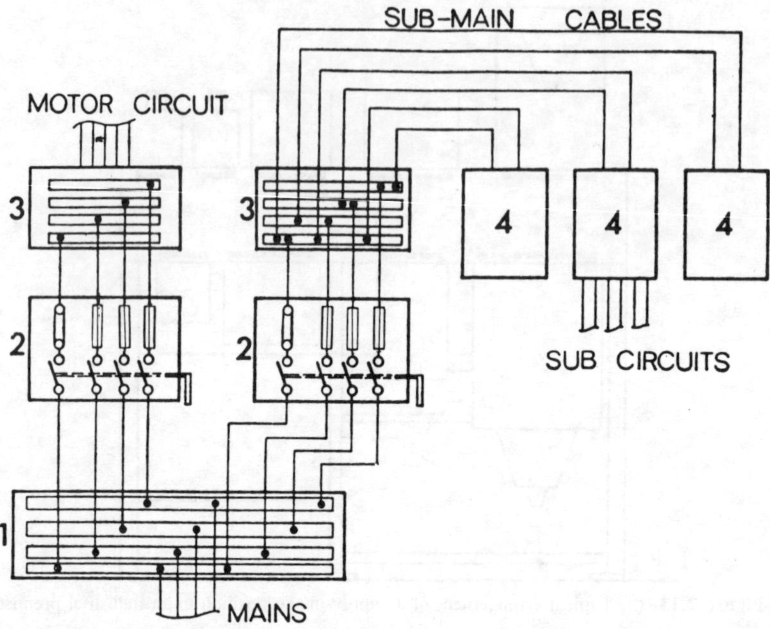

Figure 2.14. Detail of supply-intake position for a small industrial consumer. (1) three-phase and neutral busbar chamber; (2) triple-pole and neutral switchfuse; (3) sub-distribution busbar chamber; (4) sub-distribution fuseboards.

Rising mains

When rebuilding began after the last war, it was found necessary to erect numerous buildings of the multi-storied type. Originally, these buildings were five to seven storeys high. Since then, the height has been increased and, to make the most of land available for housing, twenty storeys are common nowadays. The electrical problem here is the supply of the individual dwellings in these buildings. The usual method of mains supply is to run conductors to the full height of the building and to provide convenient tapping-off points to feed the flats on one or more floors according to the number of flats per floor (Figure 2.15).

In essence, the rising mains are elongated busbar chambers supplied in lengths to suit the heights of the floors. They incorporate expansion joints between the sections. The busbars are either round or rectangular copper or aluminium bars. Boxes containing fuses may be fitted over the front of the trunking where required, or tappings can be taken off to boxes at the side, or else direct to individual flats. These systems can be provided with busbars capable of carrying upwards of 1000A. In the basement of the building the service is usually 415V, three-phase with a neutral conductor for single-phase services to the flats. The primary of the supply transformer is usually 11kV.

In deciding the system of rising mains for a particular installation, one of the most difficult problems is the determination of the allowable diversity. This diversity factor, as it is called, allows some reduction in both the size of conductors and switchgear supplying an installation. In general, the average demand of a flat is taken as 10kW, though this figure is increased if electric underfloor heating is used, which is the normal method of heating in multi-storey buildings.

In general, where bare conductors are used '... they shall be so installed that they are inaccessible to unauthorised persons and either be totally enclosed in earthed metal or fixed in a channel, trunking, or shaft specially provided for the purpose, and be of adequate strength to withstand the electro-mechanical forces that may be set up

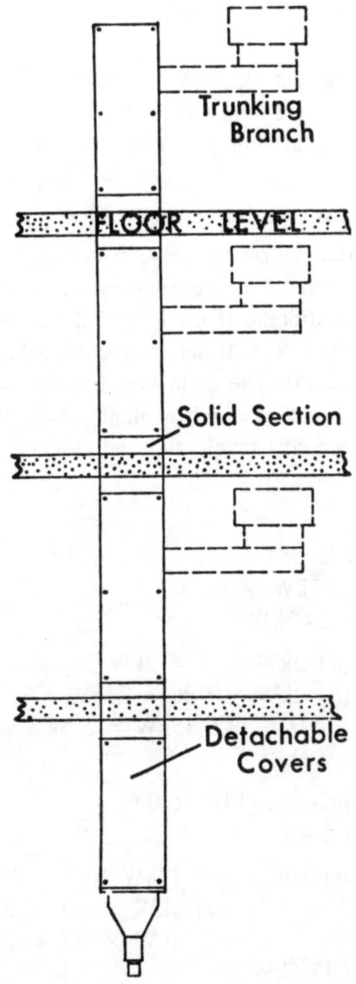

Figure 2.15. Rising main with laterals for each floor in a multi-storey building.

by the prospective short-circuit current, and be free to expand and contract as the temperature changes . . . '. In addition, where the mains pass through floors, walls, partitions or ceilings, they should pass through directly and be protected by enclosure in non-absorbent, incombustible insulating material, unless earthed metal trunking is used. If cables insulated with general-purpose rubber or PVC are to be connected to the busbars of rising mains, the insulation must be removed for a distance of 15 cm from the connection and replaced, if necessary, by suitable heat-resisting insulation.

Diversity factor

The diversity factor has an important place in the design of an installation and its final costing. IEE Regulation 311-01 deals with the subject. Diversity factor is a factor which is applied to sub-mains and mains cables and their associated switchgear to reduce (*a*) the csa of the cable conductors, and (*b*) the capacity of the switchgear.

The factor is based on the assumption that the whole of the connected load will not be on at the same time. For example, the total lighting load in a dwelling house is rarely switched on at once. Thus, it can be taken that if the total lighting load is 1000W, at any one time during the life of the installation, only 66 per cent of the load (660W) will be switched on at any one time. The factor in this instance is 0.66. A factor for diversity shall not be allowed for when calculating the size of circuit conductors and switchgear of final sub-circuits, other than specified circuits such as cooker circuits. It is noted that the provision of an allowance for diversity is a matter calling for special knowledge and experience. Indeed, the application of diversity should be decided by the engineer responsible for designing each particular installation. The amount by which they are increased or decreased for each installation is a matter for the installation engineer to decide.

There are ten types of final circuit fed from wiring to which diversity applies: lighting, heating, cooking appliances which are permanently connected, motors (other than lift motors), instantaneous-type water heaters, thermostatically controlled water heaters, floor-warming installations, thermal-storage space-heating installations, 13A fused socket-outlets and appliances fed therefrom, and other socket-outlets such as 15A. Three general groups of installation premises are also recognised:

1. Individual domestic installations, including individual flats of a block.
2. Hotels, boarding houses, lodging houses, etc.
3. Shops, stores, offices and business premises.

In the case of lighting for each type of installation, it will be noticed that the more the total lighting load is likely to be switched on over definite periods, the smaller is the allowance made for diversity. In a domestic installation, it is estimated that some two-thirds (0.66) of the lighting load will be on at any one time. In a hotel, the figure is 75 per cent (0.75). And in a shop, where virtually all the lights are on for most of the time the shop is open, the figure is 90 per cent (0.90). It should be noted that no diversity is allowable on the relevant wiring supplying certain types of load. The following is an example of the application of diversity factors:

Premises: Boarding house
Supply: 240V, single-phase ac
Connected lighting load: 2.7kW
Heating appliances: 3 × 2kW; 5 × 1kW; 3 × 0.75kW
Power appliances: One washing machine rated at 2.85kW, with power factor of 0.85
Cooking appliances: 1 × 12kW; 1 × 4kW; 1 × 4kW
Motor for overnight water-storage tank: 1.6kW; efficiency at 0.9; power factor of 0.85
Thermal-storage space-heating installation: 8kW
Socket-outlets and stationary appliances:

1. One final subcircuit (radial) protected by a fuse rating of 20A; and
2. Three ring final subcircuits each protected by fuses of rating 30A.

Total connected load:

Lighting: 2.7kW
total = 2.7kW

Heating: 6kW + 5kW + 2.15kW
total = 13.15kW

$$\text{Power appliance} = \frac{2{,}850\text{W}}{240 \times 0.85} = 14\text{A}$$

total = 14A

Cooking appliances = 12kW + 4kW + 4kW
total = 20kW

$$\text{Motor} = \frac{1{,}600}{240 \times 0.9 \times 0.85}$$

total = 8A

Thermal-storage = 8kW
total = 8kW

Radial circuit = 20A
total = 20A

Ring circuits = 3 × 30A
total = 90A

Total connected load (kW) = 43.85kW
Total connected load (A) = 132A
Therefore total aggregate (A) = 132A + 183A
= 315A

Assuming the service cable is PILC with two-core, copper conductors, the cable size would be 120 mm^2 which has a current rating of 355A in defined conditions. If the length of the service is taken as 20 m at £20 per metre, the cable cost would be £400. The main switch would be rated at 400A, the cost of which is about £240. Thus, the total service cost (cable and main switch) would be £640.

Estimated load:

Lighting: 2.7kW × 0.75
total = 2.02kW

Heating: (*a*) 2kW × 1 = 2kW
(*b*) 2kW × 0.8 = 1.6kW
(*c*) 60% of 9.15kW = 5.5kW
total = 9.1kW

Power appliances: 14A × 0.6
total = 8.4A

Cooking appliances: (*a*) 12kW × 1 = 12kW
(*b*) 4kW × 0.8 = 3.2kW
(*c*) 4kW × 0.6 = 2.4kW
total = 17.6kW

Motor: 8A × 1 = 8A
total = 8A

Thermal storage = 8kW × 1
total = 8kW

13A circuits: (*a*) 30A × 1
(*b*) 50% of (30A + 30A + 20A) = 40A
total = 70A

Total estimated load (kW) = 36.72kW (153A)
Total estimated load (A) = 87A
Therefore total estimated load = 153A + 87A
= 240A

With this estimation of the load, the size of service cable would be 70 mm^2. If extensions or alterations to the premises or installation are envisaged, the size of conductor would be taken as 95 mm^2. The size of the main switch would be the nearest practicable size, i.e. 300A.

With 70 mm^2 cable, cost = 20 m at £15 = £300.
With 300A fuse switch and isolator, cost is £200.
Therefore total cost = £500.

With 95 mm^2 cable, cost = 20 m at £18 = £360.
With 300A fuse switch and isolator, cost is £200.
Therefore total cost = £560.

It is thus seen that with 70 mm^2 cable and 300A fuse switch and isolator, the saving of £140 is due to the application of diversity. Even with the increase in cable size to 95 mm^2, the saving due to the application of diversity is £80.

3 Final circuits

A final circuit is defined as 'A circuit connected directly to current-using equipment, or to a socket-outlet or socket-outlets or other outlet points for the connection of such equipment.' In addition, the regulations require that where an installation comprises more than one final circuit, each circuit shall be connected to a separate way in a distribution board. They also require that the wiring of each final circuit shall be electrically separate from that of every other final circuit. To facilitate disconnection of each final circuit for testing, the neutral conductors shall be connected at the distribution board in the same order as that in which the live conductors are connected to the fuses or circuit-breakers.

Final circuits make up the greater part of electrical installations and can vary from a pair of 1 mm^2 cables feeding one lamp, to a heavy three-core PILC cable feeding a large motor from a circuit-breaker located at a factory switchboard. The main important regulation which applies to final circuits is No. 27 of the Electricity Supply Regulations: 'All conductors and apparatus must be of sufficient size and power for the work they are called on to do, and so constructed, installed and protected as to prevent danger.'

There are five general groups of final circuits:

1. Rated at not more than 16A.
2. Rated over 16A.
3. Rated over 16A but confined to feeding 13A socket-outlets with fused plugs.
4. Circuits feeding fluorescent and other discharge lamps.
5. Circuits feeding motors.

An industrial installation may have all five types; a domestic installation may have only 1, 2 and 3. Whatever the type of installation and the uses to which electrical energy is put, it is essential that some significant element of planning be introduced at any early stage in the design of an installation.

Before indicating the factors which are involved in the choice of final circuit types, a few brief notes on planning aspects will be relevant.

Installation planning

(*a*) *Domestic installations* seem to be the simplest to plan, but there are a number of points which are worth considering. And though these might seem obvious at first sight, a close survey of existing installations will reveal rather too many lapses in efficient planning, even for a dwelling house. For example, a room which can be entered from two points should be wired for two-way switching; a two-landing staircase should be wired for intermediate switching; and a large house should have two or more lighting circuits. A note in an older

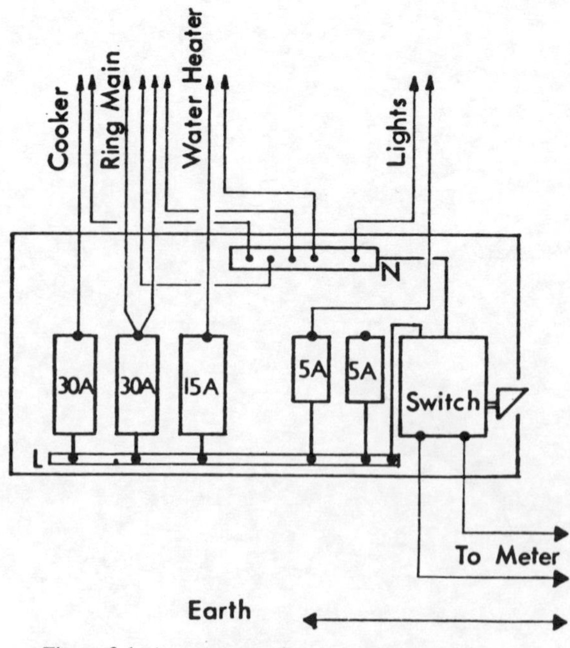

Figure 3.1. Arrangement of typical consumer unit for a domestic installation.

edition of the IEE Regulations is still relevant: 'In the interests of good planning it is undesirable that the whole of the fixed lighting of an installation should be supplied from one final subcircuit.' The reason for this is not far to seek. If an installation has two lighting circuits and one circuit fails, the house is not plunged into darkness. It is often a good point to consider a slight 'overlap' of lighting circuits: to wire one lighting point from one circuit within the wiring area of the other circuit. If this is done, there should be a note to this effect displayed at the distribution board.

The lighting in houses should be regarded as an important aspect of interior decoration, as well as supplying lighting on a purely functional basis. In living rooms and bedrooms, wall-mounted fittings can be used, controlled by multi-point switches at the entrance doors. Thought should be given to the provision of 13A socket-outlets for supplying table and standard lamps. The use of local lighting over working surfaces in kitchens is an aspect of good planning. External lighting should not be overlooked, either to light up the front and back doors or to light the way to outhouses such as detached garages, coal stores and greenhouses (Figure 3.2). In very large houses, driveway lighting may have to be considered.

To facilitate the interchange of fittings and appliances throughout the house, it is recommended that 13A three-pin socket-outlets to BS 1363 should be used exclusively. Where it might be inconvenient to withdraw plugs from the associated

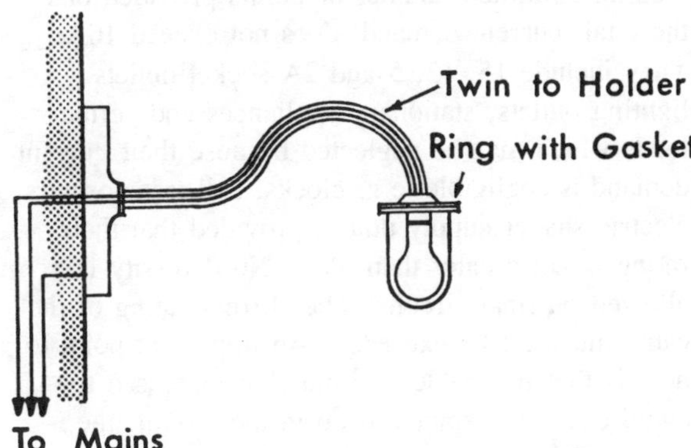

Figure 3.2. Typical waterproof outdoor lighting fitting with wellglass.

socket-outlets when appliances are out of use, switched socket-outlets should be used. Because the past few years have seen a rapid increase in the use of electrical appliances, it is essential that an ample number of socket-outlets be provided, and situated wherever there might arise the need for an electrical outlet. The table shows the provision of socket-outlets, both the desirable number and the minimum provision that can be considered as acceptable:

Part of dwelling	*Desirable provision*	*Minimum provision*
Working area of a kitchen	4	4
Dining area	2	1
Living area	5	3
First (or only) double bedroom	3	2
Other double bedrooms	2	2
Single bedrooms	2	2
Hall or landing	1	1
Store/workshop/garage	1	—
	20	15
Single study-bedrooms	2	2
Single bed-sitting rooms in family dwellings	3	3
Single bed-sitting rooms in self-contained bed-sitting room dwellings	5	5

It can thus be seen that the average house should have an adequate number of socket-outlets. In the living room, there should be a two-gang socket-outlet on each side of the fireplace. Additional socket-outlets should be located less than 2 m from the opposite corners of the room, where they are least likely to be hidden by furniture. In bedrooms, at least a single socket-outlet should be provided at each side of a bed; two-gang units can be used to good advantage (e.g. to supply a bedside lamp and an electric blanket). Additionally, there should be socket-outlets for dressing-table lamps, a heating appliance or a portable television set.

The kitchen probably places the greatest demand on the electrical service. Outlets are required for such varied appliances as washing machines, refrigerators, waste-disposal units, food mixers, can-openers, flat irons, coffee percolators and toasters. As far as possible, the outlets should be located above working surfaces and two-gang units are recommended.

In the dining room, small plate-warmers may be required. In halls and on landings the outlet is generally used for a vacuum cleaner or floor polisher, and perhaps a hall heater. No provision is made for the use of portable appliances in a room containing a fixed bath or shower. However, an electric shaver unit to BS 3052 may be installed out of reach of a person in the bath or shower. Additionally, a bathroom heater (of the enclosed-element type) or towel rail should be permanently connected through a fixed control switch out of reach of the bath or shower position.

(*b*) *Commercial installations* are often difficult to design because frequently the buildings are built as basic shells with the final requirements for lighting and other circuits not known until the office tenants sign their leases. The lighting in such buildings is 'general, special, and building services'. The general lighting is supplied by a flexible wiring system which will allow for a specific area in a new building to be sectioned or partitioned off into smaller areas for offices, stores and the like. Special lighting may include external lighting, wall points, etc. The service lighting is that associated with lifts, corridors, stairs, landings and is usually the responsibility of the landlord. Where a tenant's specific lighting requirements are not known when the building is being erected, the lighting outlets are laid out on a 'grid' system, in which the outlet points are sited at regular intervals usually related to the module of the building (that is, the basic size, multiples of which are used in the construction of the building). Generally, about 3 m are allowed between outlets. Outlets may be left on the ceiling for ceiling switches. They may also be fitted on structural columns or on the ceiling along the line of future corridors from which extensions to switch positions can be made on future partitions.

The provision of adequate socket-outlets is a particular problem, for should the electrical load increase (e.g. an office may go over to all-electric typewriters or install a computer or data-processing system), it is often difficult to extend or alter an inflexible installation. Thus, the electrical services provisions should allow for the possibility of installing new outlets or revising the positions of existing outlets without difficulty or serious disturbance to the building and its occupants. Where a tenant's requirements for socket-outlets are not known, it is usual practice to install one socket-outlet on the external wall in each building bay and make provision for spur connections to two further outlets to be installed on internal partitions as may be required. Only a limited number of bays, not more than three, should be connected to each ring circuit.

(*c*) *Industrial premises* require lighting installations which cater for the intensity of lighting required for the process to be carried out. In addition, local lighting at reduced voltages is often a requirement on machines or for portable inspection lamps. The lighting installation within the factory area should be wired with a system which will allow for extensive alteration and significant addition with ease of maintenance and rewiring when necessary.

(*d*) *Special types of premises* include hospitals, theatres, cinemas, hotels, schools and buildings of historic interest. Some of these, such as hospitals, have specific codes of practice laid down by the Ministry of Health. In places of entertainment, secondary lighting installations are required.

Circuits rated under 16A

A final circuit rated at not more than 16A may feed an unlimited number of points provided that the total 'current demand' does not exceed 16A. They include 15, 13, 5 and 2A socket-outlets, lighting outlets, stationary appliances and certain loads which may be neglected because their current demand is negligible (e.g. clocks, bell-transformers, electric shaver supply units), provided that their rating is not greater than 5VA. No diversity is allowed on final circuits. The current rating of the cable must not be exceeded. An important point to note is that if a cable size must be increased to avoid excessive voltage drop in the circuit, the rating of the fuse or circuit-breaker protecting the circuit must not be increased correspondingly. The same condition would apply if the ambient temperature of a cable were to be taken into consideration. The reason for this is that the larger cables are not being chosen for the current that they can carry under favourable circuit conditions, but to provide for the special conditions in which they are being installed. The lighting circuits of domestic installations are rated at 5A. Industrial lighting circuits are usually rated at 15/16A because of the higher wattage of the lamps used.

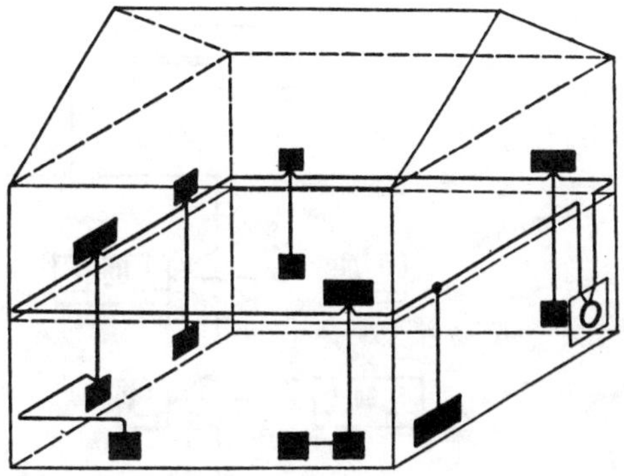

Figure 3.3. Typical ring-circuit serving two floors.

Circuits rated over 16A

With two exceptions, circuits rated at over 16A should not serve more than one point. The exceptions are circuits which feed 13A socket-outlets and cooker circuits. Final circuits for cooking appliances are assessed for current demand as follows:

The first 10A of the total rated current of the connected cooking appliances, plus
30% of the remainder of the total rated current of the connected cooking appliances, plus
5A, if the cooker control unit has a socket-outlet.

Thus, a cooker with a total load of 11kW at 240V (46A) would in fact be supplied by cables rated to carry about 26A, depending on the distance the cooker is away from the distribution board. If a large cooker which exceeds 30A is to be installed in domestic premises, and where the protection is offered by fuses, a supply service of more than the normal 60A rating may be required. In this instance, the supply authority should be consulted. Water-heater circuits are terminated in a 20A double-pole isolating switch, fitted with an earthing terminal and a neon pilot lamp.

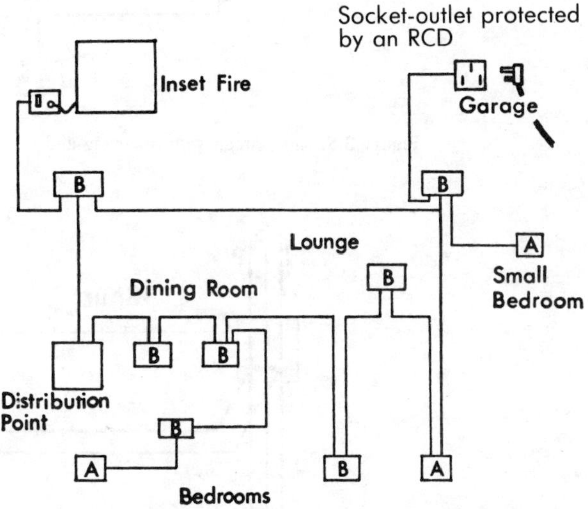

Figure 3.4. Typical ring-circuit with spurs to outlying points.

Circuits rated for 13A socket-outlets

Final circuits which supply 13A socket-outlets with fused plugs and 13A fused (switched or unswitched) connection units are provided by two types of circuit: ring and radial. Ring circuits serve a maximum floor area of 100 m^2 derived from a 30A protective device. Radial circuits serving a maximum area of 50 m^2 are also protected by a 30A device, while if the area served is no more than 20 m^2 a 20A device provides the protection. The following is a summary of the requirements relating to 13A socket-outlet circuits:

Each socket-outlet of a two-gang or multiple socket-outlet is to be counted as one socket-outlet.

Stationary appliances, permanently connected to a radial or ring circuit, must be protected by a fuse not exceeding 13A rating and controlled by a switch or a circuit-breaker.

It is important to realise that the conductor sizes recommended for ring circuits are minima. They

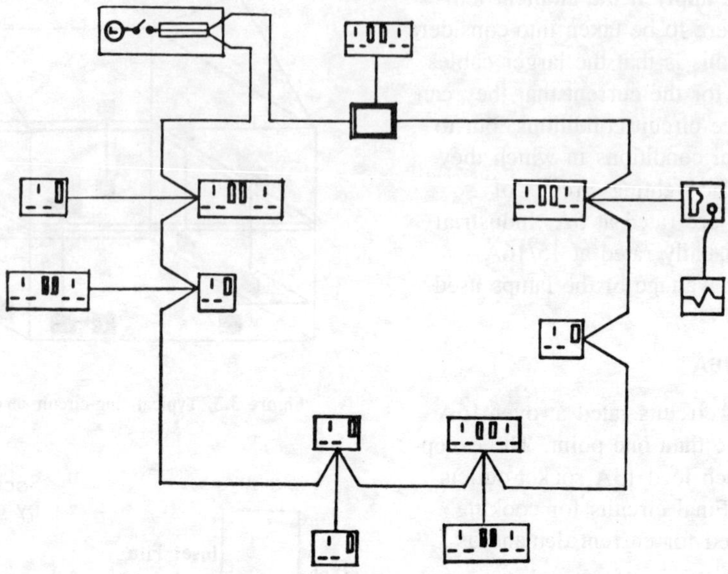

Figure 3.5. Ring circuit with one-gang and two-gang switched outlets and fused spur outlets.

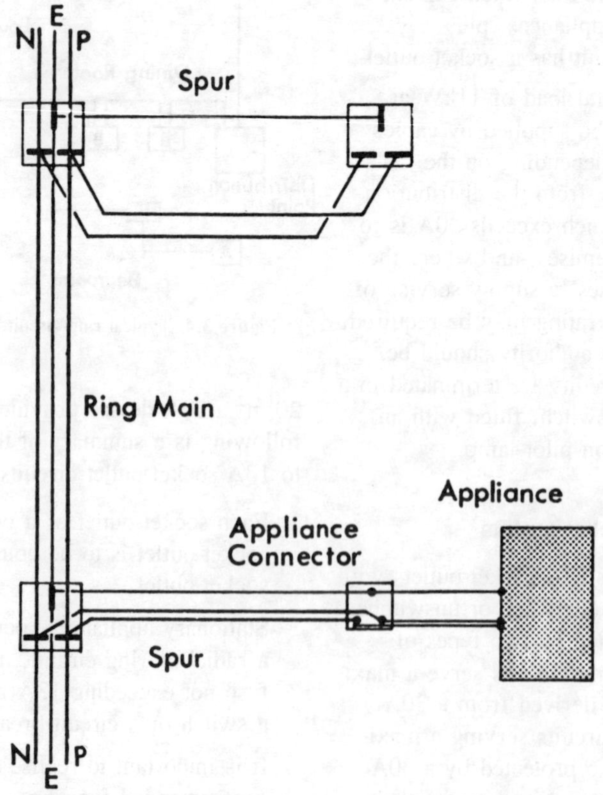

Figure 3.6. Typical spurs and the service they may supply.

must be increased if necessary where circuits are installed in groups, or in conditions of high ambient temperature, taking into consideration the class of excess-current protection provided.

The method of properly connecting circuit conductors of a ring circuit involves correct polarity and security of the terminals.

Except where a ring circuit is run throughout in metallic conduit, ducts or trunking, the CPC shall be run in the form of a ring, having both ends connected to earth at the distribution board (or its equivalent).

The total number of spurs shall not exceed the total number of socket-outlets and stationary appliances connected directly to the ring.

Fused spurs from ring circuits must be connected through fused spur boxes, and the rating of the fuse must not exceed the current rating of the cable forming the spur, and in any event must not exceed 13A.

One socket-outlet or one two-gang socket-outlet unit, or one stationary appliance fed from a connection unit, can be connected to each non-fused spur.

Circuits feeding discharge lamps

One of the main requirements is a consideration of the 'rating' of a discharge lamp outlet, for it has a rather different interpretation from that used for other lighting points. The reason for this is that,

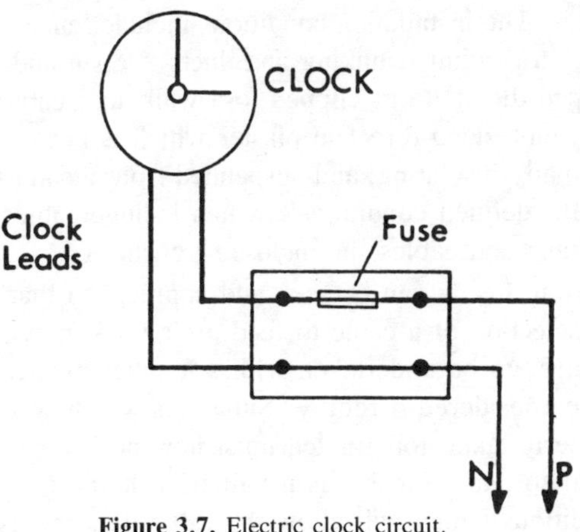

Figure 3.7. Electric clock circuit.

owing to the losses in the lamp control gear plus the low power factor (about 0.9), it is necessary to multiply the rated lamp watts by 1.8 and divide by the lamp rated voltage to obtain the actual current flowing in the circuit. It should be noted that certain switches may not be suitable for controlling the highly inductive circuits associated with discharge lighting. If a switch is not specifically designed to break an inductive load (quick-make, slow-break), it should have a current rating of not less than twice the total steady current which it is required to carry.

Circuits feeding motors

Final circuits which supply motors require careful consideration. In particular, cables which carry the starting, accelerating and load currents of a motor must be rated at least to the full-load current rating of the motor. If, however, the motor is subjected to frequent starting and stopping, the csa of the cables should be increased to cater for the consequent increase in conductor temperature. More than one motor may be connected to a 16A final circuit, provided that the aggregate full-load rating of the motors does not exceed 16A. If a motor takes more than 16A full-load current, it should be fed from its own final circuit.

Final-circuit protection

Protection of final circuits is by means of fuses, circuit-breakers or miniature circuit-breakers located at switchboards and distribution boards. The protection is for over-currents caused by short-circuits between conductors, between conductors and earth, or overloads. The protective gear should be capable of interrupting any short-circuit current that may occur without danger of fire risk and damage to the associated equipment. In large installations, where there are main circuits, sub-mains and final circuits, it is often necessary to introduce a discriminative factor in the provision of protective gear. Where circuit-breakers are used, discrimination is provided by setting sub-circuit-breakers to operate at a lower over-current value and a shorter time-lag than the main circuit-breaker. Thus, if a fault occurs on a final circuit, the associated gear will come into operation, while the main breaker remains closed. However, if the fault persists, or the sub-circuit-breaker fails to operate within its specified time (e.g. 2 seconds), the main breaker will trip out (e.g. 0.5 second later).

Fuses are often used for back-up protection of circuit-breakers. Generally, where cartridge fuses are used the fuse will operate before the circuit-breaker, particularly in the event of a short-circuit current. Where small over-currents occur (e.g. overload) the circuit-breaker is likely to operate before the fuse blows.

Where full use is made of cartridge fuses, their ratings, type and make should be consistent for each circuit protected. The rating of sub-circuit and main fuses should be chosen so that in the event of faults the sub-circuit fuses blow first. Generally, discrimination between the fuses can be obtained if the rating of the sub-circuit fuses does not exceed 50 per cent of the rating of an associated main fuse. If this margin is too large, reference should be made to the data provided by the fuse makers. Discrimination is very difficult to obtain with any degree of accuracy where cartridge fuses and semi-enclosed rewirable fuses are used together because of the many factors which are involved in the operation of the latter type of fuse. These include the type of element, its size, the ambient temperature, its age and its material.

Choosing cable sizes

The selection of the size of a cable to carry a load current involves the consideration of the rating and type of the protective device, the ambient temperature and whether other cables are run alongside the cable (grouping). There are many situations in which cables can find themselves being overheated. The more obvious are the conditions set up when overcurrents are carried due to overloading and when a short-circuit occurs. Others include the increase in temperature when a number of current-carrying cables are bunched together, for instance in conduit and trunking, which is a situation in which each cable contributes its heat to that of others and which, because of the enclosed situation, produces an environment which can quickly lead to the deterioration of the cable insulation (particularly when PVC is involved) and lead to a possible source of fire. At about 80 °C, PVC becomes very soft, so that a conductor can 'migrate' or travel through the insulation and eventually make contact with earthed metalwork. This produces a shock-risk situation, with an increase in the leakage current which could prove fatal if the installation earthing arrangement is faulty. Eventually, when the insulation breaks down completely, a short-circuit occurs and the circuit is now dependent on the ability of the over-current protection device to operate to disconnect the circuit from its supply. As is probably realised, the time of operation of the protective device is crucial: a semi-enclosed fuse will take longer to operate than would a miniature circuit-breaker. In some circumstances, particularly where PVC insulated cables are used, the time taken by a semi-enclosed fuse to operate may be long enough for the cables to burn out and create a fire hazard.

Another problem which has occurred in recent years concerns the use of thermal insulation in buildings, with cables being installed in conditions where the natural heat produced by even their normal load currents cannot be dissipated easily. The IEE Regulations recognise the fact that, in these circumstances, the ratings of cables have to be reduced quite considerably. The regulations list 20 standard methods of installation (Table 4A of Appendix 4), each of which is identified by 'Methods'. These classifications are used in the tables which give the current-carrying capacities of cables. The installation conditions include 'enclosed' (e.g. in conduit, trunking and ducts); 'open and clipped direct' (e.g. clipped to a wall, to a cable tray, embedded direct in plaster which is not thermally-insulating, and suspended from a catenary wire); 'defined conditions', which include cables in free air; and cables 'in enclosed trenches'.

From this, it can be seen and appreciated that the selection of a cable to feed a circuit is now required to be undertaken with a number of factors to be considered carefully. Situations which were formerly taken for granted must now be investigated so that the cable is installed in the best conditions which will allow the cable to carry its load current with the safety of the user of the installation in mind.

The IEE Regulations require that the choice of a cable for a particular circuit must have due regard for a number of factors, and not just the circuit current. These factors include:

(*a*) the ambient temperature in which the cable is installed;
(*b*) the installation condition, e.g. whether grouped or bunched with other current-carrying cables, enclosed or installed 'open';
(*c*) whether the cable is surrounded by or in contact with thermal insulating material;
(*d*) whether the circuit is protected by semi-enclosed (rewirable) fuses to BS 3036.

The method of choosing the correct size of conductor for a particular load condition, as recommended by the IEE Regulations, is based on the rating of the overcurrent protective device. All factors affecting the cable in its installed condition are applied as divisors to the rating of the device, as the following examples show. The requirement of Regulation 525-01-02 must also be considered. In general, the size of every bare conductor or cable conductor shall be such that the drop in voltage from the origin of the installation to any point in that installation does not exceed 4% of the nominal voltage when the conductors are carrying the full load current. Values of volt drop per ampere per metre are given in the current rating tables in Appendix 4 of the Regulations. In this context, it should be noted that conductors of large cross-sectional area have different volt drops per ampere per metre for ac circuits than those operating from dc supplies. This is because of the reactance inherent in conductors carrying ac.

The following process for working out the correct size of cables is as follows:

1. First find the load current of the circuit (I_B).
2. Determine the correction factor for the ambient temperature which of course does not include the heat generated in the cable itself, but is more concerned with the maximum temperature of the medium through which the cable runs.
3. Determine the correction factor for grouping. Here we refer to Table 4B1 of the Regulations (Appendix 4).
4. Determine the correction factor if the cable is in contact with or is surrounded by thermal insulation material. Two factors are given: 0.75 if only one side of the cable is in contact with the material (e.g. a cable clipped to the side of a joist) and 0.5 if the cable is completely surrounded by the material.
5. Select the rating of the overcurrent device. If this is offering what used to be called 'close' protection, the correction factor is 1. If, however, protection is by means of a semi-enclosed fuse, the factor is 0.725. The rating of the device must at least equal the load current.
6. Determine the size of the circuit conductor by calculating its current rating. The actual size is obtained from the current-rating tables in Tables 9D1A to 4L4A in Appendix 4.
7. Check that the volt drop does not exceed the maximum permissible allowed by Regulation 525-01-02.

If I_z represents the current rating of the conductor and I_n the rating of the protective device, then

$$I_z = \frac{I_n}{C_g \times C_a \times C_i \times C_f} \text{ amperes}$$

where C_g is the factor for grouping;
C_a is the factor for ambient temperature;
C_i is the factor for thermal insulation (0.5 if cable is surrounded and 0.75 if the insulation is in contact with only one side of the cable;
C_f is the factor for the overcurrent device. This factor is 1 for all devices except semi-enclosed fuses, when the factor is 0.725.

The following examples indicate how the installation and circuit conditions affect the final choice of cable size. It should be noted, in passing, that the current-rating tables in Appendix 4 assume that what was previously considered as 'close' protection is offered as circuit protection.

Example 1

A 240V single-phase load of 30A is supplied from a distribution board located a distance of 87 m away. The cables are to be single-core, with 85 °C insulation and are enclosed in conduit. The ambient temperature is assessed as 60 °C. Protection is by MCB.

Maximum permissible volt drop (MPVD) = 4% of 240V = 9.6V

Load current (I_B) = 30A

Rating of protective device (I_n) (Figure 4, Appendix 3) = 32A

Correction factor for 60 °C (C_a) (from Table 4C1) = 0.71

$$\text{Current rating of conductor} = \frac{I_n}{C_a} = \frac{32}{0.71} = 45\text{A}$$

Size (csa) of conductor (from Table 4E1A) is 6 mm²

$$\text{Total volt drop} = \frac{\text{VD(mV)} \times I \times \text{length}}{1{,}000}$$

$$= \frac{7.9 \times 30 \times 87}{1{,}000}$$

$$= 20.6\text{V}$$

As this volt drop exceeds MPVD, the next larger size of cable is chosen (10 mm²) which results in a volt drop of 12.26V. This is still too high and the next size of cable is chosen which is 16 mm² which gives a final volt drop of 7.56V which is less than the MPVD.

In this example, the csa of the conductor was chosen to satisfy the current-carrying requirements in the installation conditions and then increased in csa until the volt drop requirements were met.

Example 2

A 230V single-phase load of 20kW operates at a power factor of 0.7 lagging and is fed from a distribution board located 30 m away by a two-core PVC-insulated and armoured cable with aluminium conductors. The cable is clipped direct to a cable tray which also carries two similar cables. The ambient temperature is 45 °C and the circuit is protected by a BS 88, Part 2 fuse.

MPVD = 4% of 230V = 9.2V

$$\text{Load current } (I_B) = \frac{20{,}000}{230 \times 0.7} = 124\text{A}$$

Rating of fuse (I_n) (from Figure 3B, Appendix 3) = 160A

Correction factor (C_g) for grouping (Table 4B1) = 0.89

Correction factor for temperature (C_a) (Table 4C1) = 0.79

$$\text{Rating of conductor} = \frac{I_n}{C_g \times C_a} = \frac{160}{0.89 \times 0.79}$$

$$= 227\text{A}$$

csa of conductor (Table 4D4A) = 70 mm²

$$\text{Total volt drop} = \frac{0.65 \times 124 \times 30}{1{,}000} = 2.41\text{V}$$

Therefore 70 mm² satisfies the current and volt drop requirements.

Example 3

A fixed load of 80A is carried by two single-core MICS cables with bare sheath and not exposed to touch. The distance between the 240V single-phase supply and the load is 22 m. The ambient temperature has been assessed at 80 °C. The cables are run clipped direct to a cable tray with three other single-phase circuits all spaced. The circuit is protected by a fuse to BS 3036. The sheath temperature is 105 °C.

MPVD = 4% of 240V = 9.6V

Load current (I_B) = 80A

Fuse rating (I_n) (Figure 2B, Appendix 3) = 100A

Correction factor for 80 °C (Table 4C2) = 0.77

Correction factor for grouping (Table 4B2) = 0.95

Factor for BS 3036 fuse = 0.725

Current-carrying capacity of cables =

$$\frac{100}{0.77 \times 0.95 \times 0.725} = 188\text{A}$$

From Table 4J2A = 35 mm^2

$$\text{Total volt drop} = \frac{1.25\text{mV} \times 80 \times 22}{1{,}000} = 2.2\text{V}$$

As this volt drop is well within the MPVD, 35 mm^2 cable is satisfactory.

Example 4

A 415V three-phase 60kW load at a power factor of 0.8 is fed by a four-core PVC-insulated, sheathed and armoured cable with copper conductors installed in a trench in 'Method 18' of Table 4A of Appendix 4 of the Regulations. The ambient temperature is 45 °C. The length of run is 40 m and overcurrent protection is by BS 88 fuses.

MPVD = 4% of 415V = 16.6V

$$\text{Load current } (I_B) = \frac{W}{3 \times V \times \text{pf}}$$

$$= \frac{60{,}000}{1.732 \times 415 \times 0.8}$$

$$= 104\text{A}$$

Rating of fuse (I_n)
(Figure 3A, Appendix 3) = 125A

Correction factor for temperature (C_a)
(Table 4C1) = 0.79

Correction factor for Installation Method 18
(Table 4B3) = 0.87

$$\text{Cable current rating} = \frac{I_n}{C_a \times C_g} = \frac{125}{0.79 \times 0.87}$$

$$= 182\text{A}$$

From Table 4D4A, 70 mm^2

From Table 4D4A, volt drop/A/m = 0.57mV

$$\text{Total volt drop} = \frac{\text{mV} \times I_B \times \text{length}}{1{,}000}$$

$$= \frac{0.57 \times 104 \times 40}{1{,}000} = 2.37\text{V}$$

This volt drop is well within the MPVD and so 70 mm^2 csa cable is satisfactory.

Example 5

A 240V, 4kW fixed resistive load is to be fed by a PVC-insulated and sheathed cable. The cable is run alongside four other similar cables and is in contact with thermal insulation on one side only. The ambient temperature is assessed as 40 °C. Protection is by BS 3036 fuse. The length of run is 18 m.

MPVD = 4% of 240V = 9.6V

$$\text{Load current } (I_B) = \frac{4{,}000}{240} = 16.7\text{A}$$

Fuse rating (I_n) (Figure 2B, Appendix 3) = 20A

Correction factor for temperature (C_a)
(Table 4C2) = 0.94

Correction factor for grouping (C_g)
(Table 4B1) = 0.6

Correction factor for thermal insulation (C_i)
= 0.75

$$\text{Rating of cable} = \frac{I_n}{C_a \times C_g \times C_i}$$

$$= \frac{20}{0.94 \times 0.6 \times 0.75} = 47\text{A}$$

csa of cable (Table 4D2A) = 10 mm^2

From Table 4A2A volt drop for 10 mm^2 = 4.4mV

$$\text{Total volt drop} = \frac{4.4 \times 16.7 \times 18}{1{,}000} = 1.32\text{V}$$

Therefore 10 mm^2 cable satisfies both current and volt drop requirements.

4 Wiring systems and installation methods

Sheathed wiring systems

A wiring system is an assembly of parts used in the formation of one or more electric circuits. It consists of the conductor, together with its insulation, its protection against mechanical damage (sheathing and/or armouring), certain wiring accessories for fixing the system, and joining and terminating the conductors.

As implied by the term 'sheathed wiring system', this method of wiring consists of an insulated conductor provided with a sheath which serves in some degree as a measure of protection against mechanical damage. The insulating materials include impregnated paper, rubber, plastics and mineral insulation. The sheathing materials include lead, tough rubber, plastics, aluminium and textiles. Some of the cables are designed with a view to cheapness and are particularly suited to domestic installations.

PVC (polyvinyl chloride sheathed)

This is an 'all-insulated' wiring system and commonly used for domestic installations. Though it is inferior to rubber, in the context of insulation-resistance and elastic properties, it has many advantages, not least being its comparative cheapness and ease of handling. Its main disadvantage is that it tends to soften at high temperatures, which is why its maximum operating temperature is 70 °C. Above this temperature there is a tendency for the conductors to migrate through the PVC which leads to much reduced values of insulation resistance, ultimately causing a breakdown to earth. There is also a lower temperature limit, set at 0 °C. At this temperature the PVC tends to harden and becomes a difficult material to work. The PVC-insulated cables have cores which are self-coloured for identification: red, black, blue and yellow. Blue and yellow are the colours used in three-core cables for two-way wiring. The sheathed cables contain an uninsulated circuit protective conductor which must be sheathed with insulating sleeving (coloured green/yellow) whenever the cable is made off for entry to wiring accessories.

Because the sheath can be damaged, it is recommended that additional protection be provided in situations where there is a possibility of the cable sustaining physical or mechanical damage. These cables are often run in floor spaces and in attics. The IEE Regulations draw attention to the possibility of the cables, run in these situations, coming into contact with thermal insulation material. Particularly where expanded polystyrene granules are used for loft insulation, there is the real chance that some of the plasticiser material used in PVC cable sheaths will 'migrate' and produce a hardening of the sheath. The other problem with PVC cables in contact with thermal insulation is that their current-rating can be drastically reduced. The relevant factors are 0.5 if the cables are surrounded by the material, and 0.75 if only one side is in contact.

PVC-SWA cables

Cables insulated with PVC and provided with steel-wire armouring are used extensively for main and sub-main cables and for wiring circuits in industrial installations. The conductors are copper or, where lightness and easy handling are needed, of aluminium. The cables are run on cable trays, racks, or installed in trenches. Terminations are by use of cable glands; flameproof glands are available for hazardous areas. If these cables are run to motor positions, where the machine is mounted on slide rails, a loop should be left in the cable to allow movement.

PILC (paper-insulated, lead-covered)

Paper-insulated, lead-sheathed and served (compounded jute) cables are mainly used for external underground distribution systems. But this type of cable has a wide application for internal distribution in factories and other industrial premises. It can, therefore, be regarded as a wiring system. The paper is impregnated and must be protected against the ingress of moisture; hence the use of cable-sealing boxes. The current-carrying capacity of this type of cable is greater than that of an equivalent butyl cable. Bending of PILC cables must be done very carefully. Fixing is normally by cleats. Further protection against mechanical damage is provided by armouring in the form of helical-wound steel wire or tape.

MIMS (mineral-insulated, metal-sheathed)
These cables consist of copper (or aluminium) conductors contained in a copper (or aluminium) sheath; the insulant is compressed mineral magnesium oxide. The most common type is the MICS cable, with copper as the main metal for conductors and sheath. The advantages of MICS cables are that they are self-contained and require no further protection (even against high temperatures and fire); they are impervious to water and oil, and immune from condensation. Because the conductor, sheath and insulant are inorganic, the cable is virtually ageless. Installation is simple, though the ends of the cable must be sealed off by special terminations against the ingress of moisture. Fixing is by clips or saddles. Cables can be obtained with a PVC oversheath. Because of the good heat-resisting properties of the cables, the current rating is higher than that of PVC or PILC cables. Applications for the cable include industrial installations and hazardous areas (see Chapter 5). Because the sheath is copper, it offers an excellent self-contained CPC. A full range of accessories is available for the system which is adaptable to the screwed-conduit system.

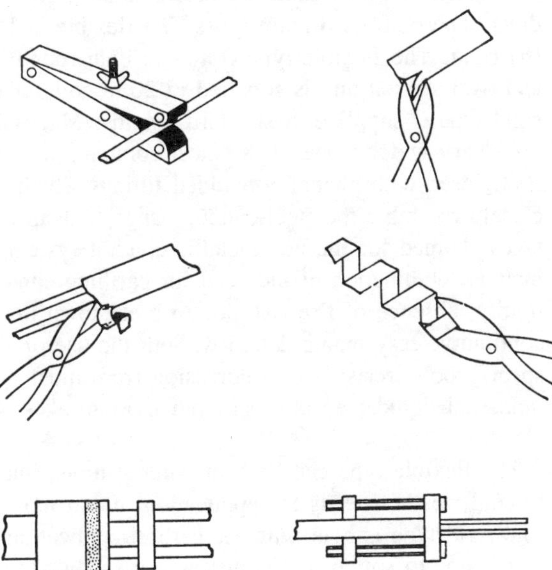

Figure 4.1. Detail of making-off MICS cable: cutting cable; sheath stripping; filling pot with compound; disc and conductor sleeve; fitted assembly before crimping.

Conduits, ducts, trunking

Steel conduit
The modern steel conduit system is available in two types or classes: Class A, plain-end conduit, and Class B, screwed-end conduit.

Class A conduit
This conduit is known as 'light gauge', plain, slip, pin-grip and lug-grip, according to the types. It has thin walls and is available as close-joint, brazed or welded joint, and solid-drawn. This type of conduit is not heavy enough to withstand threading and so presents problems where earth continuity must be maintained. Various methods for connecting the conduit with the associated accessories are available, including the more acceptable lug-grip, in which the fittings are held together by slipping the conduit end into, say, a box and holding it securely by tightening screws in the lugs. The conduit must be prepared before connecting by removing the enamel. If the contact surfaces are not cleaned, the electrical contact resistance will be too high. The applications of Class A conduit are limited to situations which are not damp and in which the wires do not require a high degree of protection against mechanical damage. Close-joint conduit cannot be bent or set because the seams tend to open. If care is used, slight bends and sets can be made in brazed or solid-drawn conduit. The standard sizes are 16 and 20 mm outside diameter. Fixing is by conduit saddles. The conduits are erected before cables are drawn into them. Unattached terminations are

fitted with push-on rubber or composition bushes to prevent the abrasion of cables.

Class B conduit

This conduit is known as heavy gauge or screwed conduit and is available as seam-welded, and solid-drawn. Alternative finishes are:

1. Black enamel for internal use in dry situations.
2. Silver grey finish for internal use in dry situations where the conduit is required to match decorations.
3. Hot galvanised or sherardised for external use where the conduit will be subjected to dampness or condensation. Because solid-drawn conduit is more expensive than seam-welded, its use is generally restricted to gas-tight and explosion-proof installation work. Welded-seam conduit is used generally for most good quality installation work. The conduits join with the wide range of associated accessories by means of screw threads, which give good mechanical strength and electrical continuity where the conduit acts as a CPC. The sizes available are from 16 to 32 mm, outside diameter. The thread is a shallow electric thread (ET). A full range of system accessories is available for screwed conduit: bends, elbows, tees and boxes. The first three can be of the inspection type (provided with a detachable lid) or 'solid' (no lid). Boxes have, of course, lids. Inspection bends, elbows and tees of the channel type are permitted, though they are not always suitable. Boxes are preferable to other fittings for drawing in cables, because they allow more space. Rectangular adaptable boxes are used at the intersection of several conduit runs. Fixings include saddles, clips and crampets.

Flexible conduit

Flexible conduits are generally used for the final connections to machinery (e.g. electric motors), where vibration and the possible need to adjust the position to an equipment makes a rigid conduit connection unsatisfactory. Flexible conduit can also deal with the need for complicated bends and sets. It is used for short runs where mechanical damage is unlikely to occur. Flexible conduit made from non-metallic material is dealt with in the following section. Flexible metallic conduit consists of a spirally wound, partially interlocked light-gauge galvanised steel strip, and may be watertight or non-watertight. It can be obtained with a PVC oversheath. As the conduit in itself is not accepted as a CPC, a separate CPC must be run between the special brass adaptors used to join the flexible to the ordinary screwed conduit. Sizes available are from 8 to 50 mm, internal diameter. Another type of flexible metallic conduit is the 'Kopex' conduit system. This consists of layers of metal and bituminised strip; it is usually supplied in 30 m coils. It is arranged to accommodate standard conduit fittings. It comes in sizes from 12 to 75 mm, outside diameter. Its great advantage is that once bent into shape it retains its position: no heating is required. The metal steel spiral of the conduit does not give satisfactory CPC facilities and so a separate CPC must be run.

Non-metallic conduit

Non-metallic conduits are obtainable in various grades and with the same diameters as steel conduits. There are two main types: (*a*) flexible and (*b*) rigid. The flexible type comes in both round and oval section and is supplied in 20 m coils. The rigid type is supplied in standard lengths. Materials used vary widely; one of the most common is PVC, used with phenolic-moulded fittings which closely resemble the steel-conduit range. Advantages claimed for the non-metallic conduit systems include: elimination of the need for earthing continuity; absence of fire risk due to breakdown in continuity; easy manipulation without the use of special tools; resistance to corrosion from most industrial liquids; no internal condensation takes place.

The flexible type can be bent without tools, but in cold weather needs the application of warmth. The rigid type is bent with the careful application of a flame to soften it. Fixings are by saddles or clips. When required, the conduit will cut its own thread when screwed into a threaded portion. But it can be easily threaded using the normal electric thread stocks and dies. If it is necessary to seal the system, the 'Bostik' type of adhesive may be used. Heavy-gauge PVC can be obtained which will withstand a fair amount of rough treatment both in erection and in service.

Trunking systems

The following advantages are claimed for trunking:

1. It is much lighter than conduits of the same capacity.
2. Fewer fixings are required for one trunking length than a run of multiple conduits.
3. Wiring is easier and quicker as the cables are 'laid-in' instead of being drawn in.
4. Erection time is reduced.
5. It is an easily adaptable wiring system.
6. Multiple-compartment trunking is available where the segregation of services is required.

Trunking is available in sections (square and rectangular). Lengths are joined by couplers

Figure 4.2. Detail of skirting trunking.

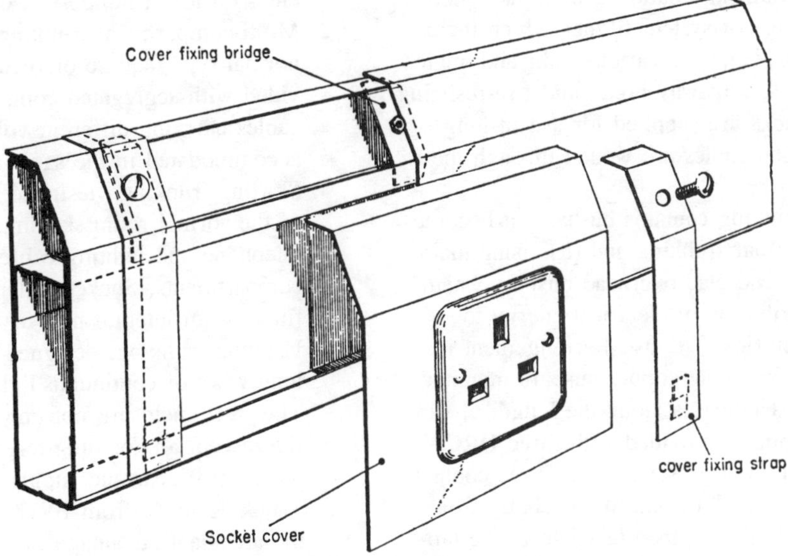

Figure 4.3. Detail of skirting trunking and accessory.

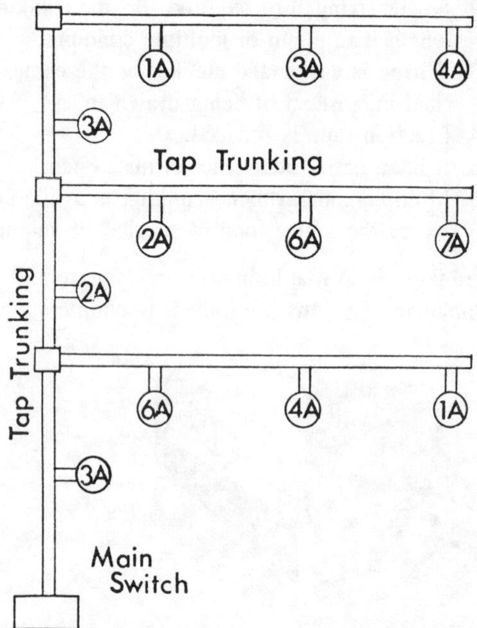

Figure 4.4. Typical layout of cable-tap trunking.

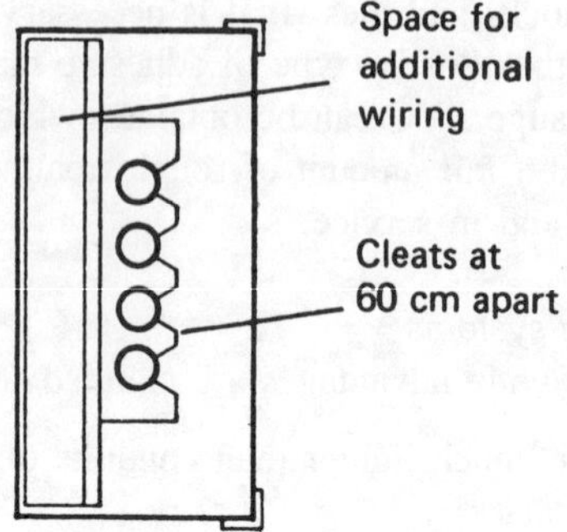

Figure 4.5. Detail of cable-tap trunking.

normally secured by screws. Earth straps fixed between each section ensure earth continuity along the trunking run. Trunking is available in both light-gauge and heavy-gauge forms; finish is generally enamel, but a galvanised finish can be supplied for certain installation conditions. There is a very wide range of system fittings which include blank ends, tees, bends of various radii and angles, elbows, couplers, four-way boxes and fire-resisting barriers. Pin-racks are supplied for use in long vertical runs. The cables are wound through the pins for support.

Where the trunking contains busbars, it becomes (*a*) overhead busbar trunking and (*b*) rising-main trunking. The metal-clad overhead busbar system is used for distribution of electrical energy to machines in factories. The usual arrangement is steel trunking containing copper busbars mounted on insulators. At intervals along the length of run a tapping-off point is provided with three HRC fuses mounted in a sheet-steel case. Three contact blades are designed to fit onto the busbars. Connections to machines are then taken from the tap-off boxes by flexible conduits, steel conduits or other wiring system. Though this system has a high initial cost, it enables much of the electrical installation work to be carried out before the machines are set in position. Additions and alterations can be carried out quickly. The factory lighting circuits can be fed from the tap-off boxes.

If long runs of busbars are installed, it is necessary to provide 'expansion' joints at approximately 30 m intervals to allow for expansion and contraction due to changes in temperature. Fire barriers must be installed at suitable intervals, particularly where the trunking passes from one room to another (to prevent the spread of fire).

Among other forms of trunking available are:

1. Flush trunking, which fits flush with walls; it entails a lot of builders' work to install.
2. Multi-compartment trunking, which is of the normal type (square or rectangular) and provided with segregated compartments so that cables carrying different voltages can be accommodated in the same trunking unit.
3. Skirting trunking, designed to take the place of the normal room skirting. It carries power, telephone and lighting cables in its various compartments. Socket-outlets can be easily fitted as an integral part of the trunking.
4. Lighting trunking, designed for use where long rows of continuous lighting are required. The steel enclosure not only carries the fluorescent and/or tungsten fittings, but also the control gear and supply cables.
5. Trunking made from PVC is available, with the attendant advantage of this material.
6. Cable-tap trunking. This type does not carry copper bars, but insulated supports which can

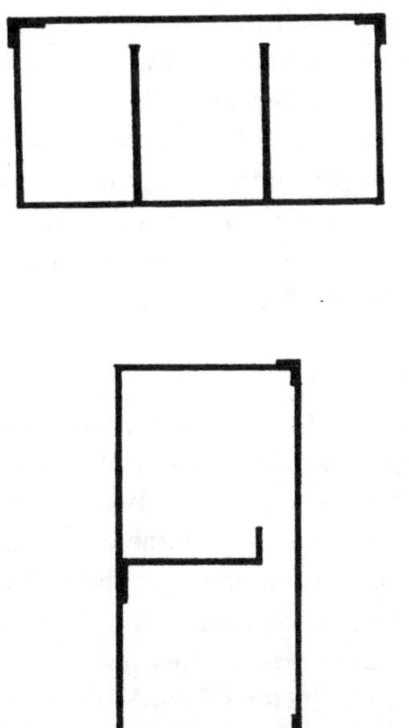

Figure 4.6. Detail of compartmented trunking.

accommodate rubber or PVC cables, from which supplies to machines and lighting circuits are tapped through fused tap-off boxes.

Rising mains are used to provide power to the various floors of multi-storey buildings. They are sheet-steel trunking containing copper bars on insulated supports. Provision is made for tapping off at each floor. Where required, distribution boards are fixed direct to the trunking.

Ducting systems

Because a majority of large buildings are now provided with solid concrete floors, the underfloor duct systems were brought into use to solve the problems of providing a distribution network of cables for power and lighting circuits. With the ducting system, the circuits are connected via surface conduits, thence to distribution boards. One of the advantages of this system is that where (e.g. in commercial buildings) a change of tenant is attended by new power layout requirements, the alterations required are easily carried out. Generally, the various ducts are arranged to feed ceiling points for the floor below and socket-outlets for the floor above. Junction boxes are provided with cover plates fixed flush with the floor finish. Because the ducting is laid out in straight lines between junction boxes, it is always possible to locate the runs. Underfloor ducting is available made from sheet metal or an insulated fibre material.

Special systems

Bare conductors

Bare conductors and/or lightly insulated conductors are installed in buildings for the following purposes only:

1. Earthing connections.
2. As the external conductors of earthed-concentric wiring systems.
3. Protected rising-main and busbar systems.
4. The conductors of extra-low voltage systems.
5. As collector wires for travelling cranes, trolleys.

Precautions must always be taken against the possibility of fire risk and earth-shock risk. In an extra-low voltage installation, the insulation must be adequate (light) for the voltage. Protection against fire risk is important because even low voltages can cause sufficient current to flow to overheat conductors and start an electric fire. In rising-main and busbar systems the conductors, which carry mains voltages of 415V/240V must, of course, be inaccessible to unauthorised persons. Strong insulators are needed to support the conductors particularly to withstand the mechanical forces set up when heavy currents flow (e.g. short circuits and switching surges). The conductors must be able to expand and contract with changes in the ambient temperature and the temperature changes caused by varying load-current conditions. The protection is generally in the form of trunking, or a channel; the metal is earthed. Bare conductors passing through walls, floors, partitions or ceilings must be protected by enclosing them in a non-absorbent incombustible insulating material. Collector wires for travelling cranes and trolleys must be protected by screens or barriers, unless they are so situated that there is no possibility of direct contact. Warning notices indicating the presence of the wires must be fixed along the length of run at intervals not exceeding 12 m.

Catenary systems
The most common system of catenary wiring is that which uses a high-tensile steel wire pulled taut between two fixing positions (e.g. between two buildings). The cable is then run along the catenary wire, being supported in some way. The extension of this type of wiring is in the proprietary wiring system known as the 'Grid-suspension System'. It consists of a central galvanised-steel, high-tensile stranded wire surrounded by a number of PVC-insulated conductors. The whole is enclosed with PVC tape and PVC sheathing. Textile filling is used to obtain a circular section. The catenary wire is secured at each end of its run by eye-bolts and strainers. Special connecting boxes are used at tees and right-angled turns. Applications include the larger types of industrial buildings and similar installations where other types of wiring system would be either difficult or expensive to install. The system can be adapted to supply feeds for lighting fittings along the length of the run.

The system has also been used for overhead street lighting and in factories instead of an overhead busbar system where the amount of power required for machines is small and the expense involved in installing the latter system would be unjustified. The advantages claimed for the system include: completely waterproof; weight imposed on a building is reduced; installation can be left until the building work is completed; reduced installation costs; the system absorbs vibration and lamp-replacement costs are reduced.

Earthed-concentric system
In its simplest form, this system consists of a single insulated conductor protected by an earthed metallic sheath which is also used as the neutral or return conductor. The sheath is then known as a PEN conductor, which combines the functions of both protective conductor and neutral conductor. The first requirement to be satisfied is that the system is supplied by a privately-owned transformer in such a way that there is no metallic connection with the general public supply. In addition, every joint in the outer conductor and every termination must be electrically and mechanically sound. No means of isolation or switching shall be inserted in the outer conductor and every such conductor shall be insulated or have an insulating covering suitable for the highest voltage to which it may be subjected. The outer conductor must be common to only one circuit, which requirement does not preclude the use of a twin or multicore cable to serve a number of points contained within one final circuit. A typical wiring system is MICS cable with PVC covering.

Overhead conductor
Though not an actual wiring system, the overhead cable does provide distribution of electrical energy between points of use, and between buildings where there is some considerable distance between the main control of supply and the point of use (e.g. between a farmhouse and a water-pump 1 km away). The cable used in this instance is PBJ. It consists of a conductor of hard-drawn copper, lapped with impregnated paper tapes, then wound with cotton impregnated with a special compound which has a red-lead base; finally, it is weatherproofed. Bare stranded conductors are also used, where heavier amounts of electrical power are required to be distributed; they are more associated with supply-authority overhead distribution than with consumers' distribution. PVC insulation is common nowadays.

Installation methods

Good workmanship
At the beginning of Chapter 13 of the IEE Regulations, 'Fundamental Requirements for Safety', it is stated: 'Good workmanship and proper materials shall be used'. This is a requirement with which all practising electricians and others must be familiar. Bad, shoddy and careless work can very easily become a source of real danger to those who are to operate electrical equipment and circuits. The good workman is the man who does not merely produce a good-looking, neat job with his tools. The job must also be the result of the sound and considered application of electrical theory. With the ever-increasing degree of complexity in circuits and apparatus which the electrician of today meets in his work, it is becoming more important than ever that theory is seen to go alongside good practice with tools, whatever the

shape or form of the latter. The good workman, then, is familiar with the best methods of installing electrical equipment and circuits, and performs his job with a knowledgeable background of the regulations, both non-statutory (e.g. IEE Regulations) and statutory (e.g. Factories Act).

General considerations

Before any electrical installation is begun, some careful thought must be given to the factors or conditions which decide the type of wiring system, its associated accessories, the wiring accessories and the electrical equipment and fittings to be installed. The following are some of the most important points to be considered:

(*a*) *The type of building*. Whether the installation work is for a permanent building, a temporary building or for an extension to an existing building.

(*b*) *Flexibility*. Whether the wiring system must be one which will allow it to be easily extended or altered at some time in the future. For instance, a building may have different tenants during its life, all of whom may require the provision of installation arrangements suitable to their needs (e.g. offices, shops, stores, showrooms or dwelling places). The more consideration given to this factor in the initial stages of installation planning, the less will be the cost of extension or alteration at a future time.

(*c*) *Installation conditions*. Whether the installation is likely to be subjected to mechanical damage, moisture, fumes, weather, abnormal or subnormal temperatures, inflammable or explosive dust, gas or vapour.

(*d*) *Appearance*. Whether the building is such that the electrical installation must be hidden, or its appearance can be allowed. For instance, surface-run conduit is not out of place in a workshop, but it would be in a suite of offices where appearance is of primary importance.

(*e*) *Durability*. Whether the installation is to last for the time of the life of the building or not. Certain systems have a 'life' in normal installation conditions. The following table shows a rough estimate of how long a system should be allowed to exist before replacement or thorough overhaul:

Wiring system		*Approximate years life in normal circumstances*
Steel-conduit system with PVC cables (concealed work)	conduit	35
	cables	20
Steel-conduit system with PVC cables (surface work)	conduit	30
	cables	20
Steel-trunking system with copper bars		35
MICS cables		25

(*f*) *Cost*. Whether the amount of money available for the electrical installation part of a building is restricted, or not. This will then dictate to the installation engineer that he must provide the best job for the smallest amount of money, while still making the installation safe to use. Cost is also related to the time of installation. It may be cheaper to install an MICS system than a conduit system. Even though the MICS system has a high materials cost, money is saved in labour costs.

(*g*) *Safety*. This is an aspect which is extremely important. Apart from minimising any danger which may arise from factor (*c*) above, safety must also be viewed from the point of view of the type of supply and the earthing arrangements available.

The estimating or installation engineer must consider these main points and other minor ones, before the final choice in favour of one or another wiring system is made. A thorough knowledge of the wiring systems, accessories and equipment used in different types of buildings will indicate to the practising electrician the initial planning considerations involved before the work began.

There are many wiring systems on the market

today. Each is designed to perform its duty in specific circumstances. Some are better than others: the cheapest system is not always the best. Nor, on the other hand, is the most expensive system. The following notes are an indication of the factors involved in the installation of some of the most common wiring systems available at the present time.

Conduit systems (metal)

There are many metal-conduit systems including heavy-gauge screwed steel conduit, light-gauge lug-grip steel conduit, aluminium conduit, copper conduit, flexible steel conduit. A conduit is a tube designed, so far as electrical work is concerned, to carry electric cables. The most common form of conduit is steel made to BS Specification 31.

There are two classes of steel conduit: Class 'A' and Class 'B'. The latter is screwed conduit made from heavy-gauge steel. It is by far the most popular system for permanent wiring installations for commercial and industrial premises. Among its advantages are that it gives good protection against mechanical damage, it allows for easy rewiring, it minimises fire risks and provides good earth continuity. To erect a good-looking and correct conduit installation requires a certain amount of skill. Among its disadvantages are its cost compared with other systems; it is difficult to install under wood floors; and it is liable to corrode in acidic, alkaline and other fumes. In certain conditions, moisture from condensation may occur inside the conduit. Class 'B' conduit is produced in two forms: solid-drawn or seam-welded. The finishes are black enamel for dry situations, silver grey for dry situations where the finish will match decorations, and hot-galvanised or sherardised finish for external use, or internal use where there is dampness.

The conduit has many different types of system accessories: boxes, fixings, terminations, all of which are necessary to complete the conduit installation.

Class 'A' conduit is light-gauge and is often called 'slip' conduit, whereas Class 'B' conduit fittings and accessories are screwed together to complete the installation. Class 'A' conduit is not screwed and the parts are connected by slipping the end of a conduit into a socket. The end is then secured by lug-grip or pin-grip. This class, limited to 12 mm maximum size, is generally used for installations at 250V or below, and where there is definitely no risk of moisture affecting the cables it carries. The conduit is cut by making a deep groove round the circumference with a file, and then bending it round the knee. This leaves a sharp edge which must be filed. Where the conduit end enters a fitting, the end must be cleaned of enamel to make a good contact between the two surfaces for providing good earth continuity. Slight sets can be made by bending round the knee. Care must be exercised, however, otherwise the conduit may collapse.

Installing Class 'B' conduit

The only type of cable excluded from being drawn into a conduit is high-voltage types. The cables usually associated with conduits are butyl and silicone rubber insulated, taped and braided, and PVC-insulated. The regulations require that live and neutral cables of associated circuits must be drawn into the same conduit. The size of conduit to be installed depends on the number of cables to be carried. The number should be such that they can be drawn in quite easily, and in no circumstances should it be greater than the recommended space factor.

There are two distinct methods of installing screwed conduit: surface and concealed. The first consideration in the installation of surface conduit is to plan the runs. For instance, where several runs are parallel, it is necessary to make sure that there is no crossing at points where directions change. Routes should be chosen to keep the runs as straight as possible. Conduits should be, as far as possible, kept away from gas and water pipes. Places where dampness might occur require special consideration. Though manufactured bends, elbows and inspection tees are available, it should be remembered that, where possible, all bends should be made by setting the conduit. Use of inspection fittings of the channel type is not good practice because they do not allow sufficient room for drawing in cables. The better method is to use round boxes. These look much better and have ample capacity, not only for drawing in cables, but to accommodate a few coils of slack cable (which should always be done at draw-in points).

Inspection boxes must be installed in positions where they will remain accessible during the life of the installation. The conduit system for each circuit should be erected before any cables are drawn in.

It makes common sense that all conduits should be securely fixed. To comply with this requirement there are a number of types of fixings available. Conduit clips are in the form of half a saddle. Though they save using an extra screw (they have only one hole), they are not satisfactory if the conduit is subject to any considerable strain. Saddles are better, and are fixed with screws — not nails. To give the conduit a good fixing, saddles should be spaced at not more than 1.3 m apart, or where required. Where fittings are to be mounted on conduit boxes, the backs of the boxes should be drilled and fixed; otherwise a saddle should be provided on each side of the box and close to it. Spacer-bar saddles are ordinary saddles mounted on a spacing plate with a slot in it. They are used where the conduit leaves conduit fittings. An ordinary saddle would become distorted when screwed down; the spacer-bar saddle takes up the thickness of the fitting and allows the conduit to run straight. Also, the spacer-bar saddle prevents the conduit from making intimate contact with damp plaster, walls and ceilings which might otherwise cause corrosion of the conduit. The distance saddle is used to keep the conduit about 10 mm off the wall, so that any dust which might collect behind conduits can be removed easily. It is for this reason that they are generally specified for places where dust traps must be avoided (e.g. hospitals).

Among other conduit fixings are multiple saddles, where two or more conduits follow the same route, and girder clips, where conduits are run across girders.

When conduit is cut with a hacksaw, burrs are formed on the inner bore of the conduit. If this burr is not removed the insulation of the cables, as they are drawn into the conduit, will be damaged. Burrs are removed with a round file, or with a conduit reamer. If steel conduits are to be installed in damp situations, they must be galvanised or sherardised, and must be Class 'B'. Fixing saddles and screws used must be of the non-rusting type. Suitable precautions must be taken to prevent moisture due to condensation forming inside the conduit. This effect is most likely to occur when the conduit passes from the outside to the inside of a building, where the temperatures are different. In all positions where moisture may collect, holes must be drilled (generally in boxes) at the lowest points in the conduit system so that moisture is drained away. It is generally advisable to use PVC-insulated or similar cables, as they are more suitable for moist conditions.

It is an important requirement to ensure that all conduit is not only mechanically sound, but that there is electrical continuity across the conduit joints. The electrical resistance of the conduit, together with the resistance of the earthing lead, measured from the earth electrode, must not exceed twice that of the largest current-carrying conductor of the circuit. So as not to exceed this figure it is necessary to ensure that all conduit connections are tight and that the enamel is removed from places where a metal-to-metal contact is made.

Before drawing any cable into conduit, the system must be fully erected. Also, the conduits must be freed from any obstruction or dampness. This can be done by pulling a small cloth through the conduit (as in cleaning a rifle); this will remove any moisture that may have collected while the conduit has been exposed to weather during building operations. When drawing in cables, the cable reels or drums must be free to revolve, otherwise the cables will spiral off the drums and become twisted, which could damage the insulation. If a number of cables have to be drawn in at the same time, a stand or support should be fixed up so as to permit all the drums to revolve freely. It is good practice to begin the drawing-in operation from a mid-point in the conduit system. This will reduce the length of cable that has to be drawn in. A steel tape should be used from one draw-in point to another. The tape is used more to draw in a draw-wire rather than for drawing the cables in. When the draw-wire has been pulled through the conduit by the tape, the ends of the cables should then be attached to the end of the draw-wire. The ends of the cables are bared for about 50 mm and threaded through a loop in the draw-wire. Always when drawing in a number of cables, one man should pull at the receiving end while another feeds the cable in carefully at the other end, making sure that no twisting takes place. When necessary, french chalk can be rubbed onto the cable insulation to make the drawing-in operation easier.

Where conduits have to be concealed, they are installed while the building is being erected and can be buried in floors and walls in such a manner that the cables can be drawn into them after the building has been completed, or nearly so. Floors and walls are either solid or hollow, made of cavity-brick, hollow tiles or wood. The conduit runs should be planned so that they run parallel to joists. Where crossing must occur, the joists are slotted to enable the conduit to be kept just below the level of the floorboards. Trap-doors, or short lengths of floorboard, must be left at the positions of all junction boxes. These traps must be screwed down and marked.

Where the floors are solid, it is not possible to leave junction boxes in the floors. In this case, the conduit system is arranged so that the cables are drawn in through ceiling or wall points. Conduits to be buried in reinforced concrete should be fixed in position before the concrete is poured. In this instance, special care must be taken to ensure that all joints are tight and painted with a bituminised paint to prevent rusting. Where the enamel has been removed from the conduit during cutting and threading, paint should be applied.

Installing flexible metallic conduit

This conduit is made from locked spirals of thin metal and is used for the final connection to motors to provide for the movement of the motor if fixed on slide rails. It also prevents any noise or vibration being transmitted from the motor to other parts of the building. Metallic conduit should preferably be of the watertight pattern and connected by brass adaptors to the steel conduit with which it is used. These adaptors are made so that they screw onto the flexible conduit and also into the steel conduit. Because metallic flexible conduit is not a good earth conductor, an earth wire must be run from the solid conduit system to the frame of the motor. Where the conduit is provided with PVC sleeving, it can be used where oil is present.

Conduit systems (non-metallic)

Non-metallic conduits come in both rigid and flexible types. They are supplied in the same diameters as steel conduits. The flexible type is available in coils of 17 m in length; rigid conduits are supplied in the standard steel conduit lengths of 4–5 m. There are a number of advantages claimed for non-metallic conduit systems: there is no need to provide earth continuity; there is an absence of fire risk due to a breakdown in earth continuity; they resist corrosion; no internal condensation takes place. When it is necessary to provide an earth continuity conductor (e.g. at socket-outlet points) a separate wire is drawn into the conduit.

Though this system does not provide great mechanical protection, it does offer many advantages and can be used for specific purposes. Accessories are modelled on the steel conduit types. Rigid conduit can be screwed in the same way as steel conduit. Heavy-gauge rigid types are available for use where unfavourable situations are likely to be encountered. Because they are easy and clean to handle, installation time is a small factor in the total cost of the job. If sealing against the entry of moisture is necessary, Bostik is used. Tools are not needed to bend conduits, though in cold weather they need the application of warmth before they can be worked. All non-metallic conduits shall be non-inflammable, non-hygroscopic, damp-proof, mechanically continuous and strong.

Metal-sheathed wiring systems

The main metal-sheathed wiring system in use today is the mineral-insulated, metal-sheathed (MIMS). The cable consists of copper conductors insulated with a highly compressed magnesium oxide (MgO) powder. The sheath is a seamless copper tube, and this makes the copper-sheathed system (MICS). Among the advantages claimed for the MIMS system is that the cables are self-contained and need no further protection; the system can withstand high temperatures (150 °C, depending on the type of termination) and fire, is impervious to oil and water and is immune to condensation.

Installation of the MICS system is comparatively simple. The cable is generally saddled to walls and ceilings. Small sizes of the cable can be bent sharply, though it is stated that a bending radius of six times the cable's own diameter will mean that the bend can be straightened out at a later date. Terminations are available for the cable. They must be made with care because the insulation must be kept absolutely dry. Although this type of cable can withstand severe hammering, it is necessary to take precautions against the sheath being punctured with possible entry of moisture to the insulation.

Where the cables pass through floors, ceilings and walls, the holes must be made good with cement to prevent the spread of fire. The sheathing and joint boxes must be bonded throughout the installation to form an earth-continuity conductor. The resistance from the earthing point to any point in the installation using the system must not exceed twice that of the largest current-carrying conductor. The range of glands, reducing nipples and sockets is designed to be accommodated in the standard boxes and fittings of the conduit system, both screw and slip type.

Trunking and ducting

Where a large number of cables have to be installed, or where the cable sizes are large, it is often preferred to use cable trunking rather than conduit. Trunking is rectangular in section, with a cap and is made from sheet steel. There are many variations of the trunking system, which has a full range of fittings and accessories to enable it to meet the specification of any installation. Steel trunking is easy to erect. It can be screwed direct to walls and suspended across trusses. When the run is vertical, the cables should be supported by pin racks. Because the trunking forms part of the earth-continuity conductor arrangement in the installation, it is necessary, as in the conduit system, to ensure that all sections, fittings and so on of the system are bonded together. This is done either by small copper bars joining each of two parts, or by running a separate conductor in the trunking, bonding this wire to the trunking itself. Cables for lighting and power circuits must not be installed in the same groove or section as cables feeding telephones, bells and ELV alarm systems. However, if the trunking is designed with segregated sections or compartments, then the regulation requirements are satisfied.

When the trunking is designed to contain copper bars, the system is known as busbar trunking, or overhead busbar trunking. The former is used generally for rising mains, supplying mains to each floor of a multi-floor building. The overhead busbar trunking system is used in industrial

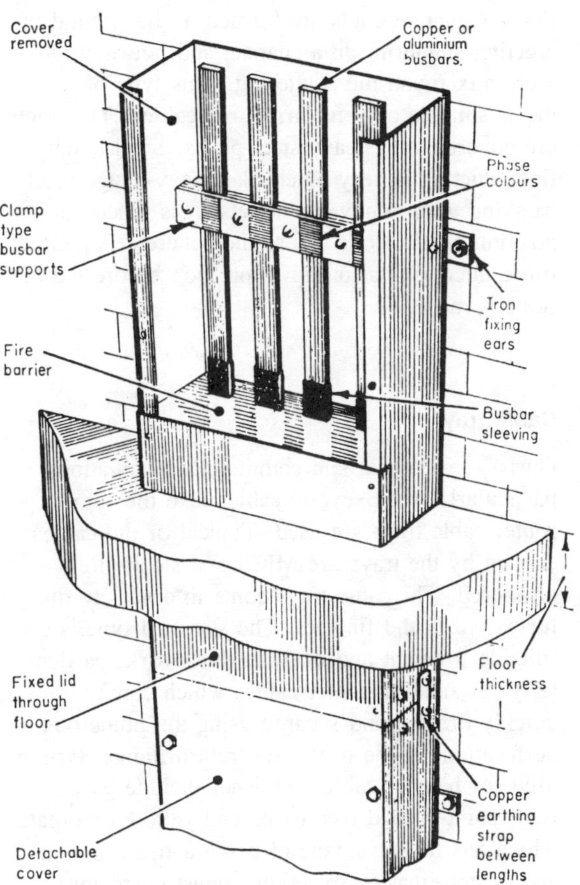

Figure 4.7. Detail of rising mains.

installations where a considerable degree of flexibility in the electrical provisions is required. Tap-on boxes can be fitted to the trunking at regular intervals throughout its length.

The main installation points which apply to trunking are: (*a*) it must not be installed where inflammable vapours are present; (*b*) fire barriers (e.g. asbestos packing) must be installed inside the trunking where it passes through floors, walls and partitions, and the holes must be made good with cement after the trunking has been installed; (*c*) allowances should be made in long sections of trunking for expansion in conditions of high temperatures. All busbar trunking should be marked DANGER and the voltage stated. Lids must fit securely.

Ducting is used to provide a network of cable ducts in concrete floors. There are three types of ducting: concrete, steel underfloor and fibre underfloor. Concrete ducts are formed in the ground by erecting shuttering in a channel and pouring concrete mix round the shuttering. This type of ducting is suitable only for armoured cables. The ducts are covered with heavy steel plates. Steel underfloor ducting is very much like heavy-gauge steel trunking with removable outlets. It is placed in position on the floor before the concrete is poured. Fibre ducting is also laid in position before the floor is made.

Cable tray

On large industrial and commercial installations, particularly when several cables take the same route, cable trays are used. Typical of the cables carried by the trays are MICS and steel-wire armoured. The cable trays come in a variety of forms, sizes and finishes. The standard type is suitable for light and medium duty work, particularly for small-diameter cables which can be quickly dressed and secured using the numerous perforations in the tray. The 'return-flange' type is used for heavier cables. Finishes include galvanised, paint-primed (red oxide and yellow chromate, which has the advantage of being a fire retardant and offers greater protection against corrosion), and plastic-coated finishes, used where protection is required against chemical contamination or where the surface must be kept clean.

When installing the trays, they must be well supported. A full range of accessories is available which can cope with most site requirements. These accessories include bends, reducers, cross-pieces and inside and outside risers. Cable ladders are used where there is a need to carry heavy cables across long unsupported spans. Expansion fishplates are needed where the installation conditions include large temperature fluctuations and long runs of cable ladder are used.

All-insulated wiring systems

This class of wiring system includes PVC (PVC-sheathed) cables. Their main disadvantage is that they do not offer adequate protection against mechanical damage, though they are relatively cheap and easy to install. The accessories associated with an all-insulated wiring system are also made from insulating material.

The following points are to be observed when installing all-insulated wiring systems. Wherever possible, the cores of the cables must be identified by colours. Note, however, that this cannot apply to a twin cable feeding a switch, where one core, the live, is red in accordance with the regulations, and the other, the switch wire, is still the live part of the circuit, though coloured black. At switches, socket-outlets and lighting fittings and junction boxes, the sheath of the cable must be taken inside the accessory. There is no objection to PVC cables being buried direct in plaster provided care is taken to ensure that there is no likelihood of damage being caused by, say, nails and screws. In such circumstances, it is best to use a conduit drop to contain the feed to switches and socket-outlets. If these isolated lengths of conduit are completely concealed they need not be earthed. Otherwise they must be earthed, particularly if they do not terminate in a hardwood or insulated accessory box.

Catenary systems

These systems are designed to take supplies from one building to another by overhead means, or else for buildings with high ceilings. In its simplest form, the system is a steel wire strained between two points on which insulated cables are carried. For short runs the steel wire carries the cables which are taped to it. The composite catenary cable consists of a high-tensile galvanised steel wire round which are located the PVC cables. Packings of jute or hemp are used to produce a circular section. When installing this type of system, it is important to ensure that the steel wire carries the weight and not the conductors themselves. The proprietary system available at present has a full range of accessories and special fittings. If the system is used out of doors it is advisable to fill the connecting boxes with a plastic compound against the entry of moisture. The catenary wire must be securely fixed at each end. The clearance between the cables and the ground must be adequate. A pole may have to be used to act as an intermediate support between the two ends. The cable, where it leaves the catenary, should pass through a suitable glazed porcelain lead-in tube. Drip-loops should be provided at entry points so that rainwater is not led into the building by running along the cable (see Figure 2.6).

New systems

In the present climate of increasing industrialised building, it is inevitable that new systems of wiring should come into existence. Just as the early days of electrical installation work were exciting because of the new products and designs that appeared on the market — some to stay and some to fade away — so our times are interesting for the newly qualified electrician. Prefabricated and prepackaged wiring is, of course, not new. But it is now having a very important impact on wiring methods, particularly where repetition jobs are to be carried out (e.g. on municipal housing sites). The systems on the market at present, or being developed, can be divided into four broad classes:

1. Surface systems in the form of skirtings, architraves and covings complete with purpose-made accessories, and supplied with wiring and consumer's main fuse units.
2. Skirting, architrave and covings to accommodate a standard range of accessories with which wiring is not supplied.
3. Cable 'harness' systems for installing where ducts, conduits or means of access are provided such as in (2) above.
4. Precut and preassembled metal or plastic-sheathed cables for incorporating in the structural members either on site or in the factory.

Some factory prewired systems of skirting and architrave trunking using push-fit connectors enable a house to be completely rewired in one day.

5 Special installations

Though most installations do not present any great problems with regard to the wiring and the equipment used, there are some types of installation which are called 'special' in that both the wiring and the apparatus used require special attention, with regard to their choice, installation or maintenance. This chapter deals with some of these special aspects. Generally, certain provisions are required to be made to render the complete installation, including the installed equipment, safe to use and as free as practicable from the risk of electric shock.

Condensation

Condensation perhaps presents the most common problems in installations and may be present to such a degree that an installation is classed as 'special' because certain requirements must be satisfied to meet installation or operating conditions. Condensation exists where there is a difference in temperature, for example where equipment is installed inside a room in which the ambient temperature is high, the equipment being controlled by switchgear outside the room and in a lower ambient temperature. If the equipment and switchgear are connected with conduit, condensation will occur inside the conduit. Condensation will also occur where a room has a high ambient temperature during the day working hours and when the temperature subsequently falls while the room is unoccupied during the night. In situations where the problem is acute, the use of galvanised fittings is recommended. Fixing materials may also be required to withstand any corrosive action which may occur (e.g. with dissimilar metals). The general recommendation is that metal conduits should not be used where condensation is likely to occur.

Cold stores

Condensation occurs frequently in cold-store chambers and around refrigeration plant. Switchgear and other control equipment should be installed outside the chambers in a position some reasonable distance away from blasts of cold air and clear of door openings where changes of temperature are likely to occur. MI and lead-sheathed cables should be glanded into totally enclosed lighting fittings. Cables should be run in the cold room on wood battens. Cable entries into the cold rooms should be sealed with a bituminous material. The aspect of working with PVC cables in low temperatures is an important installation detail. The installation of non-metallic conduit systems and associated fittings in temperatures which are below zero also require consideration.

Corrosive atmospheres

Wherever metal is used, there is often the attendant problem of corrosion and its prevention. There are two necessary conditions for corrosion: (*a*) a susceptible metal and (*b*) a corrosive environment. Nearly all of the common metals corrode under most natural conditions. Corrosion is a natural electro-chemical process or reaction by which a metal reverts in the presence of moisture to a more chemically stable form usually of the type in which it is found in nature.

In installation work, the problem of corrosion is more apparent in certain types of situation. Chemical works, salt works, cow byres and other ammonia-affected areas, all come into the class of installation which requires special attention. Corrosion, in the normal installation condition, may affect earth connections.

Generally, the precautions to prevent the occurrence of corrosion include:

1. The prevention of contact between two dissimilar metals (e.g. copper and aluminium).
2. The protection of cables, wiring systems and equipment against the corrosive action of water, oil and dampness, unless they are suitably designed to withstand these conditions.
3. The protection of metal sheaths of cables and metal-conduit fittings where they come into contact with lime, cement, plaster and certain hardwoods (e.g. beech or oak).
4. The use of bituminised paints and PVC oversheathing on metallic surfaces liable to corrosion in service.

Electrostatic situations

Static electricity is generated whenever two dissimilar surfaces are brought into intimate contact and then separated. When both surfaces are conducting, there is little apparent separation of charge, since both will be maintained at the same potential until the last moment of contact. As soon as the surfaces part, however, a spark may be observed. Generally, considerable electrification through static occurs on the separation of a good conductor and a good insulator. Many of the flammable liquids in use today have high insulating properties. When they are handled, or being poured through a pipe opening, considerable static charges may be generated to produce serious static sparks. Although precautions are taken to prevent such liquids being disturbed and so to generate static electricity, e.g. by restricting the rate of flow, the electrician may, in addition to his normal work, be called on to earth the metal pipes or tanks associated with these liquids.

Certain gases and vapours (e.g. a mixture of ether and oxygen) associated with the operating theatres of hospitals give rise to risk of explosion. Static is a problem peculiar to hospitals, where rubber is often used for sheets, flooring, trolley tyres and so on. Generally, the rubber is made conducting to reduce the incidence of static. All nylon and other materials which easily generate static are excluded, both from articles in the operating theatre and from articles of clothing worn by persons in the room. Humidification is often adopted to prevent static — all surfaces are moistened to provide an overall conducting surface to the general mass of earth.

The prevention of static involves the connection with the general mass of earth of all metal tanks, vessels, containers, pipes and the like, which are in contact with powders or fluids liable to produce static if handled or moved. Where a rubber belt runs on a metal pulley, the pulley should be bonded and earthed. Otherwise, anti-static belting is recommended; a belt dressing of graphite can also be applied, or a mixture of glycerine and water.

Temporary installations

The general definition of a temporary installation is one which is designed to be in service for not more than three months. Temporary installations are most often found on building sites, where electrical services are required during the construction of a building. As might be expected, though the installation is temporary, it is still necessary and just as important to ensure that the safety aspect, in the use of electricity on the site, is always considered carefully. Various regulations (Section 604) allude to the requirements when an installation is classed as 'temporary'. If the installation is required for use for periods longer than three months, then it must be completely overhauled at the end of the three-month period. As soon as the installation is no longer required, it must be disconnected from the supply and dismantled completely.

There are certain types of buildings, and working conditions on sites, which receive the attention of the insurance companies and local bye-laws. Thus, not only must the electrician comply with the full requirements of the IEE Regulations regarding temporary installations, but any extra requirements also. For example, though many temporary installations are carried out in some cheap form of wiring system (such as PVC-sheathed), certain types of buildings must be wired in conduit. This is particularly the case where the temporary installation is to supply services for exhibitions in permanent buildings. In many cases, the local bye-laws and insurance companies insist on the use of screwed conduit.

Many temporary installations are used to provide lighting and power for a building during the course of its construction. The regulations permit, in instances where there is adequate protection for the cables, rubber and PVC cables. However, if there is a danger of the cables being exposed to mechanical damage or being handled, then protection must be given to the cables in the form of armouring. Metal-sheathed cables, other than mineral-insulated, metal-sheathed (MIMS), must be armoured and, in addition, the relevant IEE Regulations must be satisfied. Where conduit is used to contain the cables, there must be no relaxation in the IEE Regulations relating to metallic conduit systems. All cables and wiring systems must be adequately supported. A temporary installation does not mean a 'hook-up'.

Where the wiring is exposed to weather conditions, the risk of danger is increased considerably, particularly to the building operatives handling electrical power tools. To ensure that the danger aspect is minimised or, which is better, completely eliminated, the temporary installation must be in charge of a 'competent person'. This person is generally accepted, particularly by the building industry, as a skilled, qualified electrician.

The electrician is thus fully responsible for the use of the installation and for any alteration or extension. The name and designation of such person shall be prominently displayed close to the main switch or circuit-breaker. This responsibility is given a legal and moral aspect which must be carefully considered by the electrician taking charge of the installation. Only he, or a suitably qualified delegate, is allowed to install new equipment, or make alterations to the installation. The new work must either be supervised and finally checked and inspected by the 'competent person' or by his delegate.

Of course, a temporary installation must be tested and inspected before it is put into service. It must comply, in all respects, with the requirements of the IEE Regulations on insulation-resistance and earth-continuity. In this respect, there will be no difference between a temporary installation and a permanent installation.

In the interests of safety, it is always recommended that a low-voltage supply be used. The supply should be obtained from a double-wound transformer which will reduce the supply voltage to 110V or less, and have the secondary winding centre-tapped to earth.

A voltage of 110V is now regarded as the standard voltage for supplies on building sites: the use of a reduced voltage on a correctly earthed supply-system greatly reduces the risk of accident. The bulk of the comprehensive range of power tools available for the various aspects of building work are now rated for 110V. However, though 240V will still be found on building sites, it is always recommended that the lower voltage be used.

The electrician responsible for the distribution of electrical energy on a temporary installation on a building site has to attend to many aspects of safety. In many instances, it is found that not enough socket-outlets are provided, with the result that operatives using tools powered by electricity have to use very long flexible leads, with cable couplers. Cable couplers themselves, unless maintained properly, can give trouble with faulty connections. Excessive lengths of lead (especially in the flexible cord sizes) often produce considerable voltage drops. In sites investigated some time ago, it was found that because of a shortage of plugs, it was not unusual to find flexible leads for hand tools connected to socket-outlets by wooden wedges driven into the socket contacts.

The main feature of any temporary installation is the provision of electrical services quickly and cheaply. This has too often meant PVC-sheathed cables being strung on any convenient support to cut down the cost of the time spent on the job. But the hazards in a temporary installation are far greater than those found in the more permanent installation, and so more care must be taken to see that the installation methods used are those which will go a long way to reduce, as far as is practicable, the dangers arising from shock. Building sites, in particular, offer excellent conditions for shock: wet, damp and exposure of cables to physical damage. Thus, great care must be taken with the earthing arrangements, and the positions of lighting fittings, switches and so on. If trailing leads are to be used, then watertight glands must be supplied. Fittings and accessories exposed to the weather should be of weatherproof and/or waterproof type.

The result is, of course, that unless careful attention is paid to all aspects of temporary installations, the electrician must spend much time in repairing and maintaining the system, with loss of building operatives' time.

On sites where the electrician is not always available, the use of circuit-breakers is recommended, rather than fuses of the rewirable type. Socket-outlets should be provided with hoseproof, spring-back covers, so that the socket contacts are protected when not in use. All plugs and sockets should have an indication of the working voltage and current, and coloured for clear identification (e.g. yellow for 110V).

In many instances, the cables, wiring accessories and switchgear are often dismantled from one temporary installation to be used on another site. Second-hand equipment must always be tested to ensure that its condition is satisfactory and up to the requirements of the IEE Regulations.

Electrical equipment found on sites falls into three general groups:

1. Fixed, in which the equipment is permanently installed and reliably earthed.
2. Transportable, in which the equipment is usually fairly heavy and bulky, but which can be moved about while connected to a supply although not carried when in use.
3. Portable, in which the equipment is carried by the person operating it.

Low-voltage transformers supplying portable equipment should be of an approved type having an earthed screen between the high and low voltage windings. Portable equipment which operates at no more than 25V above earth need not be earthed, and a two-core flexible cable can therefore be used. It is recommended that 'deadman' trigger-type double-pole switches be used on portable equipment and they should have a safety catch to prevent inadvertent operation. Low-voltage plugs and sockets, and lamps, should not be interchangeable with those designed for any other voltage system. Since trailing cables at normal mains voltage are a source of danger, it is preferable to have low-voltage transformers fixed permanently and effectively earthed. If this cannot be done, the mains supply cable should be kept as short as possible and be well protected.

The metal frame of all transportable equipment should be effectively earthed through the trailing supply cable to the main earthing terminal of the site supply system. The trailing cable should have both an earth core and a flexible metallic armouring or screen enclosing all the conductors. The armouring or screen should have a resistance of not more than that of the largest live conductor in the cable and should be protected overall with an insulating sheath. The screening or armouring must make sound metallic contact with the casing of the equipment and with the earth connection in the socket-outlet.

All transportable equipment and trailing cables should be identified by means of durable labels. They must be inspected regularly and a record kept. The recommended maximum period between inspections for both portable and transportable equipment should not exceed three months. For flameproof and intrinsically safe portable equipment the period should not exceed one month. An inspection must include an insulation-resistance test between conductors and earth; the continuity of the earth conductor should be measured and recorded.

Flameproof installations

There are three main types of hazard to be considered: explosive gases and vapours, flammable liquids and explosive dusts. Flammable liquids produce explosive vapours in greater or lesser degree according to their temperature. A liquid which is safe at normal temperatures may become heated to its flashpoint, above which temperature it is necessary to install flameproof equipment. Where flammable organic dusts (such as cork, sugar and flour) or metallic dusts (such as magnesium, aluminium, titanium and zirconium) are liable to be present, the electrical equipment used should be of the dustproof type. Similar precautions should be taken where explosives such as cordite and gunpowder are involved.

For the purpose of specification, flammable gases

and vapours met with in industry are classified in groups, as follows:

Group I Gases encountered in coal-mining such as methane (fire-damp).

Group II Various gases commonly found in industry, such as blast-furnace gas, propane, butane, pentane, ammonia, amylacetate and carbon monoxide, etc.

Group III Coal gas (town gas), coke-oven gas, etc.

Group IV Acetylene, hydrogen, etc.

Generally, Group I is referred to as applying to the mining industry. Group II usually refers to the petroleum industry and processes involving the use of cellulose solvents.

Equipment which is classed as 'flameproof' is so designed and constructed that it will withstand an internal explosion of the particular gas for which it is certified, and also prevent any spark of flame from that explosion leaking out of the enclosure and igniting the surrounding atmosphere. In general, this is effected by wide machined flanges which damp or otherwise quench the flame in its passage across the metal, but at the same time allow the pressure generated by the explosion to be dissipated. There are two types of apparatus: (*a*) Mining gear which is solely used with armoured cable or special mining type flexible cables; (*b*) Industrial gear, which may be used with solid-drawn conduit, MICS cable, aluminium-sheathed cable or armoured cable.

Flameproof gear is certified and consists of two or more compartments, generally constructed in either grey or malleable iron. Each compartment is separated one from the other by integral barriers having insulated studs mounted therein to accommodate the electrical connection. Where weight is important, certain articles are made in aluminium alloy. All glassware is of the toughened variety to give added strength. The glass is fitted to the item with a special cement. Certain types of gear, such as the distribution boards, are provided with their own integral isolating switches so that the replacement of fuses, maintenance, and so on, cannot be carried out while the circuit is live.

All conduit installations for hazardous areas must be carried out in solid-drawn 'Class B', with certified draw-boxes and accessories. Couplers are to be of the flameproof type with a minimum length of 5 mm. All screwed joints, whether entering into switchgear, junction boxes or couplers, must be secured with a standard heavy lock-nut. This is done to ensure a tight and vibration-proof joint which will not slacken during the life of the installation, and thus impair both continuity and flameproofness. The length of the thread on the conduit must be the same as the fitting plus sufficient for the lock-nut. Because of the exposed threads, running couplers are not recommended. Specially designed unions are manufactured which are flameproof and are designed to connect two conduits together or for securing conduit to an internally threaded entry.

Conduit of 20 and 25 mm can enter directly into a flameproof enclosure. Where exposed terminals are fitted, conduits above 25 mm must be sealed at the point of entry with compound. Where a conduit installation is subjected to condensation, say, where it passes from an atmosphere containing one type of vapour to another, the system must be sectionalised to prevent the propagation of either condensated moisture or gases. Conduit stopper boxes, with two, three or four entries must be

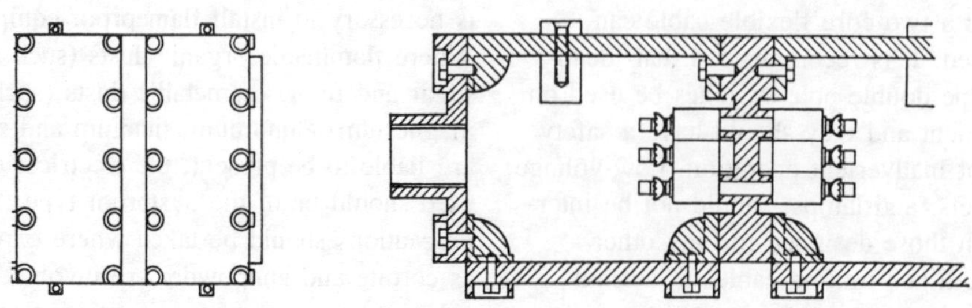

Figure 5.1. Outline and cross-section of a flameproof junction box.

used. They have a splayed, plugged filling spout in the cover so that the interior can be completely filled with compound.

When flexible, metal-sheathed or armoured cables are installed, certified cable glands must be used. Where paper-insulated cables are used, or in a situation where sealing is necessary, a cable-sealing box must be used, which has to be filled completely with compound.

The following are among the important installation points to be observed when installing flameproof systems and equipment. Flanges should be greased to prevent rusting. Special care is needed with aluminium-alloy flanges as the metal is ductile and is easily bent out of shape. All external bolts are made from special steel and have shrouded heads to prevent unauthorised interference; bolts of another type should not be fitted as replacements. Though toughened glass is comparatively strong, it will not stand up to very rough treatment; a faulty glass will disintegrate easily when broken. Protective guards must always be in place. Conduit joints should always be painted over with a suitable paint to prevent rusting. Because earthing is of prime importance in a flameproof installation, it is essential to ensure that the resistance of the joints in a conduit installation, or in cable sheaths, is such as to prevent heating or a rise in voltage from the passage of a fault-current. Remember that standard flameproof gear is not necessarily weatherproof, and should be shielded from rain or other excessive moisture.

Being essentially a closed installation, a flameproof conduit system may suffer from condensation. Stopper boxes prevent the passage of moisture from one section to another. Draining of condensate from an installation should be carried out only by an authorised person. Alterations or modifications must never be made to certified flameproof gear. Because flexible metallic conduit is not recognised as flameproof, cables to movable motors (e.g. on slide rails) should be of the armoured flexible cable type, with suitable cable-sealing boxes fitted at both ends. It is necessary to ensure that, as far as possible, contact between flameproof apparatus, conduit or cables, and pipework carrying inflammable liquids should be avoided. If separation is not possible, the two should be effectively bonded together. When maintaining equipment in hazardous areas, care should be taken to ensure that circuits are dead before removing covers to gain access to terminals. Because flexible cables are a potential source of danger, they should be inspected frequently. All the equipment should be examined for mechanical faults, cracked glasses, deterioration of well-glass cement, slackened conduit joints and corrosion. Electrical tests should be carried out at regular intervals.

The appropriate British Standard Code of Practice for flameproof installations is BS 5345, *Code of Practice for Selection, Installation and Maintenance of Electrical Apparatus for Use in Potentially Explosive Atmospheres*.

Agricultural installations

Because of their nature, agricultural and horticultural installations offer a number of problems to the electrical contractor. Specially adverse conditions are likely to be encountered, including risks arising from the presence of livestock, wet, corrosive conditions, exposure to mechanical damage, weather and neglect. IEE Regulations, Section 605 deals with the requirements which refer specifically to this class of installation. Where apparatus is exposed to a concentration of flammable dust (in grain mills, grain drying, intensive rearing houses), it should be designed for onerous dust conditions. The susceptibility of horses and cattle to extra-low voltage (in some cases to voltages below 25V) makes satisfactory control of earth-leakage currents particularly difficult for farms. Therefore, the amount of exposed non-current-carrying metalwork should be kept to a minimum, in the interest of safety of both persons and livestock.

6 Overcurrent protection

IEE Regulation 13-7 states that: 'Where necessary to prevent danger, every installation and every circuit thereof shall be protected against overcurrent by devices which (i) will operate automatically at values of current which are suitably related to the safe current rating of the circuit, and (ii) are of adequate breaking capacity, and (iii) are suitably located . . . and permit ready restoration of the supply without danger'.

Overloading occurs when extra power is taken from the supply system. The increased loading results with the addition of low resistance being connected in parallel with the existing load in a circuit. The decrease in the overall resistance of the circuit produces a proportional rise in the amount of current flowing in the circuit conductors. The increased current will have an immediate effect on the cables: they will begin to heat up. If the overload is sustained the result could be an accelerated deterioration of the cable insulation and its eventual breakdown to cause an electrical fault and perhaps fire.

A heavy sudden overload is not so serious since the overload current flows for a short time (e.g. motor starting), and the rise in cable temperature is neither rapid nor steep. However, this current must flow for a very brief period. Certain types of cable (e.g. paper-insulated and mineral-insulated) can withstand cyclic overloading. In certain circumstances, a sudden heavy overload may in fact approach the characteristic of a short-circuit.

A short-circuit is a direct contact or connection between a phase conductor and (*a*) a neutral or return conductor, or (*b*) earthed metalwork, the contact usually being the result of an accident. The result of a short-circuit is to present a conducting path of extremely low resistance which will allow the passage of a current of hundreds or thousands of amperes. If the faulty circuit has no overcurrent protection, the cables will heat up rapidly and melt; equipment would also suffer severe damage and fire is often the result.

The form which protection against overcurrent takes is either a fuse or a circuit-breaker. Each has characteristics which offer the protected circuit a degree of protection according to circuit conditions.

The fuse

The fuse was the earliest means used to protect against overcurrents in conductors. Basically, the fuse consists of a short length of suitable material, often in the form of a wire which has a very small cross-sectional area. When a current flows which is greater than the current rating of the wire, the wire will get hot. This happens because its resistance per unit length is greater than its associated circuit conductors (so giving greater power loss and heat) and because this increased heat is concentrated in the smaller volume of the material. The size of the wire is designed to carry indefinitely the normal circuit current.

The following terms are used in connection with fuses:

Current rating. This is the maximum current which the fuse will carry for an indefinite period without undue deterioration of the fuse-element.

Fusing current. This is the minimum current that will cause the fuse-element to heat up and melt or 'blow'.

Fusing factor. This is the ratio of the fusing current to the current rating:

$$\text{Fusing factor} = \frac{\text{fusing current}}{\text{current rating}}$$

Fuse-element. That part of a fuse which is designed to melt and thus open a circuit.

Fuse-link. That part of a fuse which comprises a fuse-element and a cartridge or other container, if any, and is either capable of being attached to fuse contacts or is fitted with fuse contacts as an integral part of it.

Fuse. A device for opening a circuit by means of a conductor designed to melt when an excessive current flows along it. The fuse comprises all the parts of the complete device.

There are three general types of fuse: (*a*) rewirable; (*b*) cartridge; (*c*) HRC (high-rupturing capacity), which is a development of the cartridge fuse.

The rewirable fuse is a simple device. It consists of a short length of wire, generally of tinned copper. The current at which the wire will melt depends on the length of the wire and its csa. If it is very short, the heat generated (I^2R watts) will be conducted away from the wire by the contacts or securing screws. Also, if the wire is open to the atmosphere, it will cool much more quickly than if it were surrounded by a thermal and electrical insulator such as an asbestos sleeve. In view of these and other factors, the rewirable fuse is a device with a number of variables which affect its performance; any one, or all, of these can differ between similar fuses. Though the rewirable fuse is cheap, involving only the replacement of the fuse-element, it has a number of disadvantages and limitations:

1. The fuse element is always at a fairly high temperature when in use. This leads to oxidation of the element material, which is a form of corrosion, and results in a reduction in the cross-sectional area of the element, so that it fuses at a current lower than its indicated rating. Fuses which carry their rated current for long periods generally require replacement at two-yearly periods, otherwise nuisance blowing will be experienced on the circuit.
2. It is very easy for an inexperienced person to replace a blown fuse-element with a wire of incorrect size or type.
3. When a fault occurs on a circuit, the time taken for the fuse to blow may be as long as several seconds, during which time considerable electrical and physical damage may result to the circuit conductors and the equipment being protected.
4. The calibration of a rewirable fuse can never be accurate, which fact renders this type of fuse unsuitable for circuits which require discriminative protection.
5. Lack of discrimination means that it is possible in certain circuit conditions for a 15A-rated fuse-element to melt before a 10A-rated element. Also, the type is not capable of discriminating between a transient high current (e.g. motor starting current) and a continuous fault current.
6. Owing to the fact that intense heat must be generated in the fuse-element before it can perform its protective action, there is an associated fire risk. Also in this context, should the fault current be particularly high, though the wire breaks, an arc may still be maintained by the circuit voltage and flow through the air and metallic vapour. The rewirable fuse has thus a low rupturing capacity, which is the product of maximum current which the fuse will interrupt and the supply voltage. The capacity is measured in kVA. Generally, a limit of 5000kVA is placed on rewirable fuses.

Semi-enclosed or rewirable fuses are not highly regarded as suitable means of protection against overcurrents. They can carry up to twice their current rating with no guarantee that they will 'blow'. They also present something of a fire hazard in installations.

The cartridge fuse was developed to overcome the disadvantages of the rewirable type of fuse, particularly because, with the increasing use of electricity, the energy flowing in circuits was growing larger. The main trouble with the rewirable fuse was oxidation and premature failure even when carrying normal load currents, causing interruptions in supply and loss of production in factories. Thus, the fully enclosed or cartridge fuse came into existence. Non-deterioration of the fuse-element was, and still is, one of the most valuable features of this type of fuse. The advantage, also, of the cartridge fuse is that its rating is accurately known. However, it is also more expensive to replace than the rewirable type and it is unsuitable for really high values of fault current.

It finds common application for domestic and small industrial loads. As house-service cutout fuselinks (BS 88), they are used by supply authorities for service fuses. Ferrule-cap fuselinks (BS 1361) are used in domestic 250V consumer control units, switchfuses and distribution boards. The domestic cartridge fuselinks (BS 1362) were designed for use specifically in 13A fused rectangular-pin plugs. Domestic cartridge fuselinks (BS 646) are for use specifically in 15A round-pin plugs where the load taken from a 15A socket-outlet is small (e.g. radio, TV or table lamp) in relation to the 15A fuse which protects the circuit at the distribution board. In addition, there are other cartridge fuses for particular applications (e.g. in fluorescent fittings). All these cartridge fuses are so designed that they cannot be interchanged except within their own group.

Essentially, the cartridge fuse is a ceramic barrel containing the fuse-element. The barrel is filled with a non-fusible sand which helps to quench the resultant arc produced when the element melts.

The HRC fuse was introduced in the 1930s. The modern type consists of a barrel of high-grade ceramic able to withstand the shock conditions which occur when a heavy fault current is interrupted. The end caps and fixing tags are suitably plated to give a good electrical contact. The fixing tags are also planished to ensure satisfactory alignment between contact-making surfaces. Except for very low ratings, the fuse-element is of pure silver wire or tape with a waist at its centre designed to give the required operational characteristic. The filler within the barrel is powdered silica, carefully dried before use. When used, the filler is compacted in the barrels by mechanical vibration to ensure complete filling. An indicator is sometimes provided to show when the fuse has blown. This consists of a glass bead held in position in a recess in the external barrel wall by a fine resistance wire, connected in parallel with the fuse-element. The barrels are accurately ground and the caps are a force-fit. Correct grades of solder are used for the element and tag fixings. The larger types of multi-element fuses have the elements welded in addition to soldering (Figure 6.1).

The short-time characteristics of the HRC fuse enable it to take care of short-circuit conditions in the protection of motor circuits. Tests have shown that HRC fuses have a short-circuit fusing time as low as 0.0013 second. On large ratings they will open circuit in less than 0.02 second. HRC fuses are discriminating, which means that they are able to distinguish between a high starting current taken by a motor (which lasts only a matter of seconds) and a high fault or overload current (which lasts longer). HRC fuses are often used in motor circuits for 'back-up' protection for the machines. Motors are normally protected against damage by overload by thermal magnetic devices in the motor starter; the fuses are required only to give protection against short-circuit currents and severe overloads outside the capacity of the starter protective devices. For instance, modern squirrel-cage induction motors can take up to ten times normal full-load current when stalled. The rating of a fuselink for a motor circuit should be that of the smallest current that will withstand the starting current while providing at the same time the necessary margin of safety.

When a capacitor is switched into a circuit, a heavy inrush of current results. To ensure that

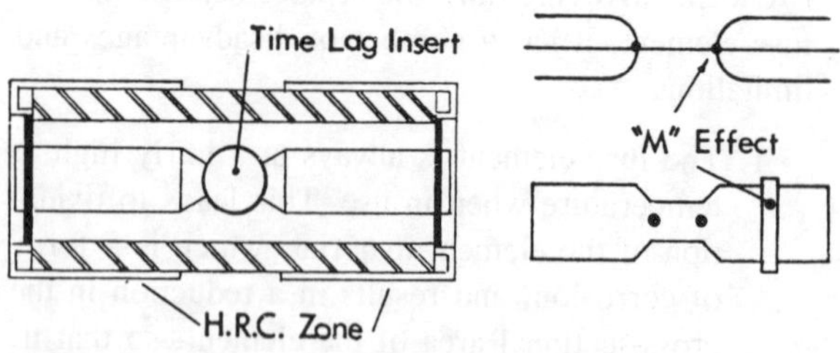

Figure 6.1. Cross-section of a typical HRC fuse. The HRC performance is obtained by the provision of restricted areas or necks and temperature control by a device known as 'M' effect. This is a plug of eutectic (tin-lead) alloy in intimate contact with the silver element (wire or strip). When the element heats up to the softening point of the alloy — about 300 °C — the silver combines with the tin-lead without altering the melting temperature so that a portion of the element now melts at 300 °C.

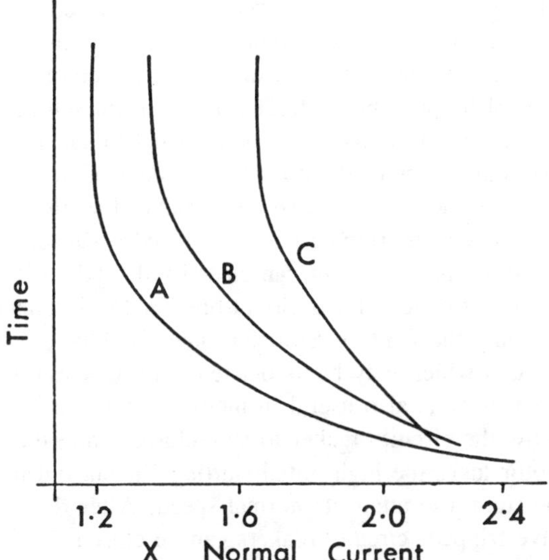

Figure 6.2. Typical tripping and fusing curves. A — Miniature circuit-breakers; B — HRC cartridge fuses; C — Rewirable fuses.

fuses do not blow unnecessarily in these circumstances, it is necessary to fit higher rated fuses. In general, if the fuses fitted are rated at 125–150 per cent of the capacitor rating, nuisance blowing of the fuses will be avoided. Transformer and fluorescent lighting circuits may also need higher rated fuselinks to deal with the inrush currents associated with this class of gear. Fuselinks with a rating of about 50 per cent greater than the normal current of the apparatus to be protected are usually found to be satisfactory.

The IEE Regulations detail many specific requirements regarding fuses and their applications. The Regulations in Chapter 43, 'Protection against Overcurrent', cover the main points to be considered. There is a general recommendation for fuses to be of the cartridge type. The main reason for this is the high fusing factors of semi-enclosed fuses, which can be as high as 1.9, which means that a fuse with a rating of 10A will require a current of 19A before the fuse-element heats up and melts. On the other hand, many cartridge fuses have fusing factors less than 1.5, which means that they can offer better protection for circuit conductors. The HRC fuses can offer fusing factors as low as 1.25, which means that these fuses will operate with an overcurrent of 25 per cent. This is obviously important when the circuit conductors to be protected are insulated with such thermoplastic materials as PVC, which cannot withstand temperatures much over their limit of 70 °C.

The circuit-breaker

The circuit-breaker is a mechanical device for making and breaking a circuit, both under normal and abnormal conditions, such as those of a short-circuit, the circuit being broken automatically. The circuit-breaker differs from the switch. Whereas the switch is capable of making and breaking a current not greatly in excess of its normal rated current, the circuit-breaker is capable of disconnecting automatically a faulty circuit, even in short-circuit conditions. A circuit-breaker is selected for a particular duty, taking the following into consideration: (*a*) the normal current it will have to carry and (*b*) the amount of current which the supply system will feed into the circuit fault, which current the circuit-breaker will have to interrupt without damage to itself.

Because the circuit-breaker is a protective device, its basic function is (*a*) to permit the installation or appliance it protects to be used up to its full rated capacity, and (*b*) to detect, and to protect equipment against dangerous conditions. Circuit-breakers are also able to provide a closer and more accurate degree of excess-current protection than that normally provided by either semi-enclosed or cartridge fuses. Circuit-breakers also perform duties as local circuit-control switches and as fault-making isolation switches. These latter types are switches capable of making and breaking rated current, and also of being closed against existing short-circuit fault.

The circuit-breaker has a mechanism which, when it is in the closed position, holds the contacts together. The contacts are separated when the release mechanism of the circuit-breaker is operated by hand or automatically by magnetic or thermal means.

The circuit-breaker with magnetic tripping (the term used to indicate the opening of the circuit-breaker contacts) employs a solenoid which is a

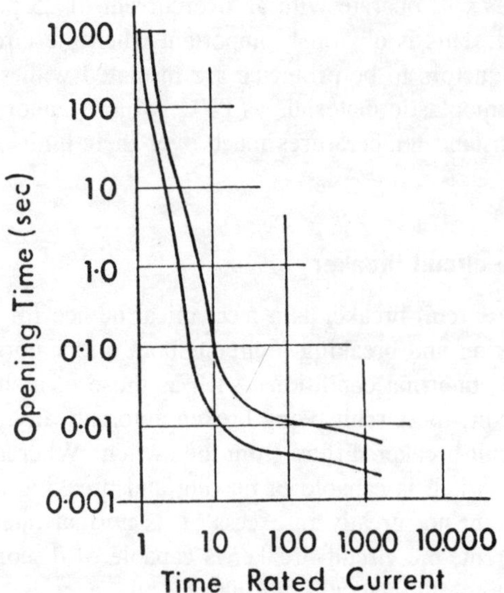

Figure 6.3. Typical operating times for a circuit-breaker.

coil with an iron slug. The normal circuit current which flows through the coil is not sufficiently strong to produce a significant magnetic flux. As soon as the circuit current increases to a predetermined level, the magnetic field strength increases to cause the iron slug to move within the solenoid and collapse the attached tripping linkage to open the contacts.

Thermal tripping uses a heat-sensitive bimetal element. When the element is heated to a predetermined temperature, the resultant deflection is arranged to trip the circuit-breaker. The time taken to heat the element to this temperature provides the necessary time-delay characteristic. The bimetal element may be arranged to carry the circuit current and so be directly self-heated. Indirect heating of the element may also be used. Because of the time lag associated with heating, tripping by this means is not so rapid as with magnetic tripping. In the circuit condition when a small sustained overload occurs, the thermal trip will come into operation after a few seconds or even minutes. However, when a heavier overload occurs, the magnetic trip coil operates quickly to disconnect the faulty circuit.

Circuit-breakers are used instead of fuses in many installations because of a number of definite advantages. First, in the event of an overload or fault, all poles of the circuit are positively disconnected. The devices are also capable of remote control by push-buttons. The over-current setting of the circuit-breakers can be adjusted to suit the load conditions of the circuit to be controlled. Time-lag devices can also be introduced so that the time taken for tripping can be delayed because, in some instances, a fault can clear itself, and so is avoided the need for a circuit-breaker to disconnect not only the faulty circuit, but other healthy circuits which may be associated with it. The time-lag facility is also useful in motor circuits, to allow the circuit-breaker to stay closed while the motor takes the high initial starting current during the run-up to attain its normal speed. After they have tripped, circuit-breakers can be closed immediately without loss of time. Circuit-breaker contacts separate either in air or under insulating oil (Figure 6.4).

The miniature circuit-breaker (MCB) has found an increasing application in domestic and small industrial installations. It is used as an alternative to the fuse and has certain advantages: it can be reset or reclosed easily while the fault is present in the circuit; it gives a close degree of excess-current protection (the tripping factor is 1.1); it will trip on a small sustained overcurrent, but not on a harmless transient overcurrent such as a switching surge (e.g. on fluorescent lamp circuits). For most

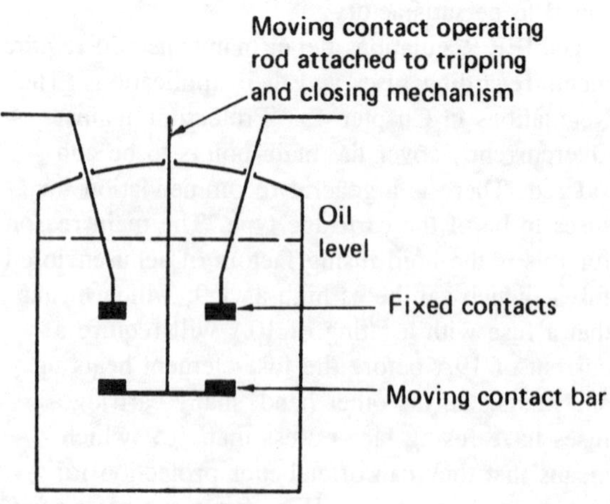

Figure 6.4. Simple earthed-tank, plain-break oil circuit-breaker.

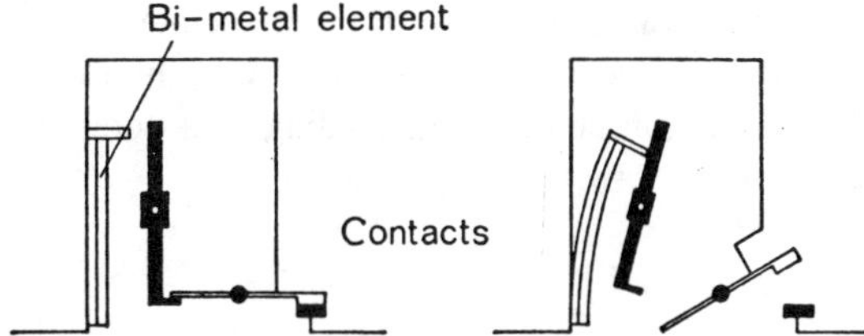

Figure 6.5. Typical thermal trip. The thermal element consists of two bonded strips of metal having different rates of thermal expansion. The heat of an excessive current will cause the element to bend. Bimetals have inverse-time elements which provide a long time delay on light overloads and a faster response on heavy ones.

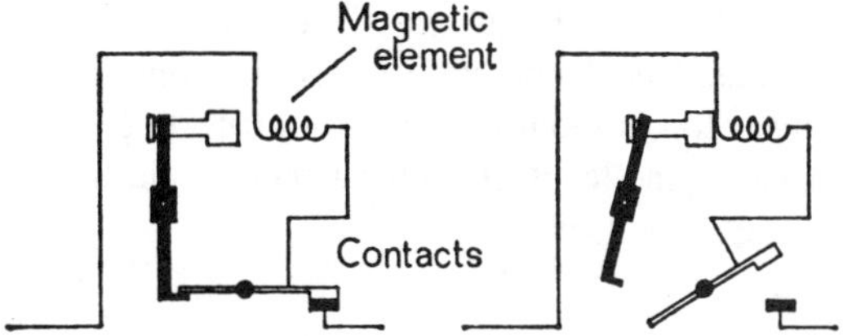

Figure 6.6. Typical magnetic trip, in which an electromagnet element is used. When a predetermined current flows through the oil, the armature is attracted, initiating an unlatching action, causing the circuit to open. A magnetic trip provides for short-circuit protection only.

applications, the MCB tends to give much better overall protection against both fire and shock risks than can be obtained with the use of normal HRC or rewirable fuses. MCBs are available in distribution units for final circuit protection.

The following are the advantages generally claimed for circuit-breakers:

1. Non-destructive determination of tripping characteristics.
2. Shorter tripping times under moderate overcurrents than with fuses.
3. Opening of all poles in every fault condition.
4. Single-phasing is prevented.
5. Re-closing can be effected at once after the fault has been cleared.
6. Switching ON and OFF without danger, even under fault conditions.
7. Factory-coordinated overload and short-circuit tripping characteristics.
8. Same tripping characteristics in all phases.
9. No stock of fuses required.
10. Immediate indication of faulty circuit.
11. Can be used as a circuit-control switch.

On the other hand, the fuse has a number of disadvantages, although cheapness is one of its merits:

1. It must be withdrawn by hand to isolate the circuit.
2. It must be replaced or repaired before the supply can be restored to the interrupted circuit.
3. If it is replaced while the fault is present in the circuit, serious personal danger could result.
4. It does not usually indicate the faulty circuit (the HRC fuse usually does), and must be withdrawn for inspection.
5. It ages in service and can cause nuisance interruption of the circuit.
6. It is liable to a makeshift repair.
7. It varies in size according to rating.

In particular, it is stressed that the tripping time of a circuit-breaker should not be altered, otherwise the degree of protection offered by the device could present a danger to wiring.

The circuit-breaker is also used for earth-leakage protection. This application is described in Chapter 7.

Both the Wiring Regulations and the 'Guidance Note', 'Protection against Overcurrent', lay justified stress on the need to understand the performance characteristics of the various types of overcurrent protective devices used to offer final circuits the correct protection they require. Appendix 3 in the main Wiring Regulations gives the time/current characteristics of various devices. Figures 1 to 8 in the Appendix take the form of graphs of prospective current against time. From any graph one can find the time taken for a certain device to carry a certain value of current, that is, the actual time of operation. For example, from Figure 2A a 30A BS 3036 rewirable fuse carrying a fault current of 100A would take 3 seconds to 'blow'. A BS 1361 30A cartridge fuse would take 2 seconds. These operating times are important because, for as long as it takes a protective device to operate, the level of fault current would be generating a rapid heat rise in the associated circuit cables and if PVC insulation was involved a serious situation could occur leading to a potential fire hazard.

7 Protection against earth-leakage currents

Electric shock

IEE Regulation 130-04-01 (in Part 1) states: 'Where metalwork of electrical equipment, other than current-carrying conductors, may become charged with electricity in such a manner as to cause danger: (i) the metalwork shall be connected with earth in such a manner as will cause discharge of electrical energy without danger, or (ii) other equally effective precautions shall be taken to prevent danger.' The basic reason for earthing is to prevent or minimise the risk of shock to human beings and livestock. The reason for having properly earthed metalwork in an installation is to provide a low-resistance discharge path for earth-leakage currents which would otherwise prove injurious or fatal to any person touching the metalwork associated with a faulty circuit. The prevention of electric shock in all installations is a matter which has been subjected to close attention in these past few years, particularly since the rapid increase in the use of electricity for an ever-widening range of applications.

An electric shock is dangerous only when the current through the body exceeds a certain minimum value. The degree of danger is dependent not only on the current but also on the time for which it flows. A low current for a long time can easily prove just as dangerous as a high current for a relatively brief period. The applied voltage is in itself only important in producing this minimum current through the resistance of the body. In human beings, the resistance between hand and hand, or between hand and foot, can easily be as low as 500 ohms. If the body is immersed in a conducting liquid (e.g. in a bath) the resistance may be as low as 200 ohms. In the case of a person with a body resistance of 500 ohms, with a 240V supply, the resulting current would be 480mA, or 1.2A in the more extreme case. However, much smaller currents are lethal. It has been estimated that about 3mA is sufficient for a shock to be felt by a tingling sensation. Between 10 and 15mA, a tightening of the muscles is experienced and there is difficulty in releasing any object gripped. Acute discomfort is felt at this current level. Between 25 and 30mA the dangerous level is reached, with the extension of muscular tightening, particularly to the thoracic muscles. Over 50mA results in fibrillation of the heart which is generally lethal if immediate specialist attention is not given. Fibrillation of the heart is due to irregular contraction of the heart muscles.

The object of earthing, as understood by the IEE Regulations is, so far as is possible, to reduce the amount of current available for passage through the human body in the event of the occurrence of an earth-leakage current in an installation.

Earthing systems

Chapter 41 of the Regulations deals with the requirements which all earthing arrangements must satisfy if an electrical installation is to be deemed safe. The main basic requirements are:

1. The complete insulation of all parts of an electrical system. This involves the use of wiring systems and apparatus of 'all-insulated' construction, which means that the insulation which encloses the apparatus is durable and substantially continuous.
2. The use of appliances with double insulation conforming to the British Standard Specifications mentioned in Appendix 1 of the Regulations.
3. The earthing of all exposed metal parts (there are some exemptions).
4. The isolation of metalwork in such a manner that it is not liable to come into contact with any live parts or with earthed metalwork.

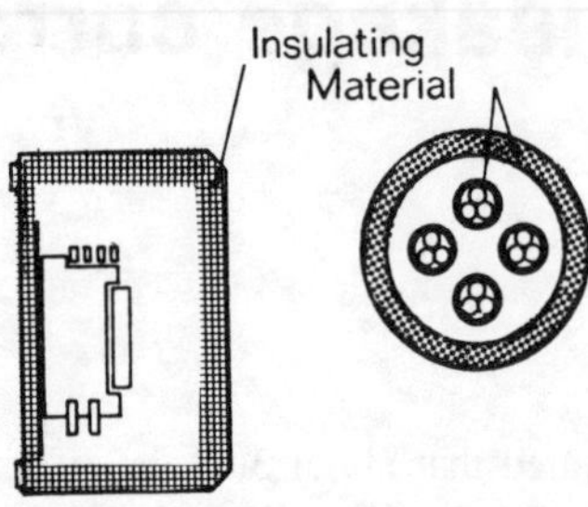

Figure 7.1. Showing the principle of protective insulation which is provided externally to the functional insulation where accessible live parts are separated from actual live parts. A contactor and a cable are shown.

In addition, the IEE Regulations, as do the statutory regulations, recognise the use of extra-low voltages (less than 50V ac or 12V dc with respect to earth) as an effective measure to prevent dangerous voltages occurring on the exposed metalwork of electrical equipment. There are certain disadvantages with this method because to satisfy modern power requirements, impractically high currents are involved. Applications of this method are restricted, for example, to control circuits, small portable tools and lighting circuits.

Wiring systems and equipment are either classed as all-insulated or double-insulated. All-insulated equipment is recognised by most of the regulations and specifications as an alternative to earthing. The principles of design of all-insulated equipment are simple and they are difficult to abuse (Figure 7.2). Double-insulation has yet to be completely recognised under the Factories Act.

The complete isolation of metallic parts associated either directly or indirectly with an installation is often difficult to achieve and is confined as a precautionary method to the following items:

1. Short isolated lengths of conduit or channelling used to protect cables, which have no metallic sheath, from mechanical damage or conduit used to protect high-voltage cables used in a discharge-lighting installation.
2. The metal clips used for fixing cables.
3. The metal caps of lamps.
4. The small metal parts which are isolated by insulating material. In this category are screws or metal nameplates.
5. Metal chains for the suspension of lighting fittings.
6. Metal lighting fittings which use filament lamps and are installed above a non-conducting floor and so mounted, or so screened in non-conducting material that they cannot readily be touched by a person standing on or within reach of earthed metal.

By far the greatest amount of work involved in the provision of protection against earth-leakage currents is the earthing of all relevant metalwork, either directly or indirectly associated with an installation and which, in a fault condition, may experience a rise in voltage above earth potential sufficient to cause a lethal amount of current to flow through a person touching the metalwork.

It should be understood that earthing cannot in itself prevent exposed metalwork from becoming electrically charged in the event of earth leakage or earth fault, but is intended to prevent the metalwork remaining 'live' at a dangerous voltage by allowing the earth-fault current to cut off the supply to the faulty circuit. If an earth fault occurs at some point in a circuit, the fault current will

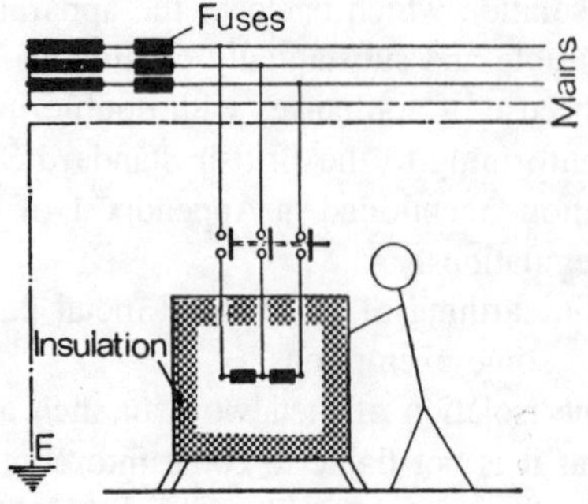

Figure 7.2. All-insulated equipment.

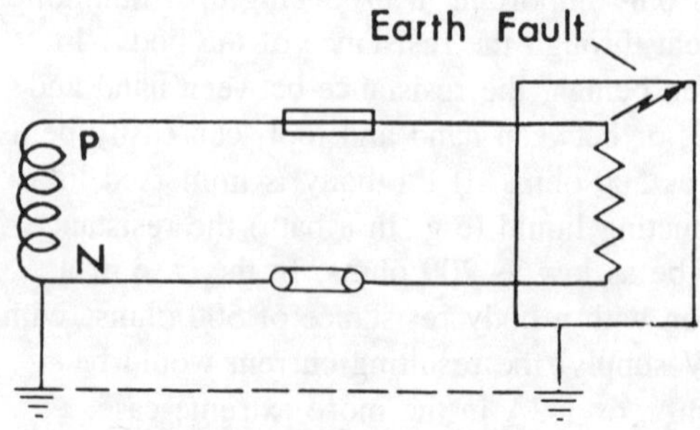

Figure 7.3. Earth-fault on an appliance with protected metalwork.

flow through what is called the earth-loop. This path comprises, starting at the point of the fault, the circuit-protective conductor, the consumer's earthing terminal, the earth conductor, the earth electrode or other metallic return path (e.g. cable sheath/armouring), the continuous earth wire of an overhead conductor (or the neutral conductor in the case of the protective multiple earthing system) or, where no metallic return path is available, the general mass of earth, and the path through the earthed neutral point of the transformer and the transformer secondary winding, and the live conductor.

Neglecting any resistance at the point of the fault, the earth-fault current will be equal to the phase-to-neutral voltage of the supply divided by the impedance of the earth-fault loop path (in ohms). If the impedance of the loop were 10 ohms, then on a 250V supply, a current of 25A would flow, the maximum possible leakage current. This current would, of course, be carried indefinitely by a 30A final circuit fuse of, say, a ring-main. As a result of the fuse remaining inoperative, because of its rating in relation to the value of current flowing, any metalwork bonded to the consumer's earthing terminal would now be permanently connected to the live circuit, and it could be live at anything up to full mains voltage.

A direct short-circuit to earth, resulting in many tens or hundreds of amperes, would blow a fuse. On the other hand, the fuse would not operate on a leakage through defective insulation of a current of, say, 100mA, which could be dangerous, if not fatal.

It is thus seen that there are a number of aspects of earthing which require careful consideration before the earthing provision for an installation is deemed adequate. The factors to be considered are as follows:

The main earthing terminal. This is required to be provided by Regulation 542-01-01. This terminal, to be of a size and type suitable for the connection of a number of conductors to it, must be located adjacent to the consumer's supply terminals. The conductors which are connected to this terminal include:

1. All circuit-protective conductors of the installation's circuits.
2. The circuit-protective conductor from extraneous metalwork (structural steelwork, etc.).
3. The earthing conductor.
4. The neutral conductor of the supply if the protective multiple earthing system (TNCS or PME) is used.
5. The conductor used as a continuous earth wire (CEW) in rural overhead supply systems.
6. The bonding conductor from a cable sheath/ armouring.

Circuit protective conductors. The CPC is the conductor which connects all exposed conductive parts

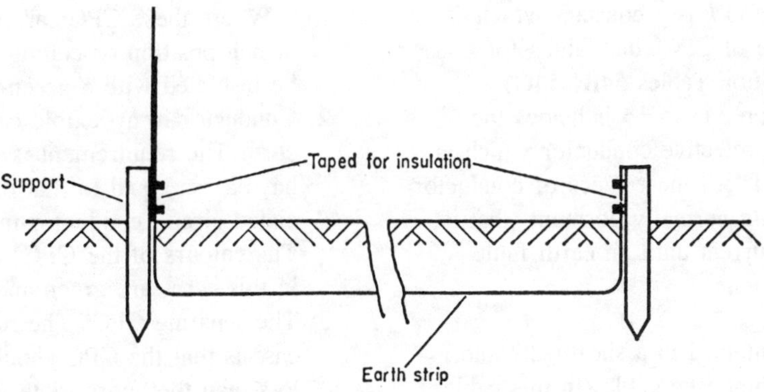

Figure 7.4. Earthing using a copper strip.

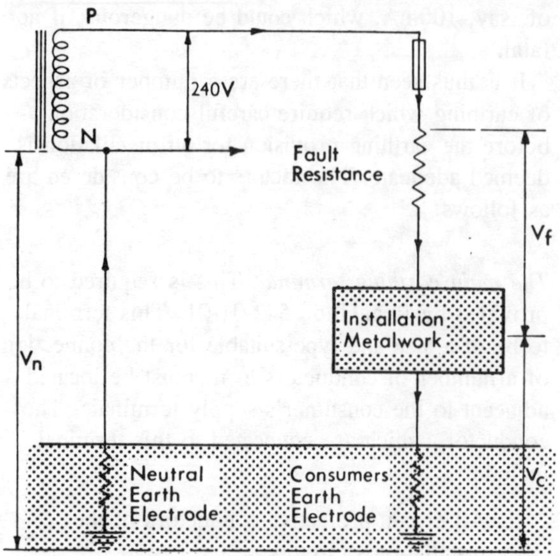

Figure 7.5. Earth-fault conditions. V_f — voltage across fault resistance; V_n — voltage between neutral conductor and general mass of earth; V_c — voltage between protected metalwork and earth.

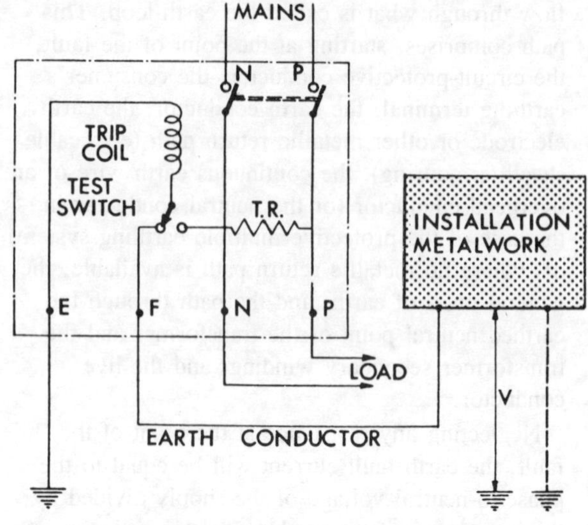

Figure 7.6. Fault-voltage earth-leakage circuit-breaker. V is the potential difference between protected metalwork and earth. Not now recommended for installation by the Regulations but may still be found in older installations.

of an installation, and equipment, to the main earthing terminal. These parts include metallic wiring systems, metal-clad switchgear, motor frames, metallic sheathing and armouring of cables and metallic enclosures of electrical equipment. Metallic conduit, however, itself may be a CPC, as would the copper sheath of MI cables.

The CPC can appear in a number of forms and must be of copper if the csa is less than 10 mm^2. The actual csa is calculated from the formula: $S = \sqrt{(I^2t)}/k$ where S is the csa in mm^2, I is the fault current, t is the operating time of the disconnecting device in seconds, and k is a constant which depends on the type of CPC (the values for k are contained in Regulation Tables 54B–54G).

Regulations Section 543 to 14 indicates the following types of protective conductor which are generally recognised. All these types of conductor are regarded as being normally dormant (that is, they do not carry current until an earth fault occurs).

1. Conductor contained in a sheathed cable, known as a composite cable. In this cable, the sheath is normally of PVC and the conductors are the circuit conductors and the CPC (e.g. 2.5 mm^2 twin with CPC). The conductor is either single-strand or multi-stranded, depending on the size of the circuit conductors. And it is uninsulated. If the sheath is of metal, the conductor is always single-stranded. Inspection of different types of such cables will reveal that the cross-sectional area of CPCs in metal-sheathed cables is less than their counterparts in insulated-sheathed cables; this is because the metal sheath and conductor are in parallel and together constitute a conducting path of very low resistance.

   Where these CPCs are made off at, say, a switch position or ceiling rose, they should be insulated with a green-yellow sleeving.
2. Conductor in a flexible cable or flexible cord. The requirement is that the CPC should have a csa equal to that of the largest associated circuit conductor in the cable or cord. The colours of the CPC, which is insulated in this case, are green and yellow.
3. The separate CPC. The requirement in this case is that the CPC should have a csa not less than the appropriate value as shown in Table 54G of the Regulations. The minimum

size is 2.5 mm^2, but in practice the size depends on the size of the associated circuit conductors. The reason for this is that if the circuit conductors are rated to carry I amperes, then the CPC should be able to carry a similar current in the event of an earth fault for sufficient time to allow a fuse to blow or to open a circuit-breaker. The resistance of a CPC of a material other than copper should not exceed that of the associated copper conductor. Additional requirements for the separate CPC are that it shall be insulated and coloured green and yellow.

4. Metal-sheath of MICS cable. Where the sheath of MICS cable is used as a CPC, the effective csa of the sheath should be not less than one-half of the largest current-carrying conductor, subject to a minimum of 2.5 mm^2. This requirement is not applicable to MICS cables used in earthed concentric wiring systems (TNC).
5. Conduits, ducting, trunking. Wiring systems which comprise metalwork, such as conduit, trunking and ducting, are used as the CPC of an installation. The requirement here is that the resistance of the CPC should be no more than twice that of the largest current-carrying conductor of the circuit. All joints must be mechanically sound and be electrically continuous. Where there is the possibility of corrosion, precautions should be taken, particularly at joints. In an agricultural installation, in those situations which are accessible to livestock, a metal pipe or conduit is not to be regarded or used as a sole CPC, though it may be used as a supplementary CPC.
6. The conducting paths as follows are not recognised as sufficient to be CPCs in their own right: gas pipes, water pipes, metallic flexible conduit, structural steelwork, and conduits or other pipes in an agricultural installation. A recognised CPC is necessary to complement the earthing requirements in these instances.

The earth conductor. The earthing lead is the final conductor by which the connection to the earth electrode, or other means of earthing, is made. It connects between the consumer's earthing terminal and the earth electrode. The minimum size of earthing conductor acceptable is 6 mm^2, and in any particular installation is related to the size of the largest associated circuit conductor. All earthing leads must be protected where necessary against mechanical damage and against corrosion. The latter requirement is particularly necessary at the point of connection to the earth electrode or other means of earthing. A label, with the words 'Safety Electrical Connection — Do Not Remove', must be permanently attached to the lead. The connection of an earthing lead to an earth electrode or other means of earthing must be readily accessible for inspection. Recommended methods of making this connection include soldered joint, or substantial clamps of non-ferrous metal, which are preferred if isolation of the electrode is needed.

Earth connection. The IEE Regulations recognise the following methods of earthing:

1. A metallic return path provided by the supply company. This can be the cable sheath/ armouring of an underground cable, or the CEW of a rural overhead distribution system.
2. An earth electrode in connection with the general mass of earth. Each earth electrode must be buried in the ground at a position as near as practicable to the consumer's earthing terminal. Neither gas nor water pipes, separately or jointly, should be used as the sole earth electrode of an installation. Electrodes come in a number of types. The pipe is generally a 150 mm diameter cast-iron pipe, about 2 m long and buried in a coke-filled pit. This type requires a certain amount of excavation and is, of course, subject to corrosion. Copper pipe, if the diameter is sufficient, can also be used, in this instance driven into the ground.

   The plate electrode is usually of cast-iron and buried vertically with the plate centre about 1 m below the surface. Copper plates may also be used. Plate electrodes provide a large surface area and are used where the ground is shallow (where resistivity is low near the surface but increases rapidly with depth). Again, excavation is required. Care

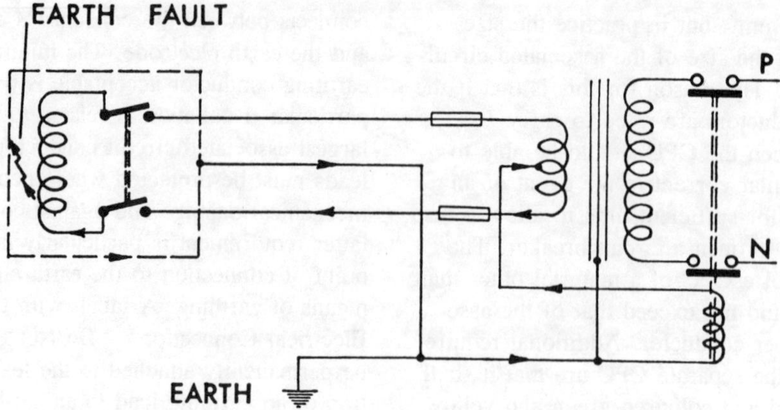

Figure 7.7(*a*). One type of earth-leakage protection for a portable appliance.

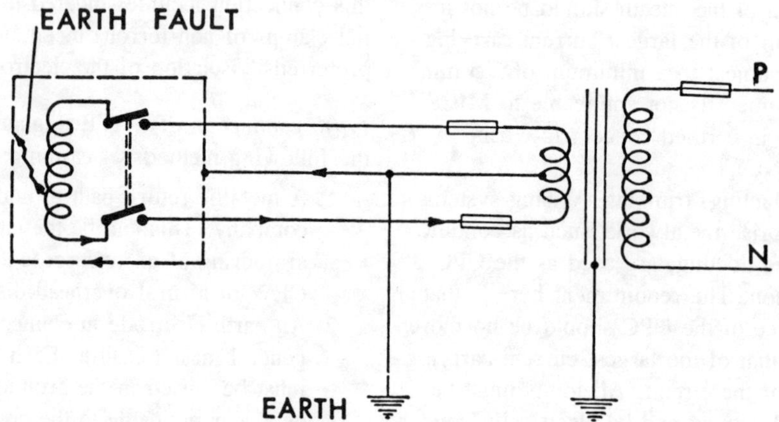

Figure 7.7(*b*). Use of a double-wound, step-down transformer for a portable appliance.

is needed to protect the earth-electrode connection (to the earthing lead) from corrosion, if iron is used as the plate metal.

Copper strip is used where the soil is shallow and overlies rock. Strip should be buried to a depth of not less than 45 cm and should not be used where there is the possibility of digging (e.g. on farmland).

Rod electrodes are very economical and require no excavation for their installation. Because buried length is more important than diameter, the extensible, small-diameter copper rod has many advantages. It can, for instance, be driven into the ground so that the soil contact with the rod is close and definite. Extensible rods are of standard lengths and made from hard-drawn copper. They have a hardened steel tip and a steel driving-cap. Some rods have a steel core running through the centre for strength while they are being driven into rocky soil. Ribbed earth rods have wide vertical ribs to give a high degree of mechanical stiffness so that they are not easily bent or deflected when driven into the ground. The ribbed section also offers increased contact area with the soil.

3. Where the protective multiple earthing (PME) system is used, the earthing lead is connected to the consumer's earthing terminal and, together with the neutral conductor of the consumer's installation, is so arranged that

connection to the neutral conductor on the incoming supply can be carried out by the supply company.

The PME system (TNCS)

The protective multiple earthing system is extremely reliable and is being used increasingly in this country. In the system, all exposed metalwork of an installation is connected to the neutral conductor of the supply, by means of the installation's earth-continuity conductors. By doing this, all line-to-earth faults are converted to line-to-neutral faults, the intention being to ensure that sufficient current flows under fault conditions to operate devices (fuses or circuit-breakers) which protect the faulty circuit (Figure 7.9).

There are two main hazards associated with PME. The first is that, owing to the increased earth-fault currents which are encouraged to flow, there is an enhanced fire risk during the time it takes for the protective device to operate. Also, with this method of earthing, it is essential to ensure that the neutral conductor cannot rise to a dangerous potential relative to earth. This is because the interconnection of neutral and protected metalwork would automatically extend the resultant shock risk to all protected metalwork on every installation connected to a particular supply distribution network.

As a result of these hazards, stringent requirements are laid down to cover the use of PME on any particular distribution system. Statutory or Government requirements indicate the full extent of provisions which must be satisfied if PME is to be used. Three points of interest might be mentioned here. First, the neutral conductor must be earthed at a number of points on the system, and the maximum resistance from neutral to earth must not exceed 10 ohms. In addition, an earth electrode at each consumer's installation is recommended. Second, so far as the consumer is concerned, there must be no fusible cutout, single-pole switch, removable link or automatic circuit-breaker in any neutral conductor in the installation. Third, the neutral conductor at any point must be made of the same material and be at least of equal cross-sectional area as the phase conductor at that point.

PME can be applied to a consumer's installation only if the supply company's feeder is multiple earthed. This restricts PME to new distribution networks, though conversion from old systems can be made at a certain cost. The supply company has to obtain permission in accordance with the provisions laid down by the Minister of Energy and Secretary of State for Scotland. Post Office approval must also be obtained for every PME installation. British Telecom approval is required since it was once thought that the flow of currents from PME neutrals to the general mass of earth could cause interference with and/or corrosion of BT equipment. In practice, however, no such problems have occurred, though BT still retain their right to approve or otherwise a proposed PME installation.

Should a break occur in a neutral conductor of a PME system, the conductor will be live with respect to earth on both sides of the break, the actual voltage distribution depending on the relative values of the load and the earth electrode resistances of the two sections of the neutral distributor. All earthed metalwork on every installation supplied from this particular distribution system would become live. High-resistance joints on the neutral can also have a similar effect, the degree of danger in all cases being governed by the values of the connected load and the various earth electrode resistances. Trouble on a neutral conductor may go undetected for some considerable time, some of the only symptoms being reduced voltages on appliances, lights, etc., and slight to severe shocks from earthed metalwork. Overhead-line distribution systems are, of course, particularly prone so far as broken or discontinuous neutral conductors are concerned.

The aspect of earthed concentric wiring is important in the context of PME. For PME systems, the conventional four-core (three phases and neutral) armoured cable can be replaced by a three-core metallic sheathed and armoured cable where the sheath and armour are used for the earthed neutral. For consumer wiring, the sheath-return concentric cable, in which the sheath acts as both the neutral and earth conductor, is a logical extension of the PME principle and is covered by IEE Section 546-02. The main advantage of sheath-return wiring is that a separate CPC is not required. This is because the chances of a complete disconnection of the earth neutral conductor without breaking the included phase conductors is remote.

Sheath return usually means that mineral-insulated cable is used. While most of the MI cable is slightly higher than other types of cable (including any necessary conduit), this is offset considerably by the saving in labour resulting from ease of handling, the small diameter and the reduced amount of chasing work required. Sheath-return wiring can result in savings in installed cost of about 30 per cent compared with a conventional direct-earthed system using plastic-insulated cable in black-enamelled screwed conduit.

For single-phase supplies, single-core MI sheath-return cables are used. Twin-core cables are used for two-way switching. Multi-core cables are used from multi-switch points and rising mains to junction boxes where a number of separate outlets are situated close together. Since the outer sheath of the MI cable is used for both neutral and earth connections, care has to be taken at terminations which are made with pot-type seals and glands into switchgear and terminal boxes at which sockets, ceiling roses, etc. are fitted. Duplicate bonding is used to ensure that the contact remains good at all times. A special seal, with an earth-bonding lead, is used.

Automatic protection

Earth-leakage and earth-fault protection are methods of protection arranged to disconnect the supply automatically from an installation or circuit when the earth-leakage or earth-fault currents exceed predetermined values. Similarly, the protection is offered when the voltage between protected metalwork of the installation and earth rises above a predetermined value. Such a system may be made to operate more rapidly and at lower values of leakage or fault current than one depending on overcurrent protective devices such as fuses, thermal trips, etc. Automatic protection is therefore used where the impedance of the earth-fault loop limits the current flowing in it to a value less than three times the current rating of the fuse or one-and-a-half times the overcurrent setting of the circuit-breaker.

Earth-leakage or earth-fault protection is generally effected by means of a device known as an earth-leakage circuit-breaker (ELCB), now known as a residual current device (RCD). For many years, the fault-voltage earth-leakage circuit-breaker was a popular method of achieving protection against small earth-leakage currents, even though it was generally recognised that the RCD was a more sensitive device for protection. When the 15th edition of the Wiring Regulations appeared in 1981, the device was still recommended. But in 1985 it was replaced by the RCD which is now the only protective device against small earth-leakage currents recommended to be used. The older type of device may still be found in installations which is why Figure 7.6 is given for information only should these ELCBs be encountered.

Residual current device. This device consists of a transformer having opposed windings which carry the incoming and outgoing current of the load. In a healthy circuit, where the values of current in the windings are equal, the magnetic effects cancel out in the transformer core. A fault causes an out-of-balance circuit condition and creates an effective magnetic flux in the core which links with the turns of a secondary winding and induces an emf in it. The secondary winding is permanently connected to the trip coil of the circuit-breaker. When the circulating current reaches a predetermined value, it is sufficient to pull out the release latch to

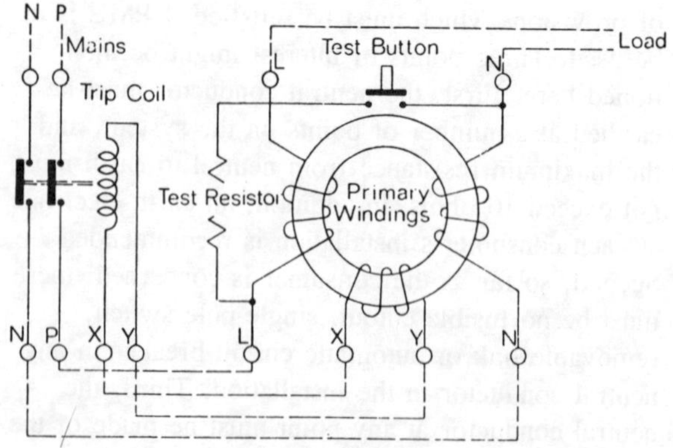

Figure 7.8. Circuit diagram of a residual-current earth-leakage circuit-breaker.

open the main contacts which are normally held closed against strong pressure springs.

In contrast to the fault-voltage ELCB, this type can be used to provide discriminative protection for individual circuits. In practice, the normal order of sensitivity ranges from about one ampere out-of-balance, for a 15A unit, up to about 3A out-of-balance for a 60A unit. These units are also known as 'low-sensitivity units' to distinguish them from the 'high-sensitivity units'. These latter units operate within 1/25 of a heart cycle and can detect a fault current of 30mA to earth, or less. The operating time is in the region of 30 milliseconds. Certain units available do not require an earth connection, relying for their operation on the actual fault current to earth through a person's body. The rapid time of operation, however, ensures that no electrical accident occurs.

One fault found with these high-sensitivity units is what is called nuisance tripping. This occurs because the units can detect very low currents of the order of 25–30mA, which are often found as normal leakage current from cooker boiling plates and immerser elements.

Section 412-06 of the Regulations deals with the use of RCDs as providing supplementary protection against direct contact. The recommended tripping or operating current is 30mA and the device must be able to trip within 40 milliseconds at 150mA. They are required to be installed when electrical equipment is to be used out of doors, that is, outside the equipotential zone represented by the complete earthing arrangements inside a building. Socket-outlets for this purpose incorporate an RCD and are identified by a warning notice: 'For Equipment Outdoors'.

Additional requirements for protection

(a) Extraneous metalwork

The Wiring Regulations require that extraneous fixed metalwork should be bonded and earthed. This is particularly important where exposed metalwork of all apparatus, which is required by the regulations to be earthed, might come into contact with extraneous fixed metalwork. Two solutions are offered; the bonding of such metalwork, or its segregation. The latter course is often very difficult to achieve and appreciable voltage differences may arise between points of contact. The extraneous fixed metalwork includes baths and exposed metal pipes, radiators, sinks and tanks where there are no metal-to-metal joints of negligible resistance, structural steelwork, and the framework of mobile equipment on which electrical apparatus is mounted, such as cranes and lifts.

(b) Bathrooms

Additional precautions are required to be taken to prevent risk of shock in bathrooms, usually associated with dampness and condensed water vapour. A bathroom is regarded as any room containing a fixed bath or shower. First, all parts of a lamp-

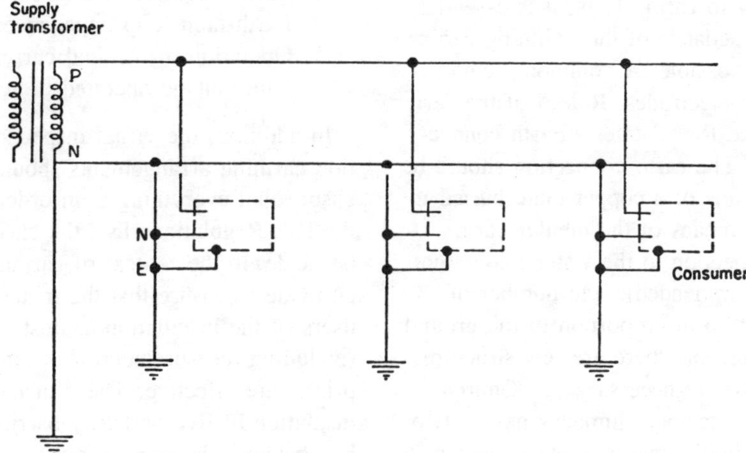

Figure 7.9. Typical distribution system with consumers connected to a common PME system of earthing (TNCS).

holder likely to be touched by a person replacing a lamp shall be constructed of, or shrouded in, insulating material and, for BC lampholders, should be fitted with a protective shield of insulating material. The regulations strongly recommend that lighting fittings should be of a totally-enclosed type. Switches or other means of control should be located so that they cannot be touched by a person using a fixed bath or shower. This means location of the circuit-control device either outside the room itself, or be ceiling-mounted with an insulating cord for its operation. No stationary appliances are allowed in the room, unless the heating elements cannot be touched. There should be no provision for socket-outlets, except to supply an electric shaver from a unit complying with BS 3052.

(c) Bell and similar circuits
Where a bell or similar circuit is energised from a public supply by means of a double-wound transformer, the secondary winding, the core of the transformer and the metal casing, if any, should be connected to earth.

(d) Lightning protection
In certain types of building, it is often the job of the electrical contractor to install an earthing system to protect against the effects of lightning discharges. Very high transient values of voltage and current may be expected when lightning surges are being led away to earth. Thus, it is essential that the overall impedance of the lightning earth path be as low as possible. A common method is the use of multiple electrodes. Rule 5 of the Phoenix Fire Office Rules states: 'Earth connections and number. The earth connection should be made either by means of a copper plate buried in damp earth, or by means of the tubular earth system, or by connection to the water mains (not now generally recommended). The number of connections should be in proportion to the ground area of the building, and there are few structures where less than two are necessary . . . Church spires, high towers, factory chimneys having two down conductors should have two earths which may be interconnected.'

(e) Portable appliances
To reduce the risk of electric shock when portable appliances are used, the appliance is often supplied with a reduced voltage. A double-wound transformer (Figure 7.7) reduces the mains voltage to a suitable level. The secondary winding has one point earthed so that should a fault to earth occur on the appliance, the shock received will be virtually harmless. Another method of protecting the user of a portable appliance from electric shock is to provide the appliance with automatic protection (Figure 7.7). In the event of an earth-fault, the supply is automatically disconnected from the appliance.

Earthing tests

These tests, as required by the IEE Regulations, are fully described in Chapter 8 of this book. Briefly, the tests are designed to ensure that the earthing arrangements for a particular installation are effective and will considerably reduce the risk resulting in the occurrence of dangerous shock conditions should an earth-leakage current (either through faulty insulation or from a direct live to earth) arise. The recommended tests include:

1. Continuity of ring final circuit conductors, particularly the circuit protective conductor.
2. Continuity of all protective conductors, including main and supplementary equipotential bonding.
3. Earth-electrode resistance.
4. Earth-fault loop impedance.
5. Operation of residual current devices and fault-voltage operated protective devices.

In addition, the visual inspection of the installation earthing arrangements should be carried out to ensure that everything is in order. Section 712 of the IEE Regulations lists the checks which should be made. In the context of earthing, a check should be made to ensure that the methods of protecting users of the installation against direct contact (including measurement of distances where appropriate) are effective. These include: protection by insulation of live parts; by barriers or enclosures; by obstacles; by placing out of reach; and by non-conducting location.

8 Inspection and testing

Whatever the quality of materials used in an installation and the quality of workmanship used to install the materials, accessories and equipment which all go to make up an electrical installation, the complete job must be both inspected and tested.

This chapter describes the types of instruments used to carry out the various tests. A look is also taken at some other types of instruments with which the practising electrician is expected to be familiar which are used to measure electrical quantities rather than perform test functions.

Recent years have seen a significant advance in the development of instruments used for testing purposes. Many use electronic devices and circuitry and are designed to be easily operated and easily read. Some instruments use the familiar graduated scale across which a needle pointer moves to indicate a reading; others use a digital read-out display and are often more accurate.

All instruments have to be checked before they are used, particularly where installation tests are carried out. Battery-operated testers should be subjected to a pre-test procedure to ensure that the instrument is able to give a reliable reading.

The batteries must be checked to ensure they are in a good condition. Most testers incorporate a 'good' or 'poor' indicator. If the batteries are healthy, the instrument should be checked for accurate readings against a known-value resistor where this is appropriate. For example, an insulation-resistance tester should be checked against a 1 megohm resistor. If these two conditions are satisfied, healthy batteries and accuracy of reading, the instrument can then be used on the test.

Calibration units can be purchased which are designed to check the accuracy of the readings of test instruments. They also have a facility which checks mains-operated testers such as the phase-earth loop instrument, thus ensuring accuracy of the readings while doing the actual test.

All test instruments should be recalibrated after a period of time. Tests should also be made with the same type (or model) of instrument to ensure that readings obtained at subsequent tests accord with each other. It is often required that the serial number of the test instrument is recorded so that the same tester can be used at a later time for a similar test.

Insulation-resistance tester

There are two types: battery-operated and those incorporating a small hand-operated generator. These instruments produce a voltage which is twice the normal working voltage of the circuit under test, e.g. 500V for a 240V system. Other test voltages include 110V and 1,000V. Most insulation-resistance testers have two scales: megohm and ohm. The former indicates the value of insulation resistance between conductors and between conductors and earth, with the scale opened out, as it were, around the minimum acceptable value for circuits: 1 megohm. The other scale, reading in ohms, is used for checking the conductor continuity of circuits, with the beginning of the scale again opened out for accurate readings. Digital display instruments give the actual value of a test reading.

The reason for the test voltage being twice the working voltage is to stress the insulation. If it has been damaged or has deteriorated, the test will show this condition. The test current actually flows through the insulation material and so any faults will readily be detected: the better the insulation the less current will flow.

Continuity tester

This instrument indicates low ohmic values, typically 0–100 ohms. It is often used to measure the resistance of conductors where accuracy is not required. If readings are expected much less than 1 ohm, a milliohmmeter is used which, typically, can measure resistance down to 1 milliohm. Some installation tests (e.g. ring-circuit continuity and CPC continuity) are best measured using a milliohmmeter. Most are battery-operated and some instruments have a digital display.

Phase-earth loop tester

This instrument is used to check the value of the impedance of the earth-loop path (Z_s). It passes, through a current-limiting resistor, a current of about 25A into the earth circuit, and the reading obtained, in ohms, is then compared with a maximum value of Z_s indicated in Chapter 41 of the Wiring Regulations. The maximum value depends on the type of protective device used for the circuit under test and its current rating. All testers have two indicating lights which must be ON before the test is carried out. The L–N light indicates that the polarity of the circuit is correct. The L–E light verifies that there is a connection between phase and earth. If one or both of these lights do not operate, the test must not be carried out. Testers are available with a digital read-out or with a graduated scale in ohms.

RCD tester

This instrument checks the operating (tripping) current of residual current devices. Most instruments offer a range of tripping currents (typically 5–500mA) and some indicate how fast the RCD has tripped (i.e. time of disconnection).

Earth tester

This instrument is used to check the effectiveness of the resistance to earth of each element of an earth installation and, in particular, where an independent earth electrode is used as the main means of earthing (e.g. in a TT earthing arrangement). The tester can also be used to measure earth continuity.

Portable appliance tester

This instrument is used to check the electrical condition of portable appliances. Three test facilities are incorporated: earth bond, insulation resistance (IR) and a flash test. The first test facility ensures that the earthing provision (e.g. CPC in the flex and the metal casing of the appliance) is adequate enough to carry a severe earth-fault current. The IR test checks the condition of the insulation in both the flexible cord and the appliance. The flash test is used for double-insulated appliances, which is stressed at a voltage up to 5kV to verify the integrity of the insulation used in the construction of the appliance.

Measuring instruments

These are used to measure voltage, current and resistance. When checking the voltage of a live circuit, it is important to ensure one's own safety by using fused safety probes to make contact with the live terminals. Instead of using a voltmeter, a potential (voltage) indicator can be used to check the voltage range of a circuit. These are safer to use.

Ammeters are normally connected into a circuit, which also raises the question of safety. On ac circuits, the clamp meter does away with the need to open up a circuit conductor to measure the level of current flow. These instruments have insulated jaws which are clamped round the insulating conductor; current values are then off a digital read-out or off a graduated scale. Most clamp meters offer a wide range of current values and some incorporate a voltage reading facility.

Resistance can be measured with an ohmmeter which is battery-operated. Some instruments are available which measure current, voltage and resistance on both ac and dc supplies. When using these multi-range instruments, care must be taken to select the correct electrical quantity to be measured and the correct scale.

Recording of test results

Any test result obtained from a test on an installation must be recorded, as it then becomes part of the history of the installation. If a similar test has to be carried out at a later date, the person carrying out the new test can then compare the new value with the recorded value. For instance, if an earth-loop test revealed an impedance (Z_s) value of

1.8 ohms which was an acceptable reading and a later test indicated, say, 2 ohms, which was still within the maximum Z_s limit, the reason for the increase should be investigated as the second reading might indicate a deterioration in part of the earth-loop path. A more than likely culprit might be the CPC connection/termination which might have become insecure. If the CPC was metal conduit, the increase might be due to slack locknuts or rusting at the conduit joints.

Except where circuits and electrical equipment are tested 'dead', all precautions must be taken to ensure safety from electric shock and burns. Attention is drawn to the Health and Safety Executive Guidance Note G538, *Electrical Test Equipment for Use by Electricians*. This publication advises on the selection and safe use of suitable test probes, leads, lamps, voltage-indicating devices and other measuring equipment.

Live electrical testing is generally limited by the Electricity (Factories Act) Special Regulations to 'authorised' or 'competent' persons where the voltage involved is more than 125V ac (or 250V dc); and these persons must be over the age of twenty-one years and under the immediate supervision of the authorised person. This age limit for a competent person may be reduced to eighteen years (under the Electricity Regulations (Competent Persons) Order 1968) provided that he/she has completed an approved training course.

Inspection and testing — general

The Wiring Regulations require that every new installation, an extension or alteration to an existing installation, must be inspected and tested on completion and before it is energised. This is to give the client some guarantee that 'good workmanship and the use of approved materials' will provide an installation which is safe to use and which, in all respects, reduces to a minimum all risks against electric shock, fire and burns.

Before any inspection and test can be carried out, certain information must be available to the inspector. This information includes drawings showing the positions of isolators, switches, outlet points, the type and rating of protective devices and the size and type of conductors. In other words, much of the information which relates to the design of the installation has to be made available. It is generally accepted in the trade that not only is the designer responsible for the quality built into the installation, but the installer (the electrician) bears some responsibility for how the installation is presented. In addition, the person carrying out the inspection and test must be fully familiar not only with the instruments used in testing but also be fully competent in their use — and be able to interpret the test results.

Visual inspection

The visual inspection of a completed installation includes checking the connections of conductors and their correct identification (by colour or numbers). The conductors must also be checked to ensure that they are able to carry the designed load current and that the voltage drop is within specified limits. All single-pole control devices (switches) and protective devices (fuses, MCBs) must be connected to the phase conductors. 'Polarised' wiring accessories (such as socket-outlets and Edison screw lampholders) must be correctly terminated.

In work areas, switches for isolation (e.g. in a motor circuit) and emergency switching must be provided. All distribution boards and consumer units must have circuit charts giving details of the function of final circuits, their conductor sizes and the type and rating of the protective devices. In situations where there are a number of switches, distribution boards, etc., these must be identified as to their purpose with labels. Danger and warning notices must also be provided (e.g. where high voltages are used for external light installations and for firemens' switches).

The visual inspection must also include checks to make sure that there is no danger to those using the installation from direct contact with live terminals.

The Wiring Regulation 712-01-03 provides a checklist which is not comprehensive but gives the inspector a good starting point from which to draw up his/her own checklist which, of course, will depend on the type of installation. The inspector must also check such simple things like: no burrs left inside conduit; all cables protected against mechanical damage; cables securely fixed with correct distances between their supports; and all materials used in the installation correctly chosen to operate in the working conditions which obtain once the installation has been energised.

Testing

The range of testing instruments available is described in the previous chapter. It is, however, worth mentioning that the instruments must be in good condition, be properly calibrated and used correctly. The tests which are required by the Wiring Regulations to be carried out do not apply to every installation. For instance, the test schedule for a domestic installation will differ from that for an industrial installation. The following list is confined to the tests applied to a domestic installation:

1. Continuity of socket-outlet final ring circuit conductors.
2. Continuity of CPCs, including main and supplementary bonding conductors.
3. Earth electrode resistance.
4. Insulation resistance.
5. Polarity.
6. Earth-fault loop impedance.
7. Operation of RCDs.

All test results must be logged so that they can be used for comparison with the results obtained at future tests. This is done to provide a historical record of the condition of the installation as it grows older and so that potential dangers can be rectified before increased risks from electric shock and fire can reach a dangerous level.

Continuity of ring final circuit conductors

This test is made to ensure the electrical continuity of the conductors of ring circuits. Ideally, there should be no break in these conductors. Normal practice, however, means that conductors are 'broken' and terminated in terminals and secured by screws. These, in fact, constitute what are called 'dry joints' which, through time, could become loose. This is easily demonstrated with the terminals of a 13A plug which is used to supply a 3kW washing machine. Over a period of time, the current taken by the appliance will tend to produce heat which results in the continual expansion and contraction of the terminal screws which eventually become loose. After a while, it is possible to get an extra half-turn or so on the screw to retighten it. If this happens in a 13A plug, it can also occur at the terminals behind the socket-outlet.

The test can be carried out using the 'continuity' range of a dual-purpose instrument (e.g. an insulation-resistance tester) or using a milliohm-meter. The latter is preferred because the instrument can give readings as low as 1 milliohm.

The test is made to ensure that the conductors (phase, neutral and the CPC) are electrically continuous and to make sure that there has been no inadvertent interconnection between socket-outlets which would constitute a short-circuit, which in effect creates an apparently continuous ring circuit. In this situation, an actual break in a conductor could exist without detection.

The test is carried out as follows:

1. Measure the resistance of the conductor (e.g. phase) by separating its ends at the consumer unit or distribution board. Call the reading obtained A.
2. Join the separated ends of the conductor and connect the instrument to the join. The other terminal of the instrument is then connected to the 'L' terminal in a socket-outlet which is judged to be midway in the ring circuit. Call this reading B. This part of the test involves the use of a long test lead.
3. Measure the resistance of the long test lead.
4. Check that the readings $A/4 = B - C$. If both sides of the equation are virtually equal, then the continuity of the phase conductor is satisfactory.
5. Repeat the test for the neutral conductor and the CPC.

Example: Reading $A = 0.4$ ohm
Reading $B = 0.2$ ohm
Reading $C = 0.1$ ohm

$$\text{Therefore } \frac{0.4}{4} = 0.2 - 0.1 = 0.1 \text{ ohm}$$

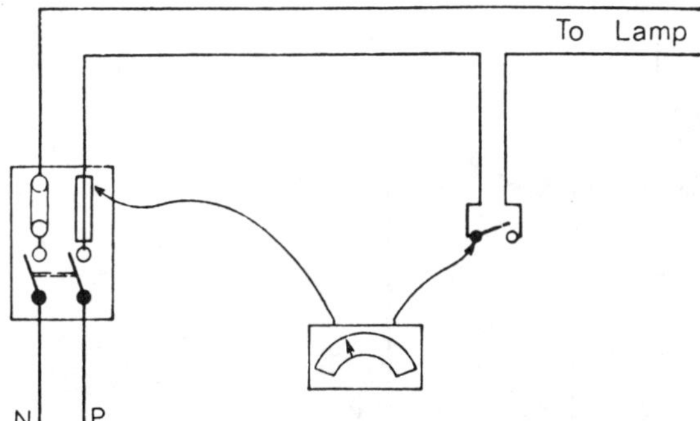

Figure 8.1. Polarity test on a single-pole switch.

Continuity of protective conductors

This test is required to verify that the conductors are both correctly connected and electrically sound. The test is carried out by using a voltage not exceeding 50V and passing a current not exceeding 25A into the conductor. This test simulates an earth-fault current and the level of current will show up any defects in the conductor and its terminations.

The resistance of a CPC can also be measured using a milliohmmeter and the reading obtained compared with the design resistance of the CPC, as used in the formula:

$$Z_s = Z_e + (R_1 + R_2)$$

where R_2 refers to the CPC. The value of R_2 can be calculated using the figures in the 'Guidance Notes', 'Inspection and Testing', of the Wiring Regulations. These tables give the resistance of different sizes of conductors in milliohms/metre at 20 °C. If one knows the length of the CPC, the total resistance can be calculated. This figure has to be used with a multiplying factor to take account of the fact that when the CPC carries a fault, current heat will be generated which will increase the CPC resistance.

Earth electrode resistance

Where the earthing arrangement is TT, with the client depending on an independent earth electrode in the ground for protection against earth-leakage currents, the testing instrument is a proprietary earth tester; or the test can be made using an extra-low voltage source.

After the earth electrode has been installed, the test ensures that the resistance of the electrode has not increased the level of earth-fault loop impedance to an unacceptable level.

The general mass of earth is used in electrical work to maintain the potential of any part of a system at a definite value with respect to earth (usually taken as zero volts). It also allows a current to flow in the event of a fault to earth, so that protective gear will operate to isolate the faulty circuit. One particular aspect of the earth electrode resistance area is that its resistance is by no means constant. It varies with the amount of moisture in the soil and is therefore subject to seasonal and other changes. As the general mass of earth forms part of the earth-fault loop path, it is essential at times to know its actual value of resistance, particularly of that area within the vicinity of the earth electrode. The effective resistance area of an earth electrode extends for some distance around the actual electrode; but the surface voltage dies away very rapidly as the distance from the electrode increases (see Figure 8.2). The basic method of measuring the earth electrode resistance is to pass current into the soil

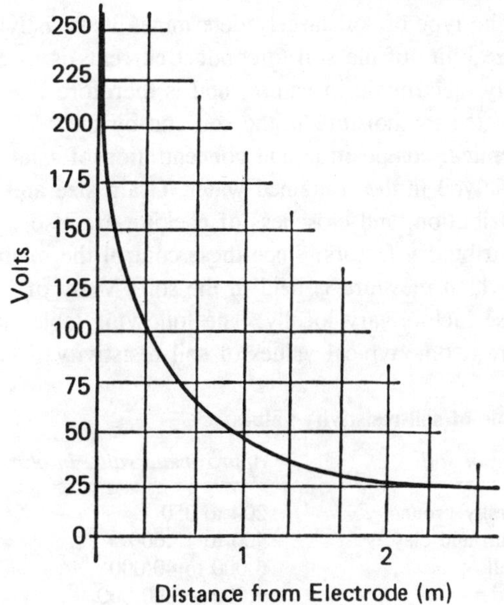

Figure 8.2. Voltage at ground surface resulting from rod earth electrode buried vertically in soil of uniform resistivity.

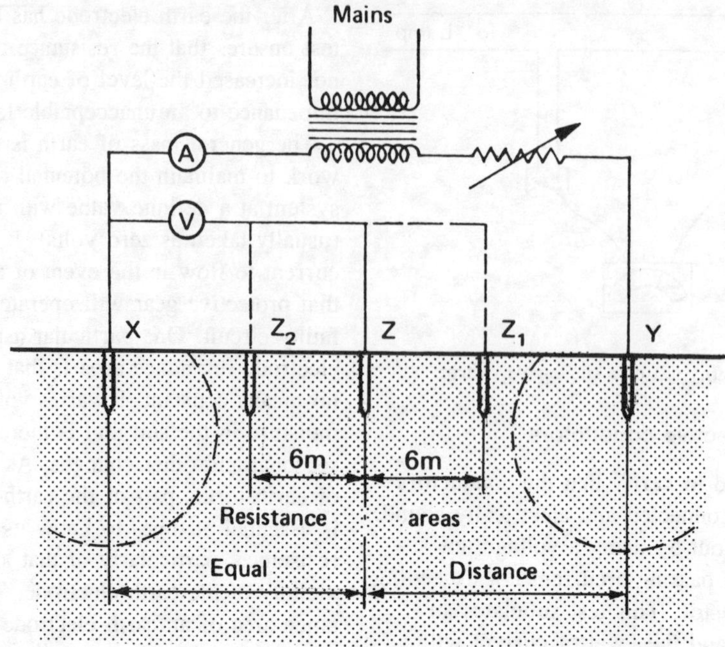

Figure 8.3. Measurement of earth-electrode resistance. X — electrode under test; Y — current electrode; Z — potential electrode equidistant from X and Y; Z_1 — first position of Z for second reading; Z_2 — second position of Z for third reading.

via the electrode and to measure the voltage needed to produce this current. The basic circuit is shown in Figure 8.3.

The type of soil largely determines its resistivity. The ability of the soil to conduct currents is essentially electrolytic in nature, and is therefore affected by moisture in the soil and by the chemical composition and concentration of salts dissolved in the contained water. Grain size and distribution, and closeness of packing are also contributory factors, since these control the manner in which moisture is held in the soil. Many of these factors vary locally. The following table shows some typical values of soil resistivity:

Table of soil-resistivity values

Type of soil	*Approximate value in ohm-cm*
Marshy ground	200 to 350
Loam and clay	400 to 15,000
Chalk	6,000 to 40,000
Sand	9,000 to 800,000
Peat	5,000 to 50,000
Sandy gravel	5,000 to 50,000
Rock	100,000 upwards

(BICC Ltd)

When the site of an earth electrode is to be considered, the following types of soil are recommended, in order of preference:

(*a*) Wet marshy ground, which is not too well drained.
(*b*) Clay, loamy soil, arable land, clay soil and clay soil mixed with small quantities of sand.
(*c*) Clay and loam mixed with varying proportions of sand, gravel and stones.
(*d*) Damp and wet sand, peat.

Dry sand, gravel chalk, limestone, whinstone, granite and any very stony ground should be avoided, as should all locations where virgin rock is very close to the surface.

Chemical treatment of the soil is sometimes used to improve its conductivity. Common salt is very suitable for this purpose. Calcium chloride, sodium carbonate and other substances are also beneficial, but before any chemical treatment is applied it should be verified that no corrosive actions will be set up, particularly on the earth electrode.

The means used to measure the resistance of the

earth electrode resistance area can be either a hand-operated tester or a mains-energised double-wound transformer, the latter requiring an ammeter and a high-resistance voltmeter. The former method gives a direct reading in ohms on the instrument scale; the latter method requires a calculation in the form:

$$\text{ohms} = \frac{\text{voltage}}{\text{current}}.$$

The procedure is the same in each case. An auxiliary electrode is driven into the ground at a distance of about 30 m away from the electrode under test (the consumer's electrode). A third electrode is driven midway between them. The connections are as shown in Figure 8.3. To ensure that the resistance areas of the first two electrodes do not overlap, the third electrode is moved 6 m farther from, and nearer to, the electrode under test. The three tests should give similar results, the average value being taken as the mean resistance of the earth electrode.

One disadvantage of using the simple method of earth electrode resistance measurement is that the effects of emfs — owing to electrolytic action in the soil — have to be taken into account when testing. Also, there is the possibility of stray earth currents being present in the area under test, these currents being leakages from local distribution systems. Because of this, it is usual to use a commercial instrument, the Megger earth tester being a typical example.

Insulation resistance

There are three tests under this heading: insulation resistance (IR) between conductors; IR between conductors and earth; and the separate IR test to be carried out on disconnected equipment such as cookers.

Before these tests are carried out, it is essential to disconnect any neons and capacitors from the circuit because they will upset the readings obtained. In addition, any control devices which contain semiconductor components must also be disconnected as they can be damaged by the test voltage.

IR between conductors. For this test, all lamps have to be removed and all switches closed. The test instrument is then connected between phase and neutral (if the supply is single-phase) and the test voltage applied. The minimum acceptable value of insulation resistance is 1 megohm. In new and otherwise electrically healthy circuits, the reading will normally be 'infinity'. If a 'zero' reading is obtained this indicates a short-circuit. If a significant resistance reading is obtained, this might indicate, say, a lamp left in the circuit (e.g. the filament resistance of a 100W lamp would be in the region of 600 ohms).

IR between conductors and earth. For this test, all fuses (or MCBs) should be in place, all switches closed (including the main switch if practicable) and all the poles or phase conductors connected together. Again, the minimum acceptable value is 1 megohm.

IR of disconnected apparatus. The tests include IR between conductors and between the conductors and earth. The minimum acceptable value is 0.5 megohm in each test.

Polarity

This test is carried out to ensure that all protective devices and single-pole controls (e.g. one-way switches) are connected in the phase conductor only. In addition, the test confirms that socket-outlet 'L' terminals are connected to the phase conductor and that the centre contacts of Edison screw lampholders are also connected to the phase side of the supply. Test are carried out with all switches closed, lamps and equipment removed. The test instrument can be a continuity tester, or a low-reading ohmmeter if no mains supply is available. If the circuit is 'live', a test lamp with approved and fused leads and test probes can be used.

Earth-fault loop impedance

The earth-fault loop path comprises the CPC, the main earthing terminal, the main earthing conductor, the metallic earth-return path (in TN systems, which could be the wire armouring of an underground cable), the earthed neutral point of the supply transformer, the secondary winding of the transformer and the phase conductor from the transformer to the point at which the fault has occurred. The impedance of the earth-fault loop is denoted as Z_s.

The instrument commonly used is a phase-earth loop tester which has two indicating lamps, both of which must be ON before a test is carried out. One lamp indicates that the polarity of the circuit is correct 'L–N' and the other ensures that a proven earth connection is available 'L–E'. There is usually a recommendation that there should be at least a 20-second interval between tests. This is to allow any heat generated in the current-limiting resistor to dissipate. The instrument passes a current of around 20A into the earth loop path.

The reading obtained must be compared with the maximum Z_s values given in Chapter 41 of the Wiring Regulations. These values vary according to (*a*) the type of overcurrent protective device and its current rating, and (*b*) whether the circuit feeds socket-outlets or fixed equipment. If the reading obtained is less than the maximum value of Z_s, the circuit is acceptable. If it exceeds the recommended figure, the circuit must be investigated to find the reason. The reading obtained should also be compared with the reading of the previous test (if this information is available) to see whether the Z_s value is on the increase, which might indicate a potentially dangerous condition appearing in the circuit. For example, if the maximum Z_s was 2 ohms and the test reading was 1.2 ohms on a previous test but was now 1.8 ohms, this indicates that the next test would produce an unacceptable reading with the possibility that an earth fault occurring in the circuit would not produce enough fault current to operate the overcurrent protective device in either 0.4 second or 5 seconds, thus increasing the risk of electric shock to persons using the installation.

RCD tests

These devices are provided with a test button which gives the client the opportunity to check that the RCD is operational at frequent intervals. The Wiring Regulations require that an RCD be tested so that it trips within the required time. An RCD with a rated tripping current of 30mA should trip within 0.2 second. RCD testers are available which give a choice of tripping currents, typically ranging from 5 to 500mA, and also display the actual tripping time. The higher the value of tripping current, the less the time of operation. It should be

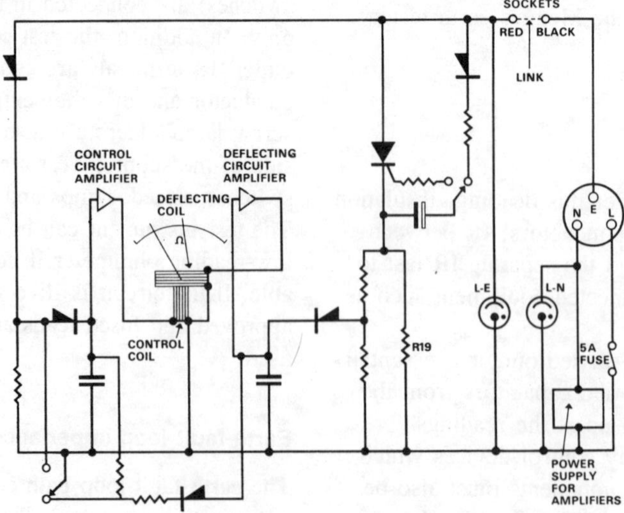

Figure 8.4. Circuit diagram of an electronic line-earth loop tester. Resistor R19 is the current-limiting resistor (value about 10 ohms).

noted that before the test is applied, all loads normally supplied through the RCD should be disconnected.

Certificates

The Wiring Regulations require that following the inspection and testing of an installation, a completion and inspection certificate should be signed by, or on behalf of, the contractor and given to the client. This certificate then forms part of the documentation relating to the installation and must be available to the person conducting subsequent tests on the installation.

Periodic inspection and testing

The Wiring Regulations require that installations be inspected and tested at regular intervals as follows:

General installations — 5 years (maximum)
Temporary installations — 3 months (maximum)
Caravan sites — 1 year
Agricultural installations — 3 years (maximum)

Other types of installations of a more specific nature are also required to be inspected and tested regularly. These include fire alarms, emergency lighting, cinemas, petrol filling stations and churches. Some of the recommended intervals between tests are recommended; others are mandatory, such as those for petrol filling stations which come under the bye-laws associated with the Petroleum Consolidation Acts.

9 Electrical apparatus

Though the contracting electrician tends to be more concerned with the actual installation of wiring systems and a restricted range of apparatus, there are certain contracts which involve the installation and connection of such equipment as heavy switchgear, transformers and rectifiers. Most often, however, he is involved with the larger types of domestic appliances. The factory maintenance electrician on the other hand, finds his work centred round the installation, commissioning and maintenance of transformers, rectifying equipment and the like. The following sections deal with each type of electrical equipment, its general physical and electrical characteristics, and its installation, maintenance and testing requirements.

Transformers

The following brief description covers the main components of transformers which are commonly found in industrial applications. The core of the transformer is built up from thin sheets or laminations of special steel. The steel is generally hot-rolled, silicon-iron alloy. To reduce eddy-current losses, the laminations are lightly insulated from one another by means of paper, china clay ('Insuline'), varnish, or a coating of phosphate. Small transformers' cores have their laminations held together by insulating tape. Larger cores are clamped together by means of bolts which pass through the laminations but are insulated from them. Modern transformers of large size have mitred-corner cores to reduce the necessity for bolts.

The windings of the transformer are either copper or aluminium conductors in wire or strip form. Each turn of the windings is insulated from adjacent turns by a thin layer of enamel or paper (in air-cooled transformers woven-glass insulation is used). The windings are generally placed over a pressboard or Bakelite cylinder which surrounds the core limbs. In core-type transformers, the primary and secondary windings are usually arranged concentrically. The windings are subdivided so that the voltage between adjacent turns and adjacent coils is kept as low as possible to avoid stressing the insulation. In most low-voltage and in many high-voltage windings, the voltage between any pair of adjacent turns is simply the normal voltage per turn of the transformer. The different sections of the windings and the hv and lv coils are separated by suitable insulation, so arranged as to provide ample and numerous ducts for the free passage of the oil or air to the inner parts of the windings, to ensure uniform cooling throughout.

When tappings for adjustment of voltage are required, they are usually provided on the higher voltage side of the transformer. They are arranged at the middle of the windings on each leg of the core. In general, the tappings recommended in BS 171 are standard at ±2½ and ±5 per cent. These ranges are sufficient for normal requirements to cater for load variations. The tappings are generally connected via removable links, with the transformer disconnected from the supply. Certain transformers have their tapping arrangements on the low-voltage side when a tapping-switch is used. Large transformers have special arrangements for on-load tap-changing which are necessary to ensure continuity of the supply.

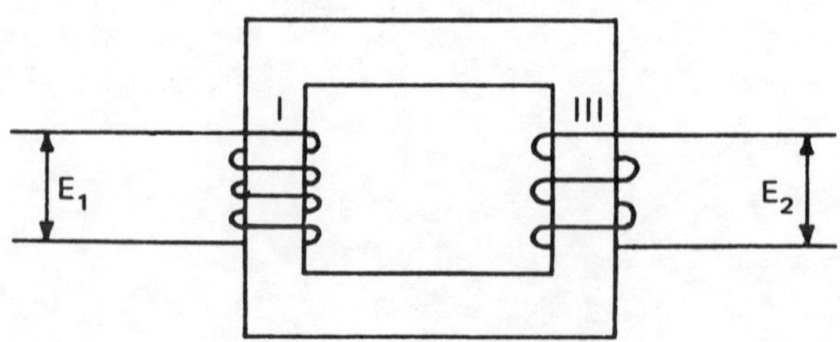

Figure 9.1. Simple transformer.

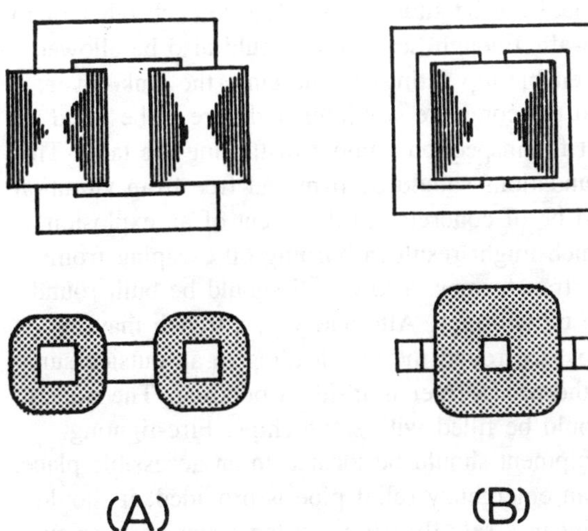

Figure 9.2. (*a*) core and (*b*) shell type transformers.

When a transformer is supplying a load, heat is generated in the windings and core. Since the rating of any electrical machine is governed by the maximum temperature which the insulation can safely withstand, cooling is necessary. Oil of mineral derivation is used. It possesses good insulation and heat-conducting properties and has a very high flashpoint. The oil has three functions: it provides additional insulation between the windings and the metal tank which houses the transformer; it excludes dirt and moisture from the coil insulation; and it cools the windings. As the heat is produced in the metal of the transformer, it passes through the insulation to raise the temperature of the oil, which circulates through pipes fitted to the exterior of the metal housing to dissipate the heat to the surrounding air. This circulation is known as natural cooling. Air-cooled transformers are usually small and are housed in a metal casing provided with louvres in the side.

Some transformers are of the hermetically sealed, oil-cooled type. The principle here is that a large air space is provided above the oil in the tank which takes up the expansion of the oil under load conditions. Outside air cannot get into the tank. Where transformers are used in hazardous areas in conjunction with flameproof equipment, they are either air-cooled or filled with a non-flammable liquid. This liquid possesses an insulation breakdown strength equal to that of mineral oil; the gaseous products evolved, should arcing take place, are non-explosive.

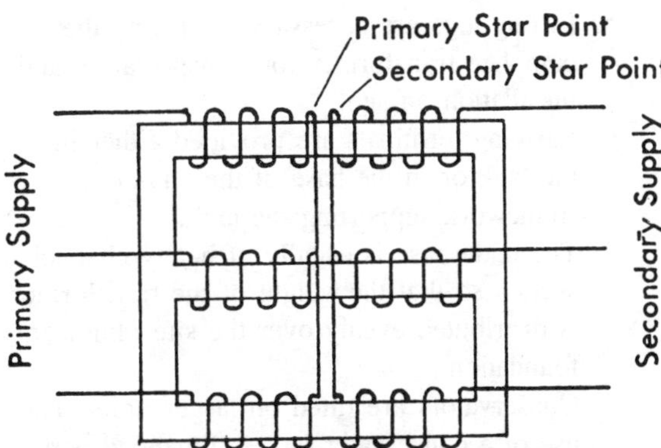

Figure 9.3. Three-phase transformer — star/star connection.

Fittings associated with the transformer tank include:

1. Drain valves, fitted in such a way that the tank can be drained completely of oil.
2. Drain plugs, which are fitted in small transformers of about 75kVA and under. They are situated in the tank wall as near as possible to the bottom.
3. Oil gauges, which are of the visual-sight glass type to show how the level of the oil varies with the loading of the transformer.
4. Thermometers are generally standard items on transformers of over 100kVA. Dial-type thermometers are fitted to very large transforming units and can be provided with 'maximum' pointers and alarm contacts.

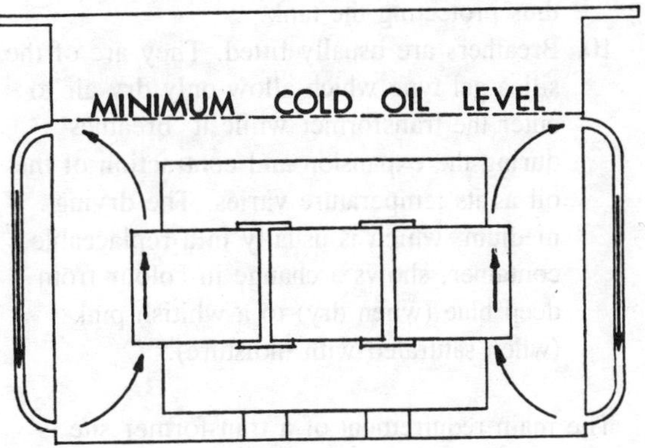

Figure 9.4. Natural oil-cooled transformer.

5. Lifting lugs are necessary for lifting the complete transformer for transportation and installation on site.
6. Earthing terminals are provided either in the tank or in the base of the chassis or framework supporting the tank.
7. The underbase is usually of heavy channel section so that the weight of the transformer is distributed evenly over the site plinth or foundation.
8. Conservators are fitted on larger units. The use of a conservator is recommended particularly on outdoor transformers where the loading is such that it gives rise to a wide variation in temperature, or where it is to operate in adverse climatic conditions. The effect of the conservator is to prolong the life of the transformer by preventing oil sludge and reducing the possibility of water entering the main tank. Conservators are supported away from the main tank and connected to it by a pipe. When in service, the tank is completely filled with oil and the conservator partially filled, thus allowing for oil expansion from the main tank when the transformer is loaded.
9. An explosion or relief vent is provided on the larger units. It consists of a welded pipe bolted to the tank cover and fitted with a diaphragm. It rises above the level of the conservator. Should a fault occur in the transformer, the resulting pressure of gas inside the tank will accumulate and appear in the vent pipe to burst the diaphragm and vent the gas and oil products to atmosphere, thus protecting the tank.
10. Breathers are usually fitted. They are of the silica-gel type which allow only dry air to enter the transformer while it 'breathes' during the expansion and contraction of the oil as its temperature varies. The drying medium, which is usually in a replaceable container, shows a change in colour from deep blue (when dry) to a whitish-pink (when saturated with moisture).

The main requirement of a transformer site is the provision of adequate ventilation. Transformers should not be situated too close to each other or to a wall. Enough headroom should also be allowed to enable top fittings of the tank, the tank cover, and the complete windings and core to be lifted out for inspection without disturbing the tank. The foundations should be firm and free from vibration and be of concrete. In the event of an explosion which might result in burning oil escaping from the transformer, a low wall should be built round the transformer. Alternatively, a trench may be provided round the unit leading to an outside sump if the transformer is inside a building. The trench should be filled with stone chips. Fire-fighting equipment should be located in an accessible place. If an emergency relief pipe is provided, it should point in a safe direction; in the event of a serious electrical fault, burning oil may be ejected from it.

Transformer maintenance is for the most part simple: keeping the tank clean and free from rust or leaking oil. Regular changing of the drying medium in breathers is essential in damp and humid situations. Otherwise, moisture in the oil will result in sludge and reduce its insulating properties. The oil level should be checked regularly, making allowance for the expansion and contraction of the oil with changes in temperature. Insulating bushings which carry the electrical connections should be cleaned regularly and their surfaces inspected for signs of chipping or cracking. The oil should be tested at least annually. There are three tests:

1. The crackle test, in which a small amount of oil is taken from the transformer and placed in a test-tube. When held over a flame, the oil in the tube will crackle as any moisture contained in it is driven off. If such a test proves positive, the oil should be changed.
2. A dielectric test should be made to test the insulation resistance of the oil, which value should conform to the maker's figure.
3. An acidity test of the oil is made to ensure that, in service at high working temperatures, it has not begun to produce acid-forming sludge. Insulation-resistance tests are also necessary on all the electrical conductors, both between conductors and between these conductors and earth. It is important that the

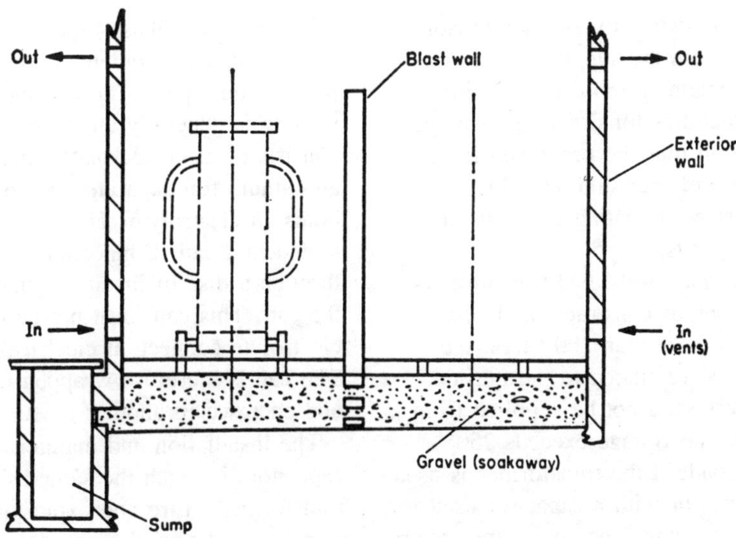

Figure 9.5. Site installation of an oil-filled transformer.

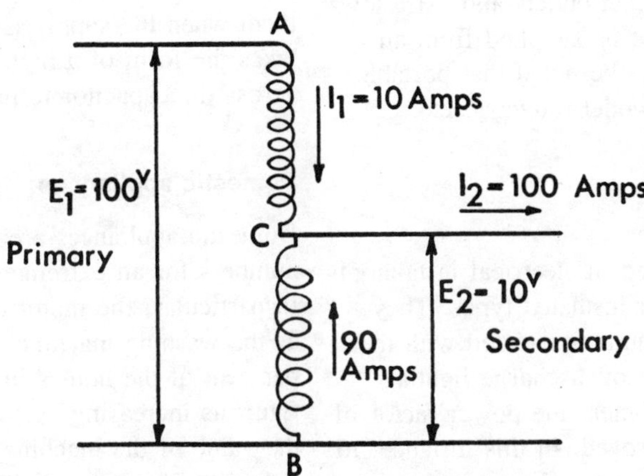

Figure 9.6. Principle of the auto-transformer.

earth connection be electrically and mechanically sound at all times and free from corrosion products.

The following is a brief summary of the main requirements of the general regulations and recommendations for the equipment listed. Full information can be found in the various Codes of Practice issued by the British Standards Institution.

1. Chokes and transformers, classified as fixed apparatus, exceeding 60W capacity are to be adequately ventilated and enclosed in a proper container or so mounted to minimise fire risks. In the latter case, the mounting must be such that no combustible material or wood, except hardwood, is within 30 cm measured vertically above the apparatus or 15 cm in any other direction from it. Combustible material protected by asbestos or other fireproof material is accepted. The housing of a choke in a discharge lamp fitting also must comply with the general regulations.
2. A step-up transformer, forming part of a consumer's installation, must be provided with a

multi-pole, linked switch to completely isolate the transformer from the supply.

3. Transformers containing more than 25 litres of oil must have facilities for draining away any excess oil. The oil must be prevented from leaking into parts of the building. This regulation is met by mounting the transformer over gravel-filled pits.
4. Buildings which house oil-filled transformers should be of fireproof construction. If the quantity of oil is more than 200 litres, the building should be ventilated to the outside.
5. Auto-transformers shall not be supplied from the mains where the voltage exceeds 250V. Exceptions are made if the transformer is used for motor-starting, or with a capacitor used for improving power factor. The auto-transformer must be installed beside the capacitor.

Portable appliances, socket-outlets and extra-low-voltage apparatus shall not be supplied from an auto-transformer. It should be noted that portable appliances include toys, model railways, etc.

Capacitors

Most of the capacitors used in electrical installation work are metal-foil, paper-insulated types. They vary in size, from small units associated with the power-factor improvement of discharge lighting circuits to the units used where the power factor of large motors is to be improved. In this instance, to give the required capacity, several capacitors are made up in banks. The banks are placed in a steel casing which is then filled with insulating oil in the same way as a transformer. Capacitors are also used for motor-starting on single-phase supplies. In the capacitor-start motor, the phase difference necessary to produce a rotating field and hence rotation of the motor rotor, is provided by a capacitor connected in series with a starting winding. The capacitor and its starting winding are disconnected by a centrifugal switch mounted on the motor shaft, once the motor has reached near full speed. In some instances, a capacitor-start, capacitor-run motor is used. A large capacitor is used for starting and a small capacitor is left in series with the starting winding. This gives the effect of a two-phase motor with a higher overall power factor and quieter running than the single-phase counterpart. The capacitor used for motor starting is generally an 'ac electrolytic' unit. It consists of electrode plates made from thin aluminium foil separated by absorbent paper which holds an electrolyte. The unit is hermetically sealed in a can. Connections are brought out through a disc of insulating material at one end of the can. This can must not be earthed as the electrolyte connects it electrically to the electrodes. The can is therefore wrapped in insulating material and enclosed in another case.

The installation and maintenance of oil-filled capacitors is much the same as that for transformers. Fire and explosion precautions must be taken and periodic samples of the oil drawn off for testing. Capacitors must always be provided with some means for automatically discharging them when the supply is disconnected. This usually takes the form of a high-value resistance connected across the capacitor terminals.

Domestic appliances

Domestic appliances are used today in great numbers for an extremely wide variety of duties. In particular, the motor-operated appliance, such as the washing-machine, is to be found in about 50 per cent of the homes in this country and this figure is increasing each year as housewives realise the value of the machine to relieve them of the drudgery of wash-day. The other two most common appliances using an electic motor are the vacuum cleaner and the refrigerator.

The main electrical feature of the washing machine is the motor. This unit is usually a capacitor-start machine of average rating 0.25kW. Split-phase-start types are also found. These motors are specially designed to deal with the variations of load imposed on them by the weight of clothes to be washed. Many often start up against a full load in the tub. A typical washing cycle on a fully automatic machine consists of the following stages: wash (10 min), spin ($2\frac{1}{2}$ min), fill with water ($2\frac{1}{2}$ min), rinse (3 min), spin ($2\frac{1}{2}$ min), fill with water ($2\frac{1}{2}$ min), rinse (3 min), and spin dry ($2\frac{1}{2}$ min).

Electricity finds a useful application in refrigerators, either to operate the various refrigerating systems or to provide a convenient means of control (switching, protection, interlocking, etc.) of cooling plants or for defrosting. To refrigerate, whether for low-temperature storage, household food preservation, or air conditioning, it is first necessary to make a surface cool. In this way, heat is extracted from the surface, known as the load, and carried away by a fluid through pipes. A fluid, when accepting heat, can do so in only two ways. It can allow its own temperature to increase, or it can evaporate from a liquid condition to a vapour (hence the use of the term 'evaporator'). This latter process is normally used since it affords by far the greater economy. Fluids are chosen which boil, while accepting heat from the load, under the most suitable temperatures and pressures. This heat is absorbed without raising the temperature of the fluid (it remains 'latent'). To remove heat from the refrigerants, it is usual to condense the vapour back to a liquid state. Assuming that one is ultimately losing the heat to the surrounding atmosphere, the condensing refrigerant must be warmer than the environment. The surface of the condenser must, therefore, be kept at a lower temperature than the warm refrigerant by the cooler atmospheric air in household and some

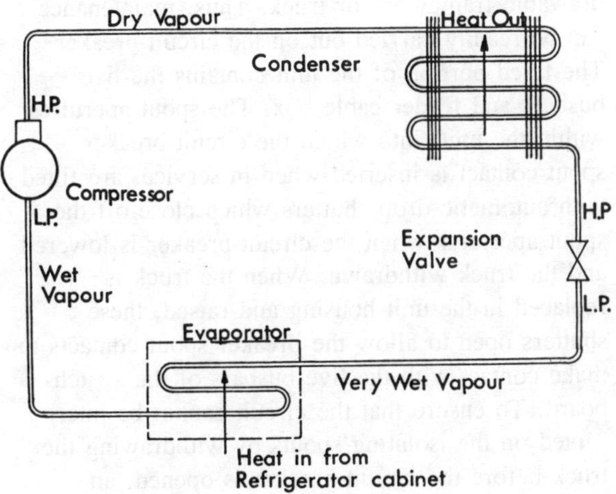

Figure 9.7. Schematic diagram of a vapour-compression refrigerator.

commercial systems, or by cooling water or brine in other systems. To make the refrigerant work, it must be driven around the circuit tubes or pipes. The electric motor is the prime mover chosen to drive a compressor. In the vapour compression household refrigerator, the compressor lifts the refrigerant at one point in its cycle from the low (evaporating) pressure to the high (condensing) pressure. Figure 9.7 shows a simple circuit diagram of a vapour-compression system. The place of the expansion valve is often taken by a long length of fine-bore tubing offering such wall resistance to the flow of refrigerant that its pressure is thereby dropped. Compression machines are normally driven by capacitor- or split-phase-start motors so that speed is constant on a given supply frequency.

Rectifiers

The continuing application of static rectifiers in electrial work is because dc supplies have certain advantages over alternating current in certain applications and are essential in others. Semiconductor rectifiers are now widely used because they have some advantages over their predecessors. DC supplies are also used for electrolytic loads in chemical engineering, plating and anodising, battery charging, cathodic protection and electrostatic precipitation. DC is an advantage in electric traction where the acceleration performances of dc motors make these machines a first choice.

The most important and generally useful type of rectifier today is the silicon diode. Germanium is also used but is generally restricted to low-voltage applications. Generally, for all equipments with outputs below 50V and for many up to 150V, the tendency is to employ germanium, provided that the temperature conditions allow. If the ambient temperature is greater than 40 °C, silicon is used. Most large-power silicon units are cooled by artificial means, either forced-air, water or oil. Small units are mounted on aluminium sections which offer a very large surface in contact with the surrounding air to dissipate heat quickly. These sections are known as 'heat sinks'.

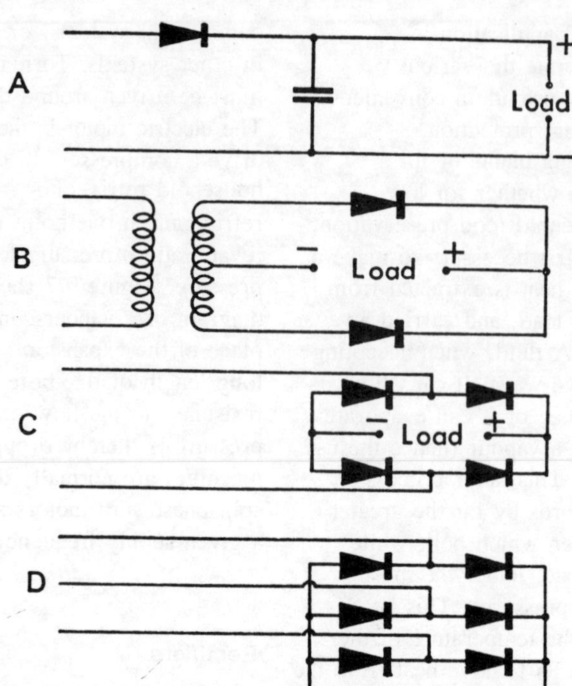

Figure 9.8. Connections of rectifier elements: (*a*) half-wave; (*b*) full-wave; (*c*) bridge connection for full-wave; (*d*) rectification of a three-phase supply.

Switchgear

Though 'switchgear' can range from small switches for domestic and small industrial installations to large outdoor 275kV units, the following deals with the type of gear associated with medium-size industrial installations. Generally, the switchgear is of one of two main types:

1. Truck type, in which the circuit-breaker (oil- or air-break) is mounted on a truck which can be withdrawn to the front of the switchboard of which the unit is a part. With this type of gear, sufficient space must be allowed for the withdrawal of the truck.
2. Metalclad, in which all parts are enclosed in metal cases, and the units are factory built. The busbars for high voltages are either oil- or compound-insulated in special chambers. Disconnection of the circuit-breaker from the busbars is made by withdrawing downwards or outwards.

In the truck-type gear, the circuit-breaker and associated current- and voltage-transformers (for the indicating instruments) are mounted in a withdrawable framework or truck. Thus, maintenance can be readily carried out on the circuit-breaker. The fixed portion of the unit contains the live busbars and feeder cable box. The spout apertures within the unit, into which the circuit-breaker spout contact is inserted when in service, are fitted with automatic drop shutters which close off the spout apertures when the circuit-breaker is lowered and the truck withdrawn. When the truck is replaced in the unit housing and raised, these shutters open to allow the breaker spout contacts to make contact with the live busbars of the switchboard. To ensure that the circuit cannot be interrupted on the isolating spouts by withdrawing the truck before the circuit-breaker is opened, an interlock is provided which effectively locks the truck in the closed position until the circuit-breaker is tripped. A further convenience of this type of

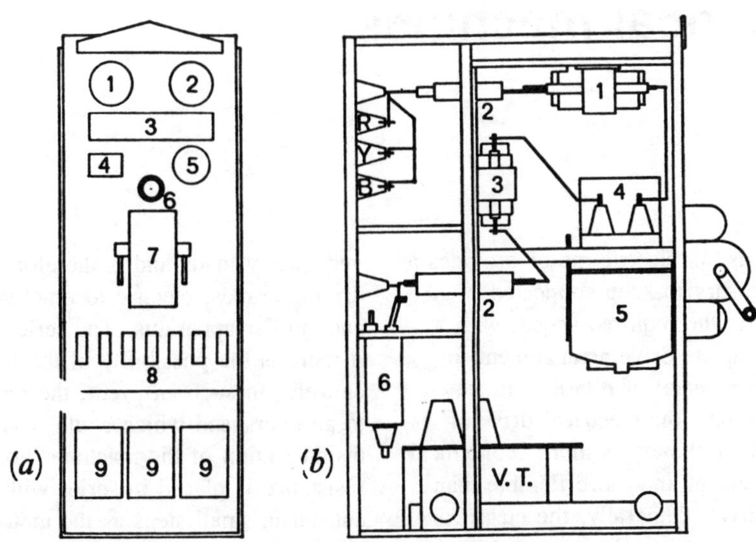

Figure 9.9. Typical cubicle switchgear with truck-mounted type oil circuit-breaker.
(*a*) 1. Ammeter; 2. Voltmeter; 3. Triple-pole overcurrent relay; 4. Earth-fault relay; 5. Three-phase ammeter switch; 6. Indicator lamp ('busbars "live"'); 7. External operating handle for circuit-breaker; 8. Fuses for switchgear protection and auxiliary circuits; 9. Relays.
(*b*) 1. Current-transformer (earth-fault detection); 2. Insulator bushings; 3. Current-transformer (overcurrent detection); 4. Phase barrier; 5. Oil circuit-breaker; 6. Cable box; 7. Voltage-transformer.

switchgear is the ease of examining the circuit-breaker contacts. When the breaker carriage is withdrawn, the switch unit can be lowered mechanically to the floor, the tank bolts removed and the switch unit raised again leaving the oil-filled tank on the floor and the switch contacts open to inspection. This type of gear is usually found on systems up to 11kV.

In the oil-filled circuit-breaker, the contacts separate under oil. The oil in this instance acts to quench the arc which is drawn out between the separating contacts when the circuit-breaker trips when there is current flowing in the circuit. Air-break circuit-breakers have arc-chutes and coolers to help dissipate the arc and its gas products.

The BS Code of Practice, *Maintenance of Electrical Switchgear*, forms a useful basis for the maintenance of switchgear of most types. An additional source of reference is BS Code of Practice, *Maintenance of Electrical Motor Control Gear*.

10 Electrical machines

In the simplest terms, an electric motor provides a driving torque necessary to keep connected machinery running at the required speed, with a provision in the complete drive arrangement for speed variation and reversal of rotation. In virtually all applications, the electrical drive of industrial and other machinery is more economical, cleaner, more convenient and more flexible than any other type of drive. Generally, the electrical motor is required to start, accelerate and drive its load, with certain limitations. In addition, the starting, acceleration and deceleration, must not damage the motor nor transfer excessive shock and vibration to the load. At the same time the motor should not blow line fuses or trip circuit-breakers under normal starting and load conditions. Also, under continuous or intermittent operation, the motor must not overheat.

DC machine types

Although ac supplies are now universal in this country, there are many applications, particularly in industry, where the dc motor finds its place because it has certain advantages over its ac counterpart. Typical applications are, for example, lineshafts (where the motor is used as a drive for a whole assembly line), traction, haulage, cranes, steel-rolling mills and billet-shearers. In addition, the dc motor offers a facility for infinite speed variation and in discrete steps. The following are the types of dc motor:

(*a*) *Series*. In this type, the field winding is connected in series with the armature. The field coils carry the armature current. When the motor is driving a light load it runs at a high speed because the resultant magnetic field is weak. As more load is applied, the current rises, the field strength increases and the speed drops rapidly. At the lower speed, the motor is able to accelerate very heavy loads and is therefore most suitable for driving cranes, electric locomotives, haulage gear and similar apparatus. The series motor is not used if there is the possibility of the load being removed entirely. In such an event, the motor would 'race' to an overspeed which could result in the complete disintegration of the machine. For starting, a resistance is placed in series with the motor and cut out in small steps as the motor speeds up. Where fine speed control is required from zero to full speed, as in colliery winders, the Ward Leonard method is used. For general speed control, the starting resistance is used. A degree of speed control is also obtained when some of the field current is by-passed through a divertor shunted across the field. In summary, this type of motor gives a high torque at starting and at low speeds. The torque is also high when heavy overloads occur during running.

(*b*) *Shunt*. This type of motor has the field winding connected in parallel with the armature. The constant supply voltage across the field winding gives a practically constant flux. The speed is therefore constant over the working range of loads. For starting, a graded resistance is placed in series with the armature to limit the starting current taken by the motor. As this resistance is cut out, the motor speeds up to reach full speed when the resistance is cut out completely. The starter used is the faceplate starter and is provided with under-voltage and over-current protection. Under-voltage protection is a requirement called for by the Regulations, and is a provision in the circuit of a dc motor (series, shunt, and compound) to prevent its automatic restarting after a stoppage of the motor owing either to an excessive drop in the supply voltage, or a complete failure of the supply. This is an important safeguard where unexpected re-starting of the motor might cause injury to an operator or

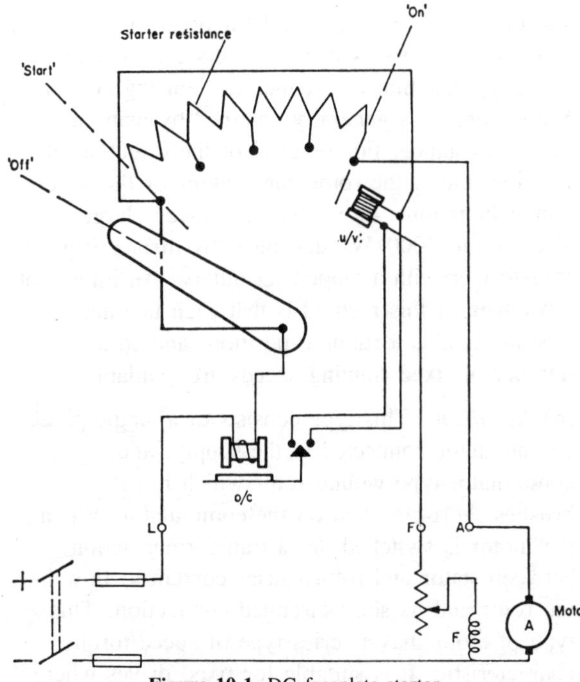

Figure 10.1. DC faceplate starter.

damage to associated machinery. In the dc faceplate starter, the undervoltage release is in the form of an electromagnet energised by the current taken by the field coil. When the starting handle reaches the limit position of its travel (when all the starting resistance has been cut out), it is held against the electromagnet. Should the electromagnet become de-energised, it will release its hold on the starter handle which will return to the OFF position of the starter under the influence of a return spring.

Overcurrent protection is provided by a second electromagnet, this time energised by the armature current. A pivoted arm carries a contact which, when the arm is attracted by the overcurrent coil (because an excessive current is flowing in the motor circuit), will short-circuit the under-voltage release coil to release the starter handle to the OFF position.

Speed control is usually be means of a variable resistance inserted in series with the field winding, to increase or decrease the current in the field winding, and so vary the strength of the magnetic field and consequently the speed of the machine.

Another method sometimes used is the addition of a variable resistance in the armature circuit. However, because this resistor has to carry large currents, there is the attendant problem of heat dissipation (I^2R watts). Shunt motors have a fairly constant speed against a varying load. The starting torque is good. In every instance it is equivalent to full-load torque, though this depends on the value of resistance incorporated in the starter. DC shunt motors up to 0.37kW can be switched direct onto the supply mains. The application of the dc shunt motor is wherever a constant speed is required — on lathes, conveyors, fans, and machine-tool drives.

(*c*) *Compound*. Compound-wound motors combine the characteristics of both shunt- and series-wound machines. The series winding gives good starting torque while the shunt winding ensures a comparatively constant speed. The motor does not race on light load. Starting is as for the shunt motor. Speed control is effected by a variable resistor in the shunt-field circuit. The actual characteristics of the compound-wound machine can be varied as the ratio of shunt to series field turns is varied. The fields are connected so that they either assist each other (strengthening the field with increased load) or oppose each other. In the first instance, a reduction in speed is produced and the motor is known as a cumulative-compounded machine. With a flywheel, this type is suitable for driving planers, shears, guillotines and other loads subject to peak loads, printing machines and power presses. In the second instance, the motor is known as a differentially-compounded machine. Because of the inherent tendency for instability, this type of machine is extremely rare.

Reversal of rotation of dc machines

A dc motor is reversed by changing over the connections to (*a*) the armature circuit or (*b*) the field circuit, BUT NOT BOTH. Reversal of the mains supply leads will result in the motor rotating in the same direction as before. Motors, other than small machines, intended for reversing duty are fitted with interpoles, placed between the main motor poles and wound with coils connected in series with the armature. These interpoles neutralise the armature's magnetic field in the neutral zone and provide a commutating field which asists in causing a quick reversal of current in the armature windings. Thus, the brushes are kept in a neutral position suitable for either direction of rotation. When reversing a motor with interpoles, the interpoles and armature are taken as a single unit.

AC machine types

In comparison with the three main types of dc machine, there are a number of ac machines, each of which offers certain characteristics compared with others. The supply available for these machines is either single-phase or three-phase. Single-phase motors are used mainly for domestic and agricultural applications. Their performance is inferior to that of their three-phase counterparts. In the fractional kilowatt sizes, they are used in large numbers for washing machines, refrigerators, etc. Three-phase machines are found in the largest sizes and have mainly industrial applications.

Single-phase motors

(*a*) *Series*. If the supply to a dc motor is reversed, the direction of rotation will remain the same as before. Thus, a direct-current series motor will run on single-phase ac. This principle is used in the 'universal' motor found in hair-driers, vacuum cleaners, floor polishers and similar equipment. The speed characteristic is that of the dc series machine: the speed falls rapidly with the application of load. Sometimes a neutralising winding or compensating winding, similar to the interpoles in a dc machine, is provided to improve both commutation and power factor. Direct-on starting is used for the small fractional hp machines. Series-resistance starters are used for the larger machines to reduce the starting current. Speed control is generally obtained by using a series resistance. For reversal of the direction of rotation, either the rotor connections or the stator connections must be reversed. For very large sizes, up to 2000kW, starting is by means of a transformer with a tapped secondary. An important advantage of this method is that each tapping position is also a running position, and so a number of fixed running speeds are available.

(*b*) *Repulsion*. This type consists of a single-phase wound stator connected to the supply, and a commutator-type wound rotor which has its brushes short-circuited on the commutator. When the motor is switched on, a transformer action between stator and rotor causes current to flow in the rotor and its short-circuited connection. This type of motor has a series type of speed/torque characteristic. It is suitable for fixed drives where a good starting torque is essential. The motor is made in sizes up to 75kW. Starting and control are done by direct-on switching or by a series-resistance starter, depending on the size of motor. The direction of rotation can be changed by moving the brushes round the commutator. Applications include lifts, cranes, centrifugal pumps, printing machinery and spinning machines. The speed can be controlled from zero to about

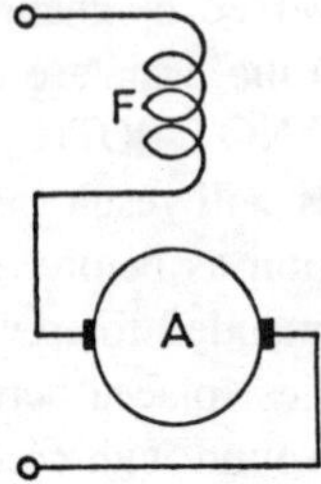

Figure 10.2. AC single-phase series (universal) motor.

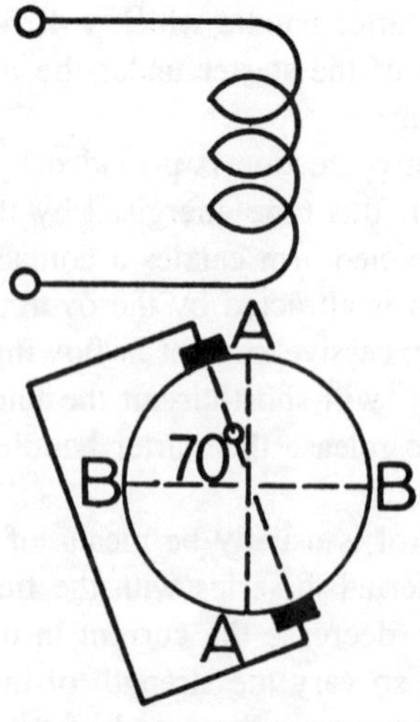

Figure 10.3. AC single-phase repulsion motor.

1.3 times synchronous speed. A large change of speed is obtained by a small brush movement.

(*c*) *Repulsion-start*. This type of machine combines the good starting characteristics of the repulsion motor with the nearly constant speed of the induction motor. The motor is started as mentioned already, but as the speed increases, a centrifugal device short-circuits all the commutator segments and also lifts the brushes from the commutator surface. In this way the motor is converted to the equivalent of a squirrel-cage induction motor, with comparative characteristics. The motor is made only in the smaller sizes. To reverse the direction of rotation, the motor must be stopped and the brush setting altered. Typical applications are desk and ceiling fans.

(*d*) *Repulsion-induction*. This motor has similar characteristics to the repulsion-start machine but is without the brush-lifting and short-circuiting device. The stator has the normal repulsion motor winding. The rotor has two separate windings in common slots. The inner winding is a squirrel-cage winding. The outer winding is the normal repulsion winding with commutator and brushes. At low starting speeds, the cage winding has little effect owing to its high reactance; the motor starts as a repulsion motor. As the speed increases, the reactance of the cage winding decreases and its torque, which is similar to that of an induction motor, is added to the torque of the repulsion winding. The overall effect is to give the good starting characteristics of the repulsion motor with a fairly constant speed at all times. Starting is by direct-on switching or by a series-resistance starter. Reversal of direction of rotation is as before.

Single-phase motor — synchronous type

Synchronous. The single-phase synchronous motor is a fractional kilowatt machine used for driving clocks and other timing devices which require an accurate constant speed. The speed is dependent on the frequency of the supply which is normally mainained within ± 1 per cent by the supply company. The form of motor known as the 'shaded-pole' motor is common. It consists of a horseshoe-shaped, laminated-iron core on which a

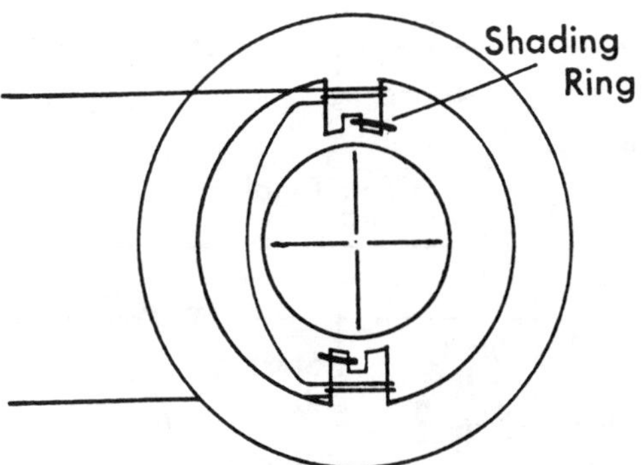

Figure 10.4. AC single-phase synchronous motor.

magnetising winding is wound. A copper ring is embedded in the face of each of the pole pieces. The effect of the ring is to split the magnetic field into two parts, out of phase with each other. The rotor is simply a slotted steel bar, or a number of slotted discs, which give the effect of salient poles by concentrating the flux paths. The two-phase flux creates a rotating field which causes the rotor to revolve. When the rotor reaches a speed near to synchronism, it locks into synchronous speed. This particular type of motor is self-starting when switched direct-on. It is used only for light loads.

Single-phase motors — induction types

A rotating field is necessary to produce the starting torque for an induction motor. The single-phase supply for a single-phase induction motor, however, will only produce a stationary pulsating field in the stator winding. Once the motor is running, a pulsating field of about equal strength is set up in the rotor winding, lagging the stator by almost 90°. The net result is a rotating field which will keep the motor running. To start the motor, the shaft is turned mechanically or by hand; the direction of rotation is indeterminate because the motor will rotate as easily in one direction as in the other. In order to produce the equivalent of a rotating field at start, an auxiliary winding is needed to produce an out-of-phase field. Several methods are used to obtain this phase displacement. To minimise losses, and to keep the overall power factor as high as possible, a centrifugal switch is fitted on the motor shaft

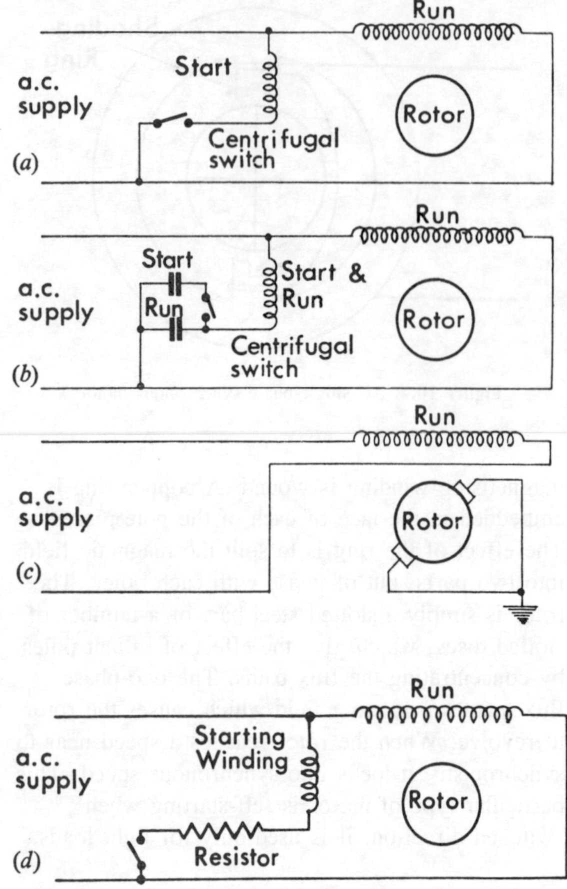

Figure 10.5. Methods of starting single-phase motors: (*a*) Reactance-start, single-phase induction; (*b*) Capacitor-start and run, single-phase induction; (*c*) Repulsion, ac commutator; (*d*) Resistor start.

which open-circuits the starting winding when the motor reaches about 80 per cent full speed. The following are the different forms of single-phase induction motor.

(*a*) *Split-phase*. This type of motor usually consists of a laminated stator wound with a single-phase winding, arranged for split-phase starting, and a cage rotor. The rotor is a laminated framework with lightly-insulated longitudinal slots into which copper or aluminium bars are fitted. The bars are all connected together at their ends by metal end-rings. No electrical connections are made to the rotor. The rotating field required to start the motor is obtained by supplying the stator with the equivalent of a two-phase supply. This is done by two stator windings (a starting winding and a running winding) wound at 90° to each other. The reaction between the stator fields and the rotor field, produced by the induced currents in the rotor, causes the rotor to revolve. When the motor reaches about 80 per cent of synchronous speed, the centrifugal switch disconnects the starting winding. Applications for this type of motor include fractional-kW, non-reversing drives.

(*b*) *Resistance-start*. This type of split-phase induction motor has a resistance connected in series with the starting winding, to produce the necessary phase difference for starting.

(*c*) *Reactance-start*. This type of split-phase induction motor has a reactor connected in series with the starting winding to produce the necessary phase difference for starting. The reactor also helps to reduce the starting current.

(*d*) *Capacitor-start*. This type is a split-phase motor with a capacitor connected in series with the starting winding. This gives a greater phase displacement between the currents in the starting and running windings than (*c*) and gives a better starting torque with a smaller line current. The motor has a constant speed and is used for drives with periodic or intermittent load, e.g. refrigerator compressors. In (*b*), (*c*) and (*d*), the starting winding circuit is disconnected from the supply during running by the centrifugal switch mounted on the motor shaft.

(*e*) *Capacitor-start, capacitor-run*. This type of motor is very efficient and is used for special applications. The motor has a double winding on the stator, the double winding being designed for continued running. Usually there are two capacitors in parallel in the starting-winding circuit. One capacitor is cut out when the motor approaches its running speed. The remaining capacitor gives permanent power-factor correction, which approaches unity. The motor has a very high efficiency.

Reversal of the direction of rotation of single-phase induction motors entails slowing the motor speed down to allow the centrifugal switch to close (to connect the starting winding) and then reversing the connections to one of the windings.

Starting is usually direct-on for the small sizes of machine. For larger types, a series-resistance can be used in the stator circuit, the resistance being cut out as the motor speeds up. Although most split-phase induction motors have squirrel-cage rotors, wound-rotor types are also used for heavier starting duties. In this instance, the slip-rings are connected to an external starting resistance.

Three-phase motors — commutator types

The three-phase variable-speed ac commutator motor provides the most efficient and positive method of speed variation with ac supplies. The stator is very similar to the squirrel-cage motor. The rotor is of the wound type which incorporates a commutator resembling that of a dc machine. Speed ranges are of the order of 2 : 1 and 3 : 1, obtained by the movement of the brushes round the commutator. The power factor and efficiency of this type is better than that of the wound-rotor motor with rotor-resistance speed control. Certain types of motor are stator-fed (not of the moving-brush type) and give a speed range of up to 10 : 1.

Control of the speed is by means of a separate induction regulator the function of which is to supply a variable voltage to the rotor winding of the motor. The motor has a smooth starting characteristic. Commutation is sparkless at all

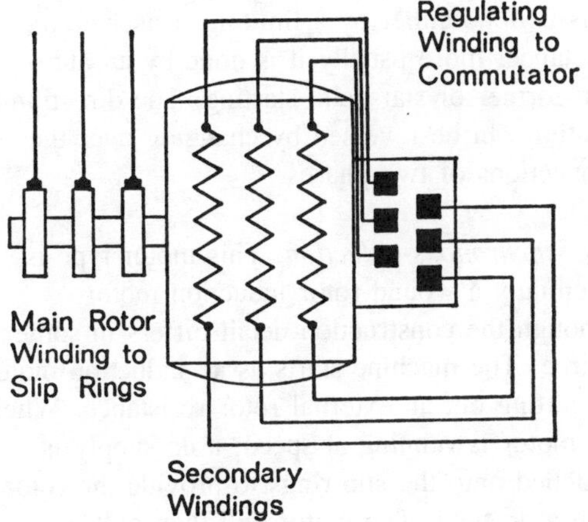

Figure 10.6. Circuit diagram of ac three-phase Schrage motor.

speeds. The supply is connected direct to the stator winding thus eliminating the use of slip-rings.

In the Schrage motor there is a primary winding on the rotor, fed from the mains through slip-rings. The regulating or auxiliary winding on the rotor is connected to the commutator. The auxiliary winding is in the same magnetic field as the primary winding and thus has an induced current at line frequency. The secondary windings have thus an induced current at slip frequency and the currents are thus of the same frequency and suitable for combination. The magnitude of the emf collected by a pair of brushes depends on the number of commutator bars between them, and the phase by their position on the commutator. It is therefore possible to vary the magnitude and phase of the emf by moving the brushes. By varying the brush positions, the power factor and the speed can be varied. At a given brush position, the characteristic of the speed/load is like that of a dc shunt motor.

The maximum operating voltage is 650V. At top speed the power factor is unity; it is lagging at lower speeds. Applications include textile mills, printing presses, large lathes, paper-making machines, lifts, fans, and pumps up to about 300kW.

Three-phase motors — synchronous types

(*a*) *The three-phase synchronous motor* has a constant speed. It consists essentially of an ac armature, normally wound on the stator frame, with a dc field winding wound on a salient-pole rotor. The ac voltage is applied to the armature and a separate dc supply — usually 110V — is connected to the rotor through slip-rings. In itself, the synchronous motor has no starting torque, and special starting arrangements are necessary. For many years, this type of motor was confined to a power-factor correction duty, most drives being the application of the induction motor. With improvements to this type, the synchronous motor is now being used increasingly for many duties because of several useful characteristics. Starting characteristics on the modern synchronous motor now compare favourably with the induction motor. Certain types are designed for direct-on-line switching taking less than $3\frac{1}{2}$ times full-load

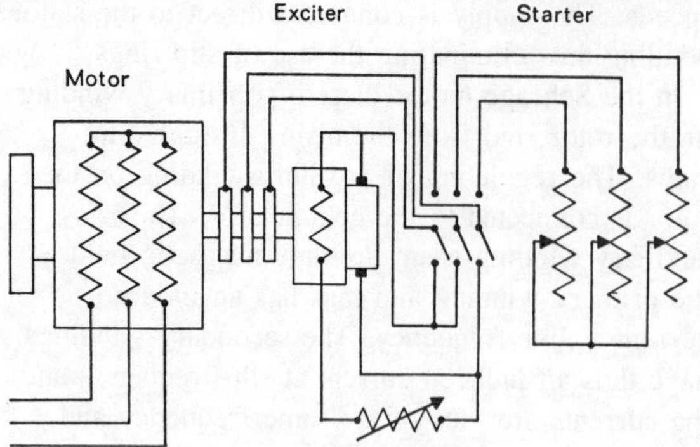

Figure 10.7(*a*). Three-phase synchronous motor with simplified starting arrangement.

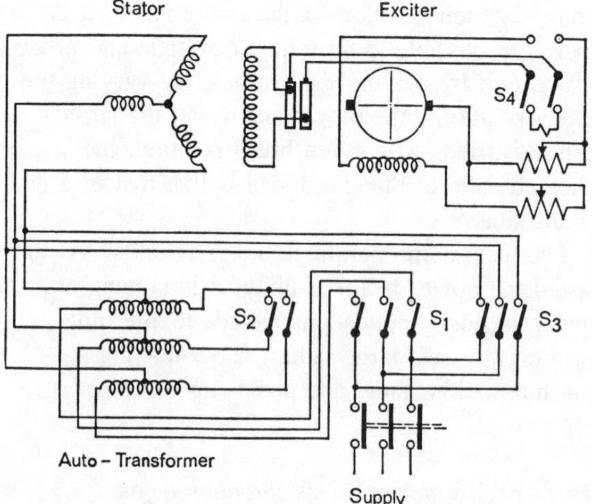

Figure 10.7(*b*). Auto-transformer (Korndorfer) method of starting a large synchronous motor with a cage winding in the field poles.

current at starting, thus reducing and eliminating the need for special starting equipment. Induction motors always operate at a lagging power factor and consequently a synchronous motor of equal output and operating at unity power factor will have a smaller kVA input rating. This means that the synchronous motor can have lower losses and a higher efficiency. It can also be a smaller machine physically, which is an advantage from the point of view of foundations and building requirements.

Typical applications for the synchronous motor include Banbury mixers (used to mix the raw ingredients for rubber products), cement-grinding mills, centrifugal compressors, motor-generator sets, mine ventilating fans, pumps, reciprocating-compressor drives and electric ship-propulsion drives.

The speed/torque characteristic is a straight line from no load to 140 per cent full-load torque. A starting torque is obtained by certain starting arrangements which allow the motor to start as an induction motor before running as a synchronous machine. The salient-pole type of motor runs constantly at synchronous speed regardless of load fluctuations. The power factor can be controlled to suit the load conditions imposed on the installation by associated plant. The sizes available are from 70kW upwards to over 10,000kW. At the higher ratings, the supply voltage is 11 or 33kV.

Starting arrangements vary. In the older type of motor, the machine had to be started by running it up to just over synchronous speed by a pony motor and then synchronising it with the mains supply. The starting method on modern types involves a number of copper bars embedded in the pole faces and connected at their ends. These short-circuited loops form a squirel-cage winding and the motor behaves like a squirrel-cage induction motor on starting. The machine pulls into step when the dc field winding supply is switched on.

During running, these squirrel-cage windings in the pole faces act as 'damping' windings in that they help to smooth out any oscillations that may occur because of sudden increases or decreases of load. Because of the squirrel-cage action, the starting current is kept low by reducing the stator voltage to about 60 per cent of the normal value. This is done either by a limiting resistance or reactance; more usually it is done by an auto-transformer or star-delta starting. The direction of rotation can be reversed by changing over the connections of two phases.

(*b*) *Synchronous-induction*. This motor type is essentially a wound-rotor induction motor, although the construction detail differs in some degree. The machine starts as an induction motor by cutting out an external rotor resistance. When the motor is running at speed, a dc supply is switched onto the slip-rings to provide the rotor with a dc field. The motor will then pull into synchronism. The main advantage of this type of motor is that if a heavy overload should occur to force the rotor to drop out of synchronism, the machine will continue to run as an induction motor, and it will pull into step as soon as the overload condition is removed. The power factor is leading or unity. This motor is replacing the usual induction motor for many applications: large fans, compressors, lineshafts, pumps and generally for machinery where a constant speed is normally required but a small decrease is permissible with overloads.

Three-phase motors — induction types

The three-phase induction motor is the simplest and cheapest of all motors and requires the least maintenance since it has no commutator. The starting torque is high. But the starting current is also high and, except for the smallest ratings, starting equipment is necessary to allow the motors to start with a reduced voltage and hence a reduced torque. The induction motor is either of the squirrel-cage (sc) or wound-rotor (wr) type.

(*a*) *Squirrel-cage*. The standard type of machine has a wound three-phase stator and a squirrel-cage (sc) rotor. The squirrel cage consists of a laminated structure with skewed slots into which copper or aluminium bars are fitted. These bars are connected together by metal end-rings, the whole forming a short-circuited winding.

Starting and maximum torque can be varied over a wide range according to design characteristics. Standard sc motors have starting torques ranging from 100 to 175 per cent of full-load torque, with starting currents of from 5 to 8 times full-load current. The speed of the machine is below synchronous speed, about 96–97 per cent. The remaining 3 per cent or so is called the 'slip'. There is no possible speed control in these motors. Because of the absence of moving parts in the circuitry, the motor is useful for duties in hazardous areas. It finds application for most industrial drives where speed control is not required. A clutch can be used to start the motor on light load. Otherwise, if the load requires a high starting torque, or where the starting current must be limited, another type of motor must be used. In this instance, use is made of the double-cage or Boucherot squirrel-cage machine. This provides a high starting torque with a low starting current. The rotor has two cage windings. One has a high resistance and is placed near the periphery of the rotor so that it has a low leakage inductance. The other is placed at the bottom of the slots and has a low resistance with a correspondingly high leakage inductance. On starting, the main current is in the high-resistance winding, to produce a good starting torque with low current. When the motor runs up to speed, the reactance of the low-resistance winding is small, so that the main current is in this winding. Reversal of direction of rotation can be achieved by changing over the connections of two phases. The power factor of this type of motor is a little lower than that of ordinary sc induction motors.

(*b*) *Wound-rotor*. This type of machine is sometimes known as the 'slip-ring' motor. The stator winding is wound three-phase as in the sc motor. The usual slotted rotor holds a three-phase winding whose ends are brought out to three slip-rings mounted on the end of the motor shaft. The slip-rings are connected, through brushes, to a three-phase starting arrangement. This machine offers a practically constant speed over the load range. The speed/torque performance can be varied by the addition of resistance in the rotor circuit via the slip-rings. The applications include high-inertia drives requiring variable speed, flywheel machine drives, air-compressors, ram pumps, crushing mills, cranes, hoists, winches and lifts.

(*c*) *Other types*. Apart from the squirrel cage and wound-rotor induction motors, there are a number of other types of induction motor available for specific duties. These include:

(i) Pole-changing motor, where the number of poles in the machine is controlled by switching. As the speed of a synchronous motor is inversely proportional to the number of poles in the stator winding, it follows that certain fixed speeds can be obtained. Generally, the speeds obtained by regrouping the poles are in the ratio of 2 : 1 and 4 : 1. This type of motor is used to drive multi-speed drilling machines and such equipment as pumps and fans which require a boost of speed at frequent intervals.

(ii) Cascaded induction motor, has two motors which are coupled together mechanically and the wound-rotor of one is connected to the stator of the other via its slip-rings. The effect is the same as changing the number of poles, several fixed speeds being obtainable by switching.

Starting three-phase motors

(*a*) *Direct-on*. The simplest method of starting squirrel-cage motors is the direct-on-line, in which the motor is connected directly to the full supply voltage by means of a hand-operated switch or contactor starter. The supply is connected to the motor stator windings. Since the motor is at standstill when the supply is switched on, the initial starting current is heavy — of the order of 6–9 times full-load current. Because the torque is proportional to the product of the rotor current and the power factor (which is very low on starting), the starting torque is not particularly high. If the motor is starting on no-load or against light loads, the starting current falls rapidly with acceleration, with little or no disturbance to the supply system. If the motor is started against a heavy load, the starting period will be prolonged with a lengthening of the time during which the peak current will flow. In this instance, the motor windings may well heat up. Generally, supply authorities impose conditions on the use of direct-on switching, usually limiting the size of the machine that may be started in this way. The general limit for the direct-on connection of medium-voltage motors is 2kW. If a high voltage is available, the limit is raised to 10kW. In brief, the direct-on method provides a quick starting at maximum torque. It is reliable, simple and cheap. The disadvantage is that it takes a heavy current from the supply system. General applications include machines for most small drives, pumps, fans, tools and small machines.

The pushbutton contactor starter consists of three pairs of contacts made by moving contacts on an armature. When the START button is pressed the contactor circuit is completed and the switch contacts close to energise the motor. The motor current passes through overcurrent coils, and if the

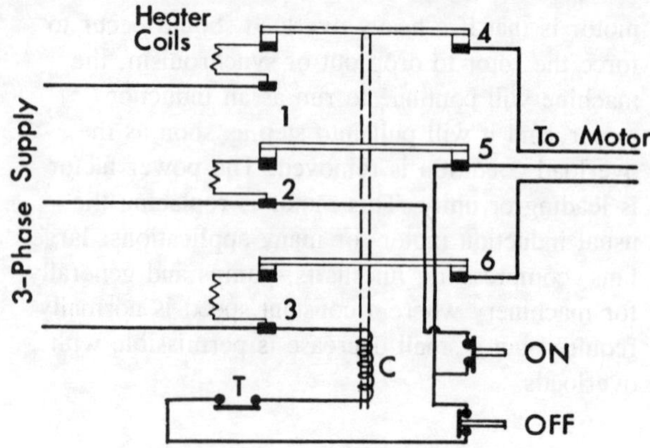

Figure 10.8. Contactor starter for direct-on-line starting of squirrel-cage motor.

current becomes excessive (during a circuit fault condition or a prolonged starting period), an overcurrent device (thermal or magnetic trip) operates to break the contactor circuit. Under-voltage protection is inherent in that failure of the supply voltage, or a drop in the supply voltage below a predetermined figure, will cause the contactor to drop out and so disconnect the motor from the supply. The STOP button is wired in series with the overcurrent contacts to break the circuit. An isolating switch is mounted in or near the starter so that the motor and its starter can be isolated. If a hand-operated starter is used, the overcurrent device actuates the mechanical linkage of the starter. In this case, the under-voltage coil is energised from two of the supply terminals and also actuates the mechanical linkage should the supply fail.

(*b*) *Star-delta starting*. There are a number of methods by which a motor can be started using a reduced voltage. The star-delta method is a two-position method of direct-on starting squirrel-cage motors. First the windings are connected in star formation to accelerate the rotor from standstill. The second position connects the windings in delta for running. This method of starting requires that both ends of each phase winding (six ends in all) must be brought out to the motor terminal block. In its simplest terms, the starter is a changeover switch.

When the windings are connected in star, the

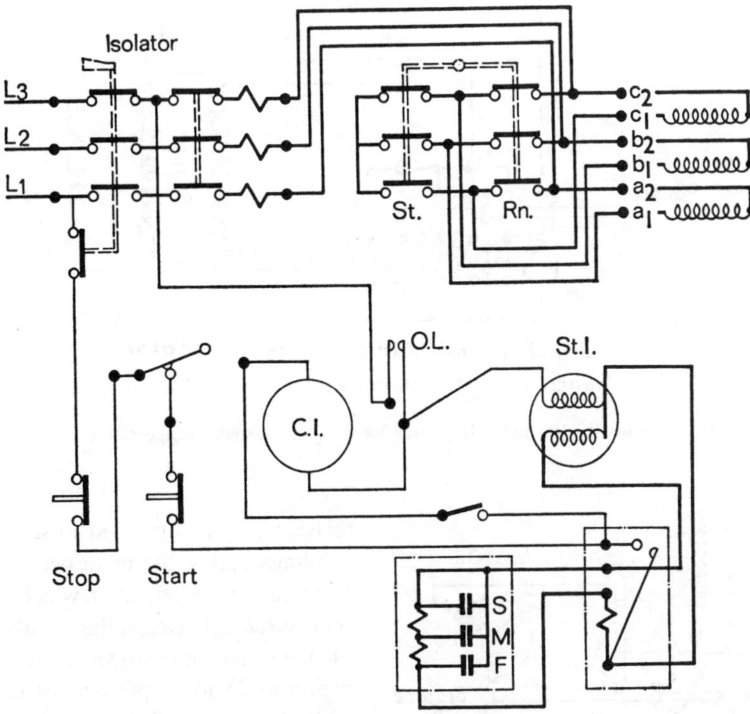

Figure 10.9. Automatic star-delta starter with thermal time-delay relay.

voltage applied to each winding is reduced to 58 per cent of the line voltage. The starting current is correspondingly reduced to 58 per cent of the normal phase current at start (i.e. one-third of line current). The starting torque available is one-third of the full-voltage (direct switching) torque. After the motor has reached a certain steady speed on star connection, the switch is placed in the delta or ON position. The changeover can be done by hand, or automatically by a timing device. The nature of the start is suitable for drives with light loadings, but which require heavy running torques. There is no variation available to the torque produced at starting, as it is fixed by the star connection. The star-delta method is cheap, simple and has the advantage that it gives a reduced starting current. On the machine side, there is the added cost of having the six terminals of the stator winding brought out to a terminal block. Applications include line shafting, and pumps and fans of the centrifugal type.

(*c*) *Auto-transformer starting*. This is another method of starting squirrel-cage motors with reduced voltage. Basically it is a two-stage method and is used where the reduction in the starting torque available with the star-delta method is not suitable, is not sufficiently high, or because the motor available has only three terminals in its connector block. The auto-transformer starter consists of a star-connected auto-transformer with a six-pole switch arranged as three double-pole switches. A choice of tapping voltages is available for supplying the motor stator windings at start. The common tappings are 40, 60 and 75 per cent of the supply voltage. For these particular tappings, the line current and the starting torque are reduced to about 16, 36 and 56 per cent respectively of the direct-on starting values. The choice of a particular tapping depends on whether the motor is to be started on no-load or light-load, since the starting torque must be sufficient to accelerate the motor at a satisfactory rate. The

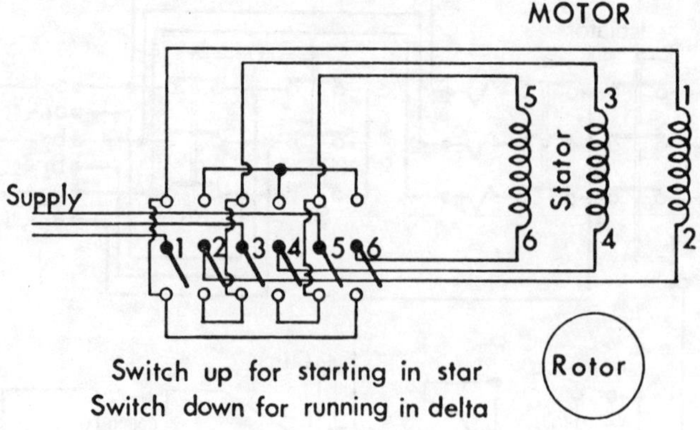

Figure 10.10. Star-delta starter for three-phase squirrel-cage motor.

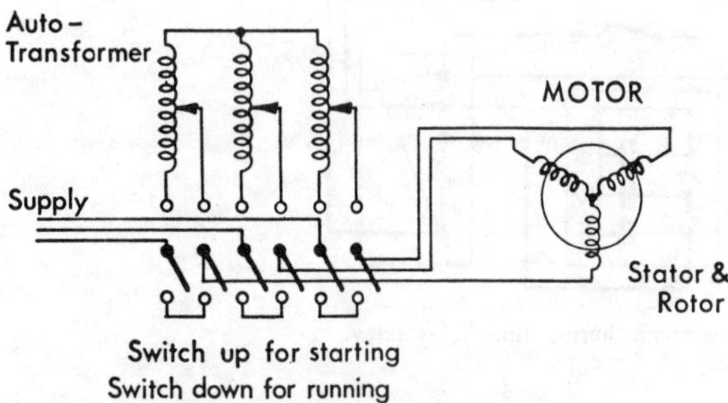

Figure 10.11. Auto-transformer starter for three-phase slip-ring motor. Variable tappings.

auto-transformer method is not suitable for starting a motor against heavy loads. Auto-transformers can be arranged to give the Korndorfer system of switching where a section of the transformer is left in circuit during the transition period (from START to RUN) to maintain a motoring torque. Most contactor-type auto-transformer starters are designed to give Korndorfer switching.

Because of the tappings available, this method of starting is adaptable for different types of starting conditions. The method tends to be costly. Applications include motor-generator sets, centrifugal machines, heavy fans and mixers.

(*d*) *Primary-resistance starting*. The conditions which govern the use of this method of starting are similar to those relating to the auto-transformer method. The method is suitable for starting squirrel-cage motors on no-load or light-load conditions. It is a two-stage method in which fixed resistances are connected in series with the motor windings during the main period of the accelerating period, after which the resistors are short-circuited. Depending on the type of resistor used, the starting torques available are in the region of 25 to 65 per cent of the direct-on value. The advantage of this method is that a smooth start can be obtained at reduced torque. The torque available at starting can be adjusted by varying the value of resistance. As with other forms of two-stage starting, a delay device is often incorporated in the circuit to prevent premature change from the START to the RUN position.

(*e*) *Rotor-resistance starting*. This method is used for wound-rotor induction motors. These motors are used when they are required to start against full-load conditions. The starting torque available with rotor-resistance starting depends on the total resistance of the rotor circuit. By connecting suitable resistors in series with the rotor windings, it can be arranged to have maximum motor torque when first starting the motor, that is at standstill. As the motor accelerates, the resistors are cut out in steps, increasing the motor torque. When the motor reaches its full speed, the slip-rings are short-circuited. Rotor-resistance starters have interlocks so arranged that the stator switch can be closed only when the rotor tapping-switch is in the START position, that is with all the resistance in the circuit and with the slip-ring short-circuiting connection open. Most starters are hand-operated,

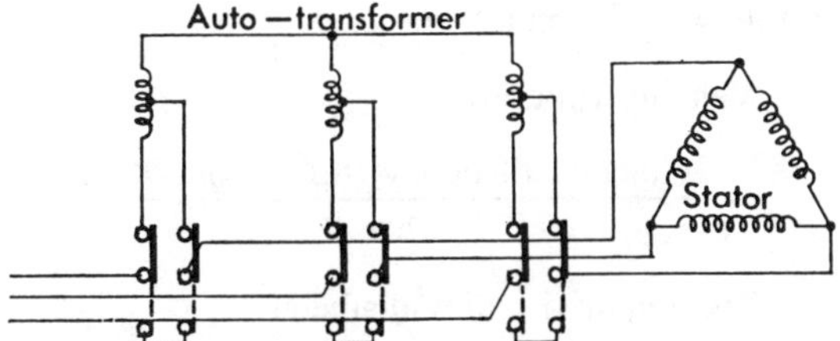

Figure 10.12. Auto-transformer starter for three-phase induction motor. Fixed tappings.

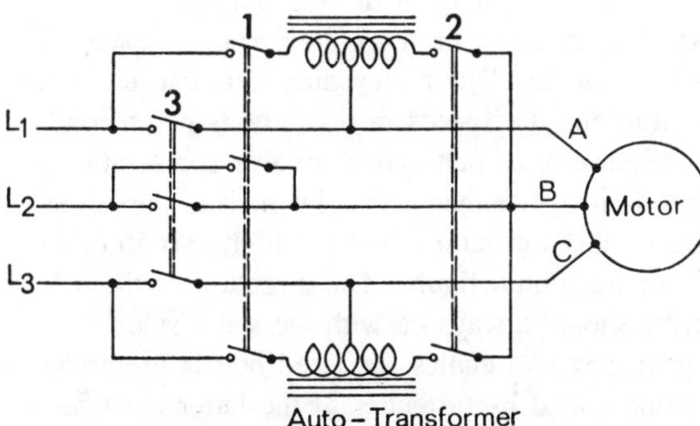

Figure 10.13. Auto-transformer (Korndorfer) starter for three-phase slip-ring motor. 1. First starting contactor; 2. Second starting contactor; 3. Run contactor.

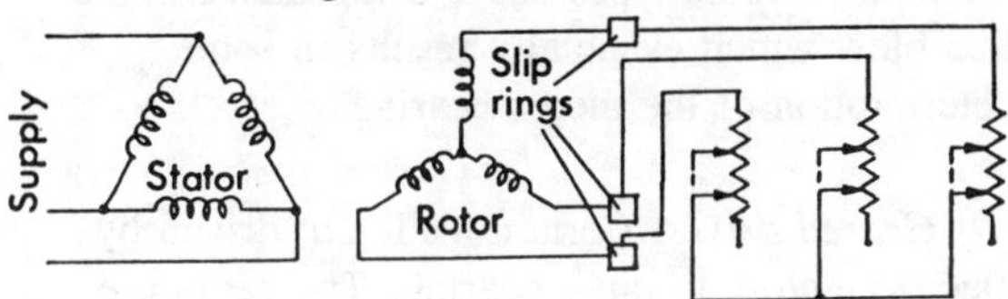

Figure 10.14. Rotor-resistance starter for three-phase slip-ring induction motor.

but automatic starters are in use, the sequence of operation being controlled by contactors. A number of motors still exist in which slip-ring short-circuiting and brush-lifting gear is fitted.

Machine ratings

There are two classes of ratings for electrical machines:

(*a*) *Continuous maximum rating* (*CMR*). This is the load at which a machine may be operated for an unlimited period in specified conditions, without the temperature of the machine rising above an upper maximum. Continuously-rated motors are generally repuired for workshop machinery drives and similar applications where the load is both fixed and steady.

(*b*) *Short-time rating* (*STR*). This is a statement of the operating limits assigned to the machine by the manufacturers, defining the load at which the machine may be operated (starting at the ambient temperature) for the period and under the conditions specified on the motor rating-plate. Short-time ratings are usually one-hour and half-hour. Short-time rated motors are used for lifts and cranes, where momentary over-loads are experienced, yet which do not last so long that the temperature of the machine will rise above the limit fixed for the machine.

Motor-circuit protection

(*a*) *Overcurrent*. This circuit condition arises from (i) a circuit fault such as a short-circuit or fault to earth; (ii) an overload, which is a load in excess of the rated load for which the motor is designed; (iii) sustained overload, which is an overload sustained for a sufficiently long period to affect appreciably the temperature of the machine and which causes the motor to draw more current from the supply system to produce the increased torque; (iv) momentary overload, which is an overload the duration of which is so short that it does not affect appreciably the temperature of the machine; (v) single-phasing — described later.

There are two methods used to protect the motor and its circuitry against significant overcurrents: the thermal trip and the magnetic trip. The former is the simplest type. It consists of a heat-insulated bimetallic strip which is enclosed by a heating coil carrying the motor current. In the event of an overcurrent, the strip will bend sufficiently to open contacts in the motor-control circuit through a mechanical trip. The time taken for the coil to heat up is usually longer than that taken for the motor to start up so that the heavy starting current flowing during this period does not affect the thermal trip. Magnetic-type overcurrent devices consist of a solenoid with a plunger, usually fitted with a time-lag arrangement to delay the action of the trip. The time-lag is introduced by either an air or oil dashpot. Some motor starters incorporate both thermal and magnetic trips with independent trip-current and time-lag settings. The thermal type trip has an inherent inverse time-lag, but since it is operated by the heating effect of the current, it is more closely related to the thermal capacity of the motor it protects.

Protection against single-phasing conditions on a three-phase supply is very important. The normal three-phase induction motor, when once running, will continue to run even though one phase becomes open-circuited owing to a fuse blowing or some other fault. Under these conditions, the motor will endeavour to produce something approaching full-load output, but at the expense of drawing excess current in the two remaining phases. In a star-connected machine, where the motor phase current is the same as the line current, the normal overload protection will react suitably, as long as the motor is operating over three-quarters load. However, as most motors are delta-connected under the single-phase condition, the circulating currents in the windings will not operate the overcurrent devices. Some thermal overload trips embody a differential tripping feature which ensures that the relay will operate when two elements are carrying normal current and the third is cold.

(*b*) *Under-voltage*. This form of protection is required by the IEE Regulations (552-4) so that a motor is disconnected from the supply in the event of either complete failure of the supply voltage or the reduction of the supply voltage to a predetermined minimum value.

Motor drives

(*a*) *Belt drives*. Most flat belts are either of leather or a similarly constituted fabric. The width of the belt is always a little less than the pulley face. Wide belts should be run at slow speeds; narrow belts can be run at high speeds. The maximum speed of belts should not exceed 1,500 metres/minute, though no hard-and-fast rule can be laid down, because much depends on the driven-shaft speed, the size of the pulleys, the torque to be transmitted, and the width of the pulleys.

For the velocity of belt drives in metres/minute, the following formulae are used:

Velocity (m/min)

$$= \frac{\text{diameter of pulley (m)} \times \text{rpm} \times 22}{12 \times 7}$$

The required pulley diameter

$$= \frac{d \times \text{rpm}}{\text{RPM}}$$

where d = diameter of driving pulley; RPM = speed of driven pulley; rpm = speed of driving pulley. The pulley diameters can be in cm or mm and the speeds in revolutions per second.

Because most belt drives involve some ratio of speed change, either up or down, it is important to ensure that the ratio is not too high. Six to one is a fair maximum figure. The direction of the belt drive should always be with the slack side uppermost. An endless or laced belt is preferable to one joined by fasteners. If the latter must be used, they should be of the type that allows sufficient flexibility to conform to the diameter of the pulley. Some types cause a repeated hammer-like blow which eventually results in some deterioration of the motor bearings.

(*b*) *Geared drives*. Certain loads are driven by electric motors through gearing. The gears are usually contained in a unit. The gears include straight spur wheels and pinions in single, double and triple reductions, worm gears and combinations of both. Final speeds obtainable are usually from 1 rpm and upwards. The choice of gearing depends on the required reduction. For very low speeds it is usual to have a worm reduction gear. For best results, worm gears should run in oil. Bevel gearing is extensively used where the direction of motion is changed by 90°. Double-helical gearing is used for heavy work, where it has the advantage of continuous engagement and silent running.

Pinion and spur wheel drives may use pinions of phosphor-bronze, raw-hide, paper, fibre in mesh with spur wheels of cast iron. If a raw-hide pinion is used, grease must not be allowed to come into contact with it. A very light brushing with linseed oil is sufficient to preserve the hide should it

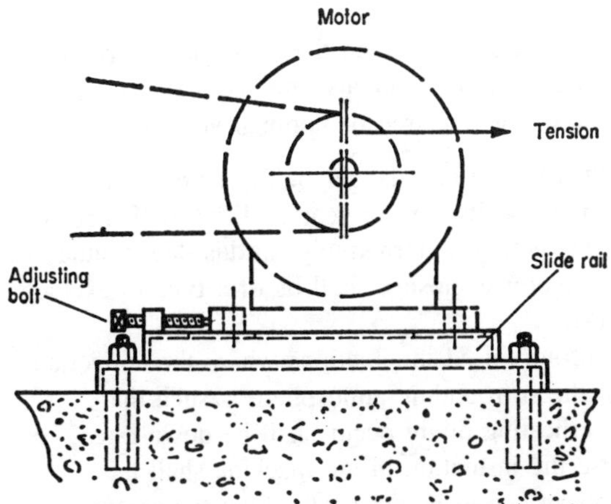

Figure 10.15. Motor mounted on slide rails.

become dry. Nylon is used extensively because it tends to be self-lubricating.

(*c*) *Direct coupling*. These are used where the motor is mounted in the same plane as the machinery to be driven (e.g. pump, motor-generator set). Flexible couplings are usually employed as they take up any slight mis-alignment between the two shafts.

Slotted slide rails (Figure 10.15) are a convenient means of fixing a motor where it is necessary to provide for belt adjustment and to take up any slackness in a new belt as it stretches in use. The slide rails are fixed to the motor's concrete plinth by means of rawlbolts. The feet of the motor are then dropped onto bolts set in the slots of the slide rails. The position of the motor is adjusted by the locating bolts on the rails and fixed by tightening the holding-down bolts of the motor.

Machine enclosures

All machines must be protected against any installation condition which might result in damage to them or to their associated control gear and circuit wiring. There are a large number of types of enclosure today which are used in specific circumstances. The most common are:

(*a*) *Screen-protected*. This is a protected machine in which all the ventilating openings in the frame and end-shields are protected by wire screen, expanded metal or other suitably perforated covers. Contact with any internal rotating parts is made impossible by the use of metal grids.

(*b*) *Totally enclosed*. Such a machine is so constructed that the enclosed air has no connection with the external air. This machine is not necessarily air-tight. The air within the machine is circulated by an internal fan which allows the heat generated to be drawn off through the motor casing. The surface area of the motor casing is increased by providing a number of fins. Because cooling is less efficient in this machine than with the screen-protected motor, it is physically larger.

(*c*) *Drip-proof*. This machine has holes for the circulation of air which are arranged so that they point downwards. Cowls are fitted to prevent the ingress of moisture or dripping water from condensation. This machine is not waterproof.

(*d*) *Flameproof*. Flameproof machines are totally enclosed and have wide flanged bolt-on covers to flameproof specification. These motors are used where flammable liquids and gases or vapours are present. The motor is not completely enclosed inasmuch as there are designed passages between the inside and the outside to allow any gas which collects inside the maching to pass to the outside. Similarly, if any explosive gas passes inside, its explosive properties can be dissipated to the atmosphere. To obtain a flameproof certification, a motor must withstand the following test. The inside of the motor is charged with and surrounded by a flammable gas. When the initial charge is ignited, the windings of the motor must not be damaged, nor must the explosion ignite the gases outside. As might be expected, the flameproof machine is expensive, its cost being in the region of three times that of the screen-protected motor.

Maintenance and testing

The detailed maintenance requirements of rotating electrical machinery are outside the scope of this book. In general, each machine is supplied with both installation and maintenance instructions and these should be followed closely. The table which follows, indicates in summary the types of fault and the corrective procedure to be carried out with machines. For detailed maintenance requirements, the reader is referred either to the maker's instructions or to BS Code of Practice CP *Maintenance of Electric Motor Control Gear*.

The testing of machines involves insulation-resistance testing of windings, between coils and between coils and earth. In particular, any earthing arrangement should be proved at regular intervals. Periodical testing of the insulation of a machine is desirable. The circuit should be isolated from the supply and the tester connected between the motor conductors and the frame of the machine, with the starter closed. Tests may also be made between the phases of a three-phase motor used with a star-delta starter, when the starter is in the OFF position. However, it may be necessary to hold the starter midway between START and RUN, and/or interrupt the circuit of the under-voltage release coil by separating the overload contact in this circuit. Secondary circuits, such as the rotor circuit of a slip-ring or repulsion type of motor should also be tested. In most instances it will be necessary to raise the brushes of the repulsion motors to test the rotor. Any reading of insulation-resistance below 0.5 megohm should be investigated, by disconnecting the various parts of the machine and conducting individual tests. If all parts of a machine have low values of insulation-resistance, the cause may well be dampness, in which case the machine should be dried out. This is achieved by passing a suitable value of current at a low voltage through the windings or preferably using a drying oven. It is important to remember when testing, that the values for insulation-resistance will vary depending on the amount of humidity in the atmosphere at the time of test.

Summary

There are available a number of publications giving recommendations for the installation, commissioning and maintenance of motors, their control gear and associated circuitry. The following is a brief summary of the main points:

The volt drop between the consumer's terminals and the motor terminals must not exceed 4 per cent of the declared or nominal voltage.

Where there is a danger of fire or explosion, the motor and its control gear shall be of flameproof construction. Alternatively, in dust-laden situations, the motor enclosure shall be of a type to exclude dust.

Motors used in situations where the temperature of the surrounding atmosphere is such that overheating might occur shall be down-rated, or else the insulation in the machine shall be appropriate to withstand the high temperature. Means for forced ventilation, or pipe-ventilated enclosures, can be used as an alternative.

Every electric motor shall be provided with efficient means of starting and stopping. This control shall be within easy reach of the operator. In addition, motors of more than 0.37kW shall be provided with control gear with the following devices: (*a*) means to prevent self-starting in the event of the restoration of the supply after failure; (*b*) protection against overcurrent in the motor and in the cables supplying the motor; and (*c*) means of isolating the motor and all its associated apparatus.

In modern factories, use is made of group control where several motors are automatically started from a group of contactors on a single control board. It is useful to have a stop-button close to each motor position. Normally, this stop-button is of the lockable type and in addition, an isolator can be provided at the motor position. The main isolator on the control board should be lockable also, to comply with safety requirements.

The final circuit supplying a motor shall be protected by fuses, the current rating of which should not be greater than twice the cable rating. Where fuses are used in conjunction with control gear, the rating can be twice that of the cable. The rating of cables in rotor circuits, or commutator circuits, of induction motors is also included. These cables must be suitable for the starting and running conditions.

Fault	*Possible cause*	*Corrective action*
Vibration	Uneven foundations	Check level and alignment of base and realign.
	Defective rotor Imbalance	Uncouple from driven machine, remove motor pulley or coupling. Run motor between each of these operations to determine whether imbalance is in the driven machine, pulley, or rotor. Rebalance.
Frame heating*	Excessive load	
	Foreign matter in airgap or cooling circuit	Check airgap, dismantle motor and clean.
	Excessive ambient temperature	Motors are normally intended for operation in an ambient temperature not exceeding 40 °C. Where this exceeds 40 °C a motor of corresponding lower temperature rise should be used.
	Partial short or open circuit in windings	Check windings with suitable meter. If defective, repair or return to manufacturer.
Bearing heating	Too much grease	Remove surplus grease.
	Too little grease	Wash bearings and replenish with grease.
	Incorrect assembly	Ensure bearing assembled squarely on shaft.
	Bearing overloaded	This may be due to misalignment of the drive, excessive end thrust imposed on motor, or too great a belt tension. Take appropriate steps to reduce the load on the bearing.
Brushes heating	Excessive load	
	Brushes not bedding or sticking in holders	Carefully rebed or clean brushes and adjust pressure.
	Brush chatter	Ensure that commutator is true without high or low bars and adjust brush pressure.
	Incorrect grade of brushes	Ensure that brushes used are those specified by the motor manufacturer.
No rotation	Supply failure, either complete or single phase	Disconnect motor immediately — with a single-phase fault serious overloading and burn-out may rapidly occur. Ensure that correct supply is restored to motor terminals.
	Insufficient torque	Check starting torque required and compare with motor rating, taking into account type of starter in use. Change to larger motor or to different type of starter.
	Reversed phase	Check connections in turn and correct.
Steady electrical hum	Running single phase	Check that all supply lines are alive with balanced voltage.
	Excessive load	Compare line current with that given on motor nameplate. Reduce load or change to larger motor.
	Reversed phase	Check connections in turn and correct.
	Uneven airgap	Check with feelers. If due to worn bearing fit new ones.
Pulsating electrical hum	Defective rotor	Check speed at full load. If it is low and if there is a periodic swing of current when running, a defective rotor is indicated, and the matter should be referred to the manufacturers.
	Defective wound rotor. Loose connection, partial short-circuit, etc.	On a wound-rotor machine check should be made of rotor resistance and open-circuit voltage between slip-rings. The rotor should be at standstill. Note these voltages can be higher than the supply voltages.
Mechanical noise	Foreign matter in airgap	Check airgap, dismantle rotor and clean.
	Bearings damaged	Check with a listening stick or screwdriver. If confirmed try rotating outer race of bearing 180°. If still unsatisfactory fit new bearing.
	Couplings out of line	Check coupling gap and realign.

* The frame temperature should be checked with a thermometer; the reading so obtained will be approximately 10 °C lower than the actual temperature of the windings.

11 Electric heating

The use of electricity for heating purposes has long been favoured because it offers certain advantages over other sources of heat. There is an absence of fumes; heat is available immediately at any desired temperature; there is a particular ease of control; cleanliness is an important factor; and there is a reduction in the amount of labour required for operation as compared with other fuel systems. In recent years there has been an increase in the applications of electricity to provide heat, not only for domestic purposes, but also for industrial processes. This chapter gives a broad view of electric heating in the forms which are most likely to be encountered in normal practice.

Summary of element materials

Most of the resistive conductors which we know as 'elements' are made from nickel-chromium-iron alloys. These alloys stand up fairly well to the cyclic heating to which they are subjected when they carry an electric current. Elements are found in fires, space heaters, toasters, flat irons, kettles, immersion heaters, hair-driers, boiling plates, grill boilers, oven elements and other appliances. The operating temperature of the elements is around 1,000 °C, depending on the actual composition of the alloy metal.

The table on page 99 gives some details of the resistive materials used for elements, and some of the more common applications.

Direct heating

This is the term used for heating which is directed at an object to be heated to raise its temperature. The method is suitable for producing heat in a very short time for short periods. It is generally in the form of 'radiant' heat. There are two classes of radiant heating: high temperature and low temperature. The advantage of radiant or direct heat is that it can be switched on and off when and where it is required. High-temperature heating has been described as 'personal warming', in that the heat (from a bright-red element) is radiated direct to a specific area; to be warm a person must be in that area.

The radiant fire is probably the most common direct-heating appliance. It is produced in two forms: (*a*) where the element is a spiral of wire fitted in the grooves of a refractory material (fireclay); (*b*) where the element is a wire wound round a long ceramic cylinder and mounted in front of a reflector of polished metal. A variation of type (*b*) is the heating element protected by a tubular sheath of metal or silica and mounted in front of an adjustable angle reflector. These are sometimes called 'infra-red' heaters and are particularly suitable for intermittent heating. They are also the type recommended for bathrooms and

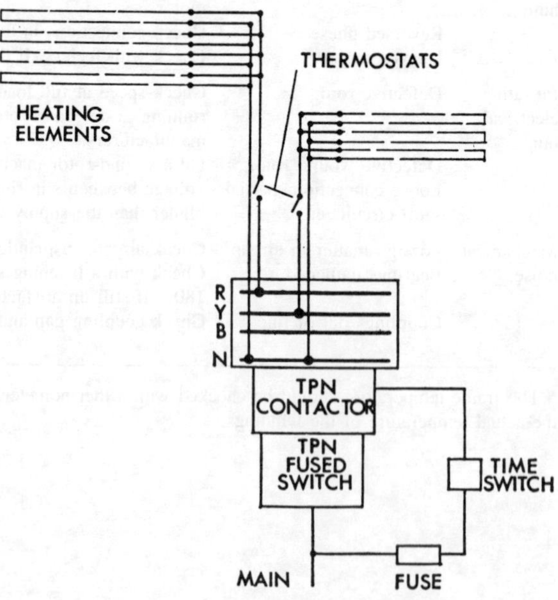

Figure 11.1. Typical circuit diagram for single-phase heating circuits from three-phase supply.

Material	*Composition (%)*	*Working temperature (°C)*	*Characteristics*	*Applications*
Brightray 'C'	Nickel 80 Chromium 18 Silicon 1.5 Iron 0.5	1,150	Can withstand switching operations resulting from frequent and wide temperature fluctuations	Most domestic heating appliances
Brightray 'S'	Nickel 80 Chromium 18.2 Iron 1 Silicon 0.8	1,150	Does not become brittle during use	Furnace resistors
Brightray 'B'	Nickel 60 Chromium 15.7 Iron 24 Silicon 0.3	950	—	Low-temperature domestic heating; control resistors, starters,etc
Ferry	Nickel 4.6 Copper 54	400	Good ductility and resistance to corrosion	Instruments and resistances; thermocouples; low-temperature heating
Nichrome V	Nickel 80 Copper 20	1,150	Can withstand high temperatures for long periods	Industrial and domestic equipment; precision resistors for electronics
Nichrome	Nickel 65 Chromium 15 Copper 20	950	—	All types of domestic heating equipment; rheostat and resistance units
Tophet 'A'	Nickel 80 Chromium 20	1,150	Resistançe to corrosion and scaling	Heavy-duty industrial furnaces and radiant element heaters
Tophet 'C'	Nickel 60 Chromium 16 Iron 24	950	—	Low-temperature resistance units; motor starters; radio rheostats; multipliers and shunts for instruments; electric blankets and heater pads

similar situations where moisture or condensation is present. Radiant fires are often used to provide 'top-up' heating, to supplement the general heating from say, a central heating system.

Low-temperature heaters are those in which the heating element temperature is low and the element does not glow bright red. This type of heat is usually known as 'black heat'. The radiated heat is given off in small quantities. Sometimes the elements are embedded between sheets of non-inflammable material such as asbestos, and the sheets fixed to a ceiling. Wall-mounted heaters using embedded elements are also used for direct heating. Surface temperatures vary from 50 to 65 °C. Load ratings are from 8 to 17W per square metre of surface.

Tubular heaters are cylinders of sheet-steel containing black-heat elements and have surface temperatures of about 200 °F. The average loading is about 20W per metre run of single tube. Most of the heat produced is convected and the units are normally placed along skirtings, particularly below windows, singly or in banks of two or three.

Indirect heating

Low-temperature convection heating uses the black-heat principle, but instead of producing radiated heat, the air surrounding the element is warmed to create convection currents in the air. This form of heating is known as 'indirect'. Basically, the convection heater is constructed to

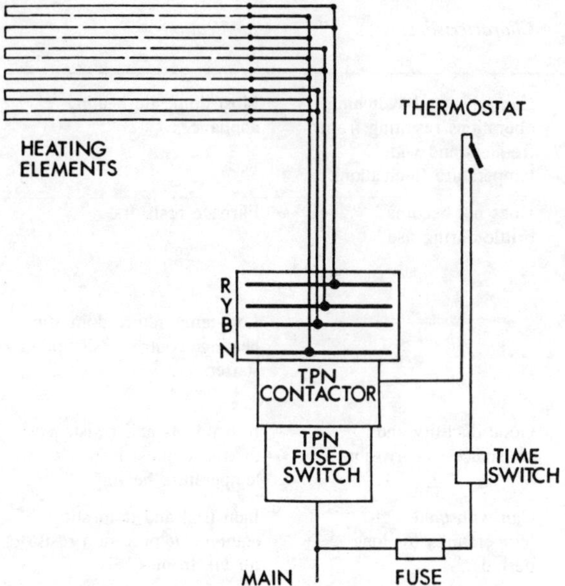

Figure 11.2. Typical circuit diagram for heating circuits on three-phase supply.

draw cold air in from an inlet at the bottom; the rising air is heated by the element and escapes through an outlet at the top. Convector heaters are used for background heating. The tubular heater described above tends to act as a convector heater though heat is also radiated from its surface. Convector heaters are often fitted with a thermostat situated in a suitable position in the room. Some types have fans to give a more positive air circulation.

Thermal-storage heating

This form of heating uses the principle that material such as concrete can be heated and then allowed to release its stored heat over a period of time. The typical storage heater consists of heating elements embedded or surrounded by refractory material, such as concrete. The whole is enclosed in a metal case. Each heater unit is designed to take a charge of electricity during certain periods in a 24-hour period. Some units are fitted with fans to give a boost of heat.

Thermal-storage radiators are easy to install. The heating elements are automatically switched on by time-switches during off-peak hours, thus storing heat in the surrounding storage material.

The 'Electricaire' system of heating consists of a thermal-storage unit, generally situated centrally in a building. Ducts lead off to the various parts of the building from the unit. The heat from the unit is directed through ducts by a fan the speed of which can be varied to control the amount of heated air being delivered to a particular room. Small units are available for individual room heating.

Space-heating by means of elements buried in

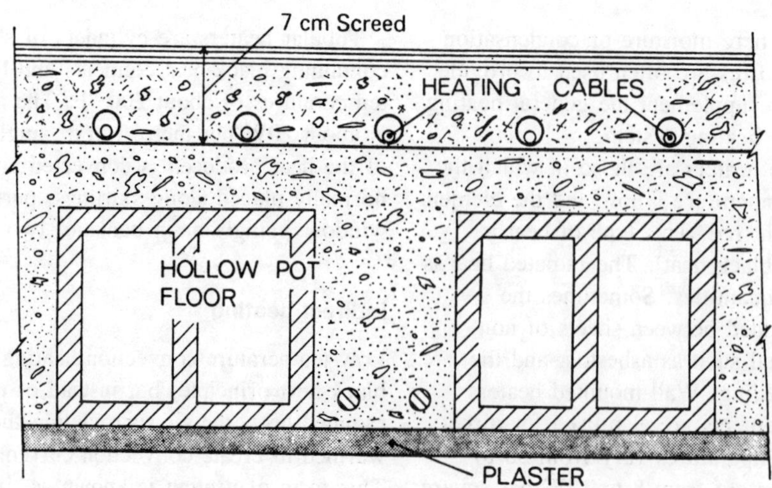

Figure 11.3. Typical floor construction with withdrawable heating system.

Figure 11.4. Heating cables in tongue and grooved hardwood flooring.

the concrete of a floor, wall or ceiling is another form of thermal-storage heating. The high level of comfort all over a building using floor-warming methods is due to the fact that the floor in which the elements are laid becomes a low-temperature radiant surface. The system can be operated continuously on standard tariffs and the temperature controlled thermostatically within prescribed limits. More usually, these systems are arranged for connection during periods of off-peak supply at reduced tariffs. The capital cost of electric floor-warming equipment and its installation is very much lower than any comparable central-heating system.

There are a number of floor-warming element types with conductors of chromium, iron, aluminium, copper, silicon and manganese alloys. Conductor dielectrics include asbestos, mineral insulation, PVC, butyl and silicone rubber, and nylon. These dielectrics are normally covered with a plastic sheath for protection against mechanical damage. Floor-warming elements are usually directly embedded, or they may be contained in a metal housing in the concrete floor. The latter system, known as the 'rewirable', is more costly to install than the directly embedded system, but it can be renewed, replaced or modified without disturbing the floor.

The rewirable system comprises elements which are drawn into tubes or other ducts running between transverse trunkings which accommodate connections and to which access can be gained by removing the trunking covers. The system layout is usually dictated by the range of elements available since the access trunkings require to be spaced at a distance apart which will exhaust the element in a single run, or after making several runs resulting in a serpentine formation with the bends in the trunking. The access trunking is usually placed at the foot of a wall. Control of the

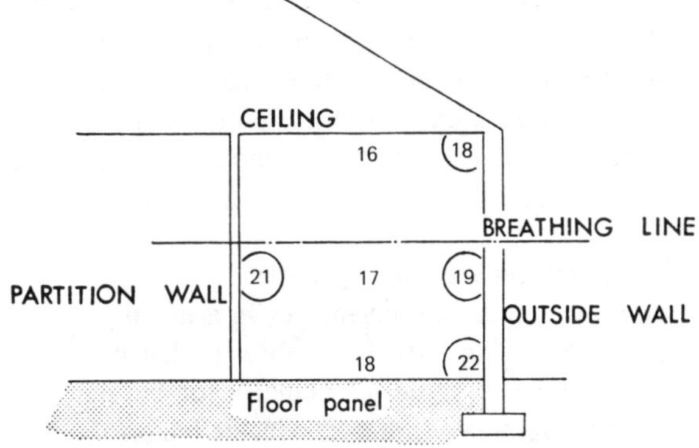

CEILING
21
17
BREATHING LINE
PARTITION WALL
19
19
16
OUTSIDE WALL
14
12
CONVECTION SYSTEM

Figure 11.5. Temperature distribution in single-storey building with floor-warming and convection heating systems. Figures show air temperature and surface temperatures in °C.

surface temperature is by means of thermostats.

The directly embedded system employs an element buried in the floor screed. There is no access for replacement purposes. Various types of element are available. Some have fixed lengths and loadings. Others are rated on conductor size and resistance per metre only, leaving the designer of the heating system to determine his own convenient lengths and loadings within certain limits as to element temperatures. The usual procedure for installation is to lay the selected cable, or cable and housing, in the constructional floor, on the concrete floor or on the precast concrete members of the floor ensuring that the heating elements, or their containers, are covered with a concrete screed of about 5 cm thick. The floor-heating elements are arranged as far as possible to cover the whole of the floor area in order to obtain an even diffusion of heat. In general, loadings are in the region of 9–12W per square metre.

Fault-location in buried systems
One of the main disadvantages in a heating conductor being buried in a floor is that it becomes inaccessible, particularly for the purpose of locating breaks in the conductor length. It is good practice to prepare a layout drawing of the system, both for installation and record purposes. There are a few methods of pin-pointing the fault position. They can locate a fault within 6 mm on any floor size and under any type of finish. Thus the total excavation for both the location and repair of a fault usually does not exceed an area of some 220 by 70 mm.

Some fault-location methods use loop tests, resistance or capacity bridges, but the accuracy of these tests to pin-point the fault position depends on an exact knowledge of the characteristics of the heating cable and its layout. In addition, there are some types of fault which cannot be found by these methods.

The 'induction' method is used mainly for plastic-insulated types of cable. The 'hot-spot' method is used for MICS cables. For the induction test, any valve or transistor amplifier with a simple search coil of small dimensions can be used. The signal source can vary from a simple buzzer operated from a dry cell or a 50 Hz supply, to a valve or transistor oscillator producing a signal in the rage up to 10kHz. Commercial instruments are available on the market.

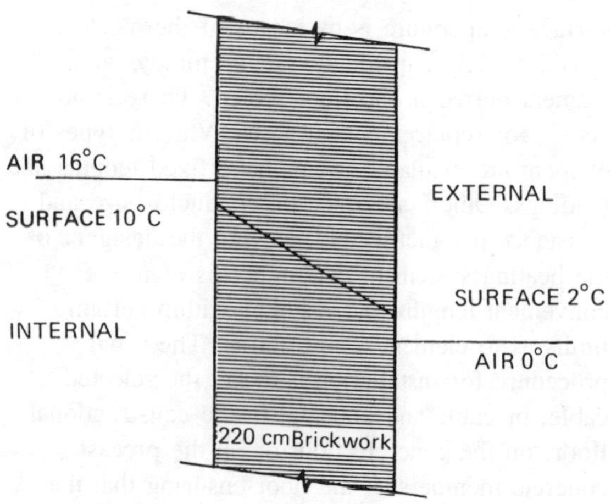

Figure 11.6. Temperature gradient through a wall.

In all cases of fault finding, the first step in the procedure is to isolate the circuit and establish the fault conditions by insulation-resistance and continuity tests (faults to earth, or break in conductor continuity). Next the cable layout is checked. Even where accurate records exist of the layout, sometimes the heating cables have been moved either during the concrete screeding process or by an electrician using up a piece of 'surplus' length in an unexpected place. The preliminary test should be made by using the induction method.

This involves injecting a signal current along the cable core (assuming the use of single-core cables). The magnetic field set up by this current can then be detected at the floor surface. Maximum field-strength readings will be obtained directly over the cable run, and the actual position marked off on the floor surface with chalk.

The presence of faults, except open-circuits with insulation-resistance values between ends or to earth higher than one megohm, will not affect this test, provided that suitably sensitive apparatus is used. Subsequent procedure then depends on the type of cable and faults.

When plastic or other non-metallic cables are already faulted to earth, it is only necessary to pass the test signal between one end of the core and earth. Then, with the induction set, find the point where the signal ceases. This will be the fault position. The test current can be as low as one milliampere. 'Earth' in this test means the concrete floor.

A point of importance to note is that if the ratio between depth and cable spacing is less than 1 (approximately), not all the cable runs may be indicated by the test. If the ratio is greater than unity, only the 'outside' cable runs will be indicated. So far as the faulty length of cable is concerned, however, the fault position will be indicated by a sharp decrease in signal strength as the search coil traverses the run containing the fault. This sharp decrease or 'dip' is caused by the

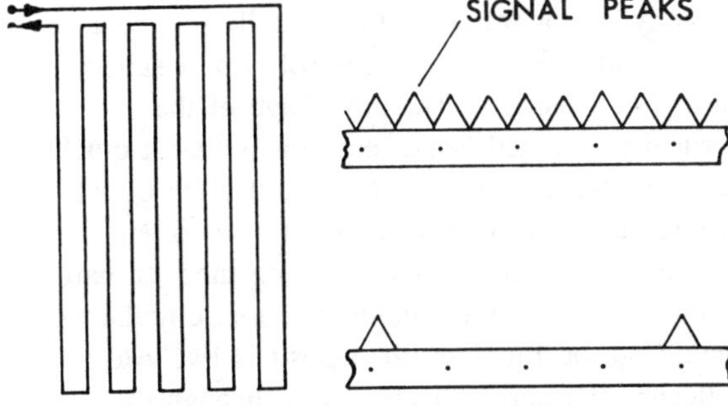

Figure 11.7. Location of cable layout before locating fault. Note that every cable run will be indicated when the depth/space ratio is less than 1. Only the outside cable runs will be indicated when the depth/space ratio is greater than 1.

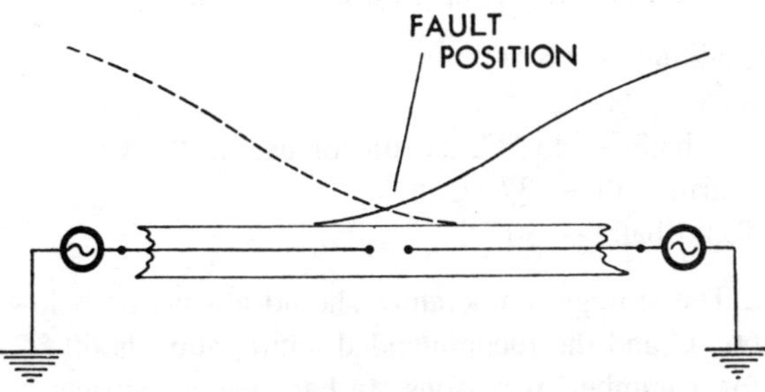

Figure 11.8. Location of open-circuit faults (non-metallic sheath). The fault position is indicated by the overlap of two tests.

search coil being under the influence of two opposing fields exactly at the fault position.

If the fault-resistance to earth is too high to pass sufficient test current it will be necessary to reduce the resistance by applying a dc or ac voltage between the core and earth. Only limited power (not more than 100W) must be used in the 'breaking-down' procedure on plastic-insulated cables otherwise further damage will result to the cables. If more than one fault to earth occurs, a similar test from each cable end will be necessary.

When the fault position has been found, the smallest area possible should be excavated carefully and the repair effected.

Another fault-position location method used with MICS cables is the 'hot-spot'. This involves creating a small arc at the fault position, the power being fed into the arc being of the order of 70W. The heating effect of this arc is local and can be detected at the floor surface within about fifteen minutes. The hot-spot is about 40 mm diameter and about 12 °C hotter than the surrounding floor. The hot-spot can be detected either by hand or by using heat-detecting devices.

Water heating

Electic water-heating is very efficient because the heating element is entirely immersed in the water to be heated. The greatest proportion of electric water-heating is represented by immersion heaters, most of which are fitted in storage cylinders or tanks which sometimes have complementary means of heating. There are two types of immersion heater. The withdrawable type is a heater so constructed that the heating element can be withdrawn from the enclosing sheath without breaking a water joint. The non-withdrawable type is a heater so constructed that the heating element cannot be removed without breaking a water joint. As for the storage vessels, there are four general types in use:

(*a*) *Non-pressure or open-outlet*. This has a capacity of from 56 to 450 litres, with an immersion heater of rating in the region of $1\frac{1}{2}$kW. This type is controlled by a stop valve fitted on the water-inlet pipe and is usually fed directly from a water main or, alternatively, from a cistern. A non-return valve is usually fitted in the inlet pipe. The heating element and the associated thermostat are located in the bottom of the container. For domestic purposes, this type of heater has a capacity of about 12 litres and is most often used to provide hot water in an instant for washing-up duties. The type is also used in cloakrooms where there is an intermittent demand for hot water for hygiene. The tank is insulated against heat losses by a lagging of fibreglass or granulated cork. When the inlet valve is opened, the incoming cold water pushes the less-dense hot water into the outlet pipe.

(*b*) *Pressure*. Water heaters of this type are connected to a cistern. Capacities range from 15 to 370 litres. The heater ratings are 1kW and above. In domestic installations, the usual rating is a 3kW heater in a 100-litre tank. The water supplied from the mains to the cistern is controlled by a float-ball valve. Hot-water outlets are thus fed under pressure supplied by the head (vertical height) of the cold water available.

(*c*) *Cistern*. This type incorporates a feed tank with ball-valve, arranged for direct connection to the water main. A connection for an overflow pipe is also provided, for which any special requirements of the local water-supply undertaking should be observed. They must always be installed above the level of the highest hot-water tap in the house. The feed pipe, draw-off and vent pipes are all inside the heater unit. Capacities range from 15 to 100 litres; heater ratings are between 1 and 3kW.

(*d*) *Dual-heater*. This is a special development of the pressure-type of heater. The unit of 60 or 100 litre capacity is designed primarily for installation under the draining board next to the kitchen sink. This position is taken because the kitchen tap is the most frequently used hot-water outlet in a dwelling. The unit is usually also coupled to the bathroom hot-water taps. The unit is provided with two heaters, each controlled by a thermostat. One heater, located near the top of the tank, is of low rating (usually 0.5kW). It provides sufficient hot water for ordinary domestic purposes. The main heater, of a higher rating (2.5kW) is placed near the bottom of the tank and can be switched on manually before a bath is required. The complete unit, as manufactured, comprises a thermally insulated cylinder, electric-heating elements, thermostats and pipe connections. The unit of 100-litre capacity is often designed to be coupled to, and to operate in conjunction with, a fuel-fired domestic water-heater.

Immersion heaters are available in the two types mentioned already. The removable-element type is the more popular since the element can be withdrawn from the sleeve or pocket permanently fixed to the tank, so enabling a replacement to be made without emptying the tank of water. Immersion heaters are designed for both horizontal and vertical fixing, with the terminal head at the top. The advantage of horizontal fixing is that the whole body of water above the heater element will be raised equally in temperature, giving maximum capacity of hot water. A horizontally-mounted heater under thermostatic control is best suited for hard-water districts. The advantage of the vertically-mounted heater element is that it quickly heats the top layers of water, the heating effect progressing downwards. This action is often assisted by a draught or circulating tube. In hard-water districts it is recommended that circulators should not be fitted as fur deposit is likely to collect in the narrow water-ways through the circulator. Another advantage of the circulator is the quick delivery of hot water to the top of the tank which can be drawn off in small quantities soon after switching on the element. The use of vertical heaters and circulators is mostly confined to soft-water districts.

The following temperatures are common:

Scalding – 66 °C
Sink – 60 °C
Hot bath – 43 °C, as run for use at 40 °C
Warm bath – 37 °C
Tepid bath – 30 °C

The storage temperature should always be below 66 °C and the recommended temperature is 60 °C, for a number of reasons. In hard-water districts furring troubles usually begin to increase rapidly above 60 °C. This temperature is also adequate for washing greasy dishes and reduces standing losses. At higher temperatures there is the risk of scalding the skin.

There are two basic types of thermostat for the control of domestic hot-water systems: the long, thin-stemmed type (usually known as the rod thermostat) and the short-stem type. The rod-type thermostat operates on the principle of differential expansion between 'invar' and copper, and usually takes the form of an invar rod (which is the lower expansion material) housed within a copper tube which has a higher coefficient of expansion. The lower end of the copper tube is brazed to the invar rod, while the upper end is brazed to a solid portion of the switch mechanism. The invar rod is thus free to move up and down, which it does with the contraction and expansion of the copper tube under the effects of varying temperature. These thermostats are made in 18, 22, and 44 cm lengths. The 22 and 44 cm lengths are most

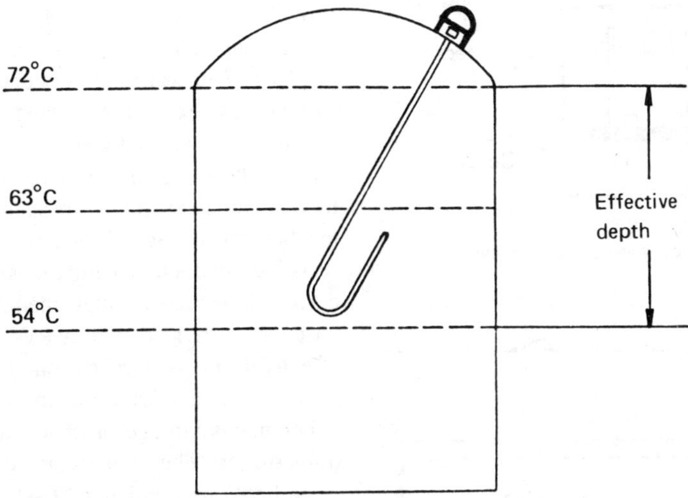

Figure 11.9. Water-heater layout showing typical temperature gradient.

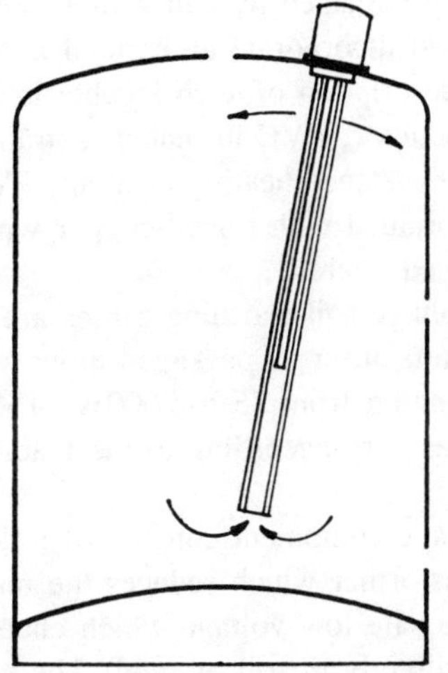

Figure 11.10. Water heater with circulator.

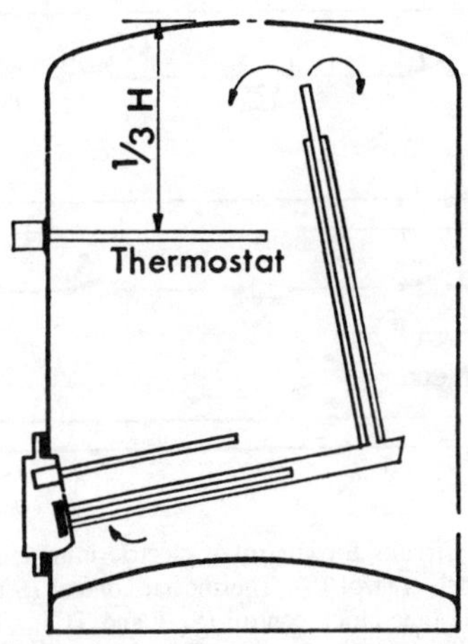

Figure 11.11. Water heater with vertical circulator.

commonly used for the control of vertical domestic heaters. The 18 cm model is generally used for horizontal or side-entry heaters. The short-stem thermostat contains a snap-action switch similar to that used in the rod-type thermostat. However, operation of the switch is by means of a piece of bimetal which replaced the combination of invar rod and copper tube.

In most water-heating installations, the immersion-heater with its associated thermostat is installed in the conventional hot-water cylinder in such a way that both heater and thermostat hang vertically downwards. Horizontal mounting is also a less-common practice. With horizontal mounting, the heater lies horizontally across the cylinder which means that it imparts maximum turbulence to the water above the heater. Thus, virtually all the water in the tank is heated to the temperature at which the thermostat is set, before the latter trips the circuit. With vertical mounting, the degree of turbulence in the cylinder is not so great, because the heated water tends to flow

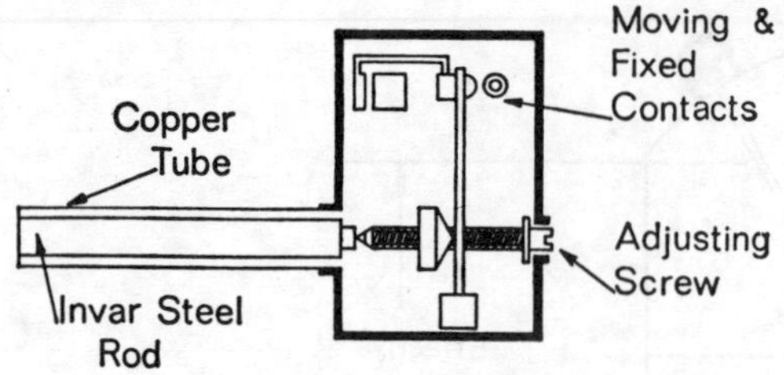

Figure 11.12. Typical water-heater thermostat.

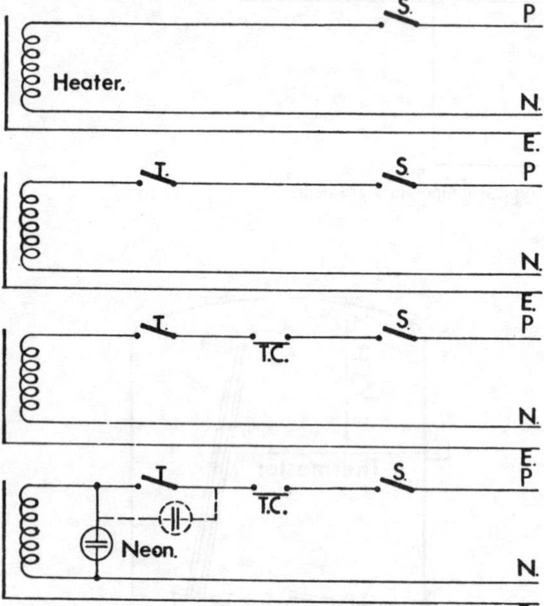

Figure 11.13. Circuits for control of electric immersion heaters: Simple switch control (S); Thermostat control (S and T); Thermostat and time-clock control (S, T and TC); Circuit with neon light indication (Neon across T will glow brightly when the cylinder is full of water).

upwards along the elements of the heater. Consequently, when the thermostat switches off, there is a gradient between the top and bottom of the heater element of some 20 to 30 °C.

Soil warming

Electrical soil warming is used to provide a controlled root temperature so that plants and seedlings can be brought to advanced stages of growth in a short time, thus enabling the grower to take advantage of out-of-season markets for his produce. Soil-warming conductors are generally supplied for extra-low voltage application and are usually bare, specially-selected galvanised-steel wires. The gauge depends on requirements. The larger gauges are more resistant to corrosion and mechanical damage. These wires are in effect resistive conductors which dissipate heat when a current is passed through them. Some heating wires are provided with a PVC sheath to effectively prevent corrosion (Figure 11.15).

Soil- or bench-warming installations operate at either mains voltage or at low voltage fed from a transformer. The mains-voltage method (used for large beds) uses either PVC-sheathed wire or MI cables. As these cables are 'live', they should not be installed where there is a likelihood of the sheath being damaged by cultivating tools. Such cables should incorporate an earthed metal screen. A typical description of such a cable is a central copper conductor, PVC-insulated, spiralled with an enamelled resistance heating element, PVC-insulated, braided with tinned-copper wire and PVC-sheathed overall.

Mains-voltage soil-warming cables are supplied by the manufacturer as packaged units with loadings ranging from 75 to 2000W. The lengths of the cables vary according to the loading per metre run.

Low-voltage equipment consists of a double-wound transformer which reduces the mains voltage to a safe low voltage which energises the wires laid directly in soil or sand. The voltage used varies between 6 and 30V depending on the

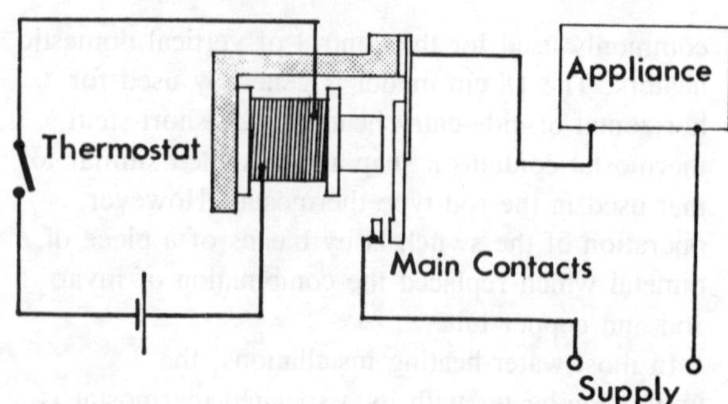

Figure 11.14. Simple contactor circuit operated by thermostat.

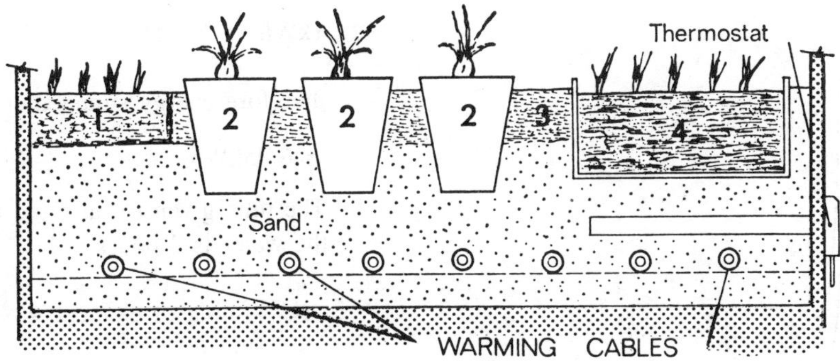

Figure 11.15. Soil warming. 1. Peat and sand mixture placed on sand bed for rooting and cutting. 2. Pots pressed into sand bed and surrounded with peat. 3. Peat bed. 4. Seed boxes direct on sand bed.

size of the installation. Although the wires can be handled with complete safety, the current should always be switched off during the cultivation of the soil. The wires are laid in loops and held in place. For any particular installation the wires are selected for correct size and resistance to suit the associated transformer. As galvanised iron wire is not normally made with special regard to its electrical properties, and the resistance of two pieces of such wire of the same gauge and length may differ quite considerably, it is best not to cut the wire to shorten it or replace a piece. Regulations 554-06-01 to 554-06-04 refer to the requirements relating to heating wires and cables.

Process heating

Process heating is used for industrial applications and takes many forms. The heat treatment of metals is usually carried out by indirect heating in resistance furnaces. Induction heating is based on the current carried by a coil of large cross-section copper conductor inducing circulating currents in the surface of the object to be heated, which is placed beside the coil though not in contact with it. The induced currents cause heat to be developed in the metal subject. Infra-red heaters are those which heat the charge purely by radiation. These generally take the form of silica or quartz lamps with internal or external reflectors, sheath-wire elements with reflectors, or indirect panel heaters. Infra-red units are widely used for paint stoving, strip-metal annealing and billet heating for forging temperatures up to 1,250 °C. Fluid heating is achieved with either heaters external to the fluid container or by using heaters immersed direct in the fluid.

Heating calculations

Although the provision of heating in a building is correctly the task of the professional heating engineer, at times the electrician is required to assess the heating requirements of small premises and domestic dwellings. The following notes and examples are intended as a rough guide only and are provided for general information.

To obtain the greatest efficiency from a water-heating installation, it is important to ensure that the storage tank and all associated hot-water pipes are lagged to retain the heat. As an example, if a thermostat controlling the immersion heater is set at 60 °C, the losses from an unlagged tank will be in the order of some 90kWh per week, costing on average about £3. The following formula is used to determine the efficiency of the thermal insulation which can take the form of glass-fibre, bagging, polystyrene, etc. (Figure 11.16).

Thermal-insulation efficiency per cent

$$= \frac{\text{dissipation from bare metal} - \text{dissipation from insulated metal}}{\text{dissipation from bare metal}} \times 100$$

Example 1

Assume a 95-litre tank the losses of which are

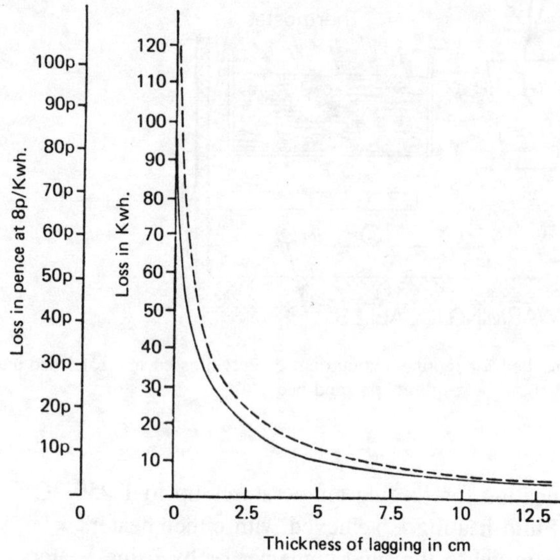

Figure 11.16. Weekly loss from a 100-litre copper cylinder storing hot water.

(unlagged) 10.8kWh per day, when the water-to-air temperature difference is 50 °C. From a similar tank thermally insulated on all external surfaces with mineral slag wool to a thickness of 7.5 cm, the losses for the equivalent conditions are 1.125kWh per day.

The thermal efficiency of the insulated tank is

$$\frac{10.8-1.125}{10.8} \times 100 = 89.6 \text{ per cent}$$

Example 2

To calculate the rating of an element for an immersion heater for a tank containing 100 litres of water. The water is to be heated from 10 to 60 °C in 2 hours. The efficiency of the heating system is 85 per cent. One litre of water has a mass of 1kg; 1kWh = 3.6MJ; specific heat of water is 4.2kJ/kgK.

Heat reqired in kJ:
= mass × specific heat capacity in kJ/kg K × change in temperature
= 100 × 4.2 × 50 = 21,000kJ = 21MJ.

$$\text{Heat supplied} = \frac{\text{heat required}}{\text{efficiency}} = \frac{0.85}{21}$$

= 24.7MJ

1kWh = 3.6MJ,

$$\text{therefore energy supplied} = \frac{24.7}{3.6}$$

= 6.85kWh

The time given to raise the temperature of the water is 2 hours

$$\therefore \text{kW rating of element} = \frac{6.85}{2} = 3.42\text{kW}$$

Example 3

To find the time taken to heat a tank with a capacity of 90 litres and a 3kW immersion heater. The temperature is to be raised from 10 to 60 °C. The efficiency of the lagged heater tank is 90 per cent.

Heat required = 90 × 4.2 × 50 = 18.9MJ

$$\text{Heat supplied} = \frac{\text{heat required}}{\text{efficiency}}$$

$$= \frac{18.9}{0.9} = 21\text{MJ}$$

1kWh = 3.6MJ

$$\therefore \text{Energy supplied} = \frac{21}{3.6} = 5.85\text{kWh}$$

Rating of the heater element = 3kW

$$\therefore \text{time taken in operation} = \frac{5.85}{3}$$

= 1.95 hrs

Heating appliance element repairs

In most cases, elements are best replaced as a unit, but occasionally it falls to the electrician to effect repairs to a unit with a resistive conductor for which no spare is immediately available or if the pattern of element is obsolete. The following general rules will enable a satisfactory result to be obtained.

The rating of the element must first be determined, from which the length and size of resistance wire can be found. For example, a 1,000W panel-type fire element is rated at 240V.

$$I = \frac{W}{V} = \frac{1{,}000}{240} = 4.16\text{A}$$

This current can be carried by a 25 swg wire of the 'Brightray C' type.

Figure 11.17. Heating-wire terminations: simple wire-twisted, used with a porcelain connector, and crimped joint.

$$\text{Resistance} = \frac{V}{I} = \frac{240}{4.16} = 57.8 \text{ ohms}$$

The length of wire can be found either by measurement, or

$$\frac{\text{resistance of element}}{\text{resistance per metre of wire}}$$

$$= \frac{57.8}{5} = 11.56 \text{ m}$$

The weakest point of an otherwise sound element is usually the end connection. Loose end connections, or connections made simply by screwing the element wire under a steel washer, frequently lead to arcing and early failure. The joint between the conducting lead wire and the heating wire may be made mechanically, by welding, brazing or by silver-soldering. A mechanical joint can also be made by inserting the element and lead wires in a small-bore tube. Terminal nuts, and screws and washers, should be rustless and heat-resisting so that they can be unscrewed without breaking the refractory material. In particular, the selection of the correct type of flexible cord for use with a heating appliance should be related to the possible transfer of heat. It also requires that insulating sleeves, or leads suitable for the temperature likely to be encountered, be fitted over the individual cores of the cable or flexible cord within the heating appliance. This is done so that the normal insulation is not relied on in the event of its being affected by the heat.

12 Illumination

Filament lamps

Filament lamps fall into a group of light-producing devices called 'incandescents'. They give light as a result of heating a filament conductor to a very high temperature. In 1860, Sir Joseph Swan produced the first lamp using carbonised paper strip. Later, carbonised filaments made from silk were used. Until 1900, carbon-filament lamps enjoyed an undisputed field of use. Then the metal-filament lamp appeared and by 1910 it had superseded the carbon lamp. The carbon lamps which are made today have a limited application: for lamp resistances (battery-charging), and radiant-heat apparatus. The modern carbon lamp has a filament of Swedish filter paper which is dissolved in zinc chloride solution. The resultant viscous solution is squirted slowly through a fine die into a jar of acidified alcohol. Tough cellulose threads are the result. They are wound on formers which are packed into a crucible filled with finely powdered graphite. The crucibles are then baked in a furnace at 1400 °C when the cellulose threads become pure carbon. The temperature limit for a carbon filament is about 1800 °C. The light output is low, at about 3.6 lumens per watt (ℓm/W).

The tungsten-filament lamp first appeared about 1910 and has since been the main incandescent lamp in use. It operates at a temperature of about 2300 °C and has a light output of about 8 ℓm/W. The first lamp to use a tungsten filament had the air evacuated from the glass bulb — the so-called vacuum lamp. Later, the bulb was filled with argon and nitrogen which are inert gases and do not support combustion. This development enabled the filament to be operated at a higher temperature without the undue evaporation of the filament which tends to take place in a vacuum. The operating temperature of the gas-filled lamp is about 2700 °C. The light output is in the region of 12 ℓm/W. The early lamps had a single-coil filament. Later the coiled-coil lamp was produced, that is, the coiled filament was itself formed into a coil. The light output of this lamp is about 14 ℓm/W. The main advantages of the coiled-coil lamp are (*a*) the filament has a more compact formation and (*b*) the heat losses due to convection currents in the gas are reduced, so giving a higher light-output efficiency.

Tungsten has a resistance which increases with temperature. The resistance when cold is about 6 per cent of that when operating at normal temperature. This means that when the lamp is switched on, a current of about fourteen times the running current flows. The increase in the temperature of the filament is rapid, however, and the current surge does not harm the filament. The resistance of the filament increases as rapidly and has a stabilising effect on the power consumed.

There are many types of metal-filament lamps available today. Signal lamps are small and are used on indication boards to show the flow of chemicals, the passage of trains past a given point, and the energising of a circuit in a definite sequence. Spot and flood lamps are made from pressed glass and are internally mirrored to radiate a defined beam of light. The flood lamp has a relatively broad beam and is used for outdoor illumination such as gardens, monuments, parks and sports grounds. The spot lamp has a narrow beam and is found in shop windows and showcases. They are also used to highlight an object which has a general illumination. Thermal-radiation lamps are used in piglet and chicken rearing. They are hard-glass bulbs and are internally mirrored for use for short-periods at a time. They are also to be found in bathrooms, and in industry for drying processes (e.g. stove enamelling).

Discharge lamps

The discharge lamp consists of a glass tube containing a gas. At each end of the tube there is an electrode. If a sufficiently high voltage is applied across these electrodes a discharge takes place between them. The gas now becomes an electrical conductor and light is produced. The colour of the light produced by a discharge lamp depends on the gas in the tube: Neon – red; mercury vapour – bluish-white; helium – ivory; sodium vapour – yellow.

There are a number of electric-discharge lamps available today, each of which has a particular application or advantage over another.

Low-pressure mercury-vapour

This lamp is popularly known as the 'fluorescent' lamp. It consists of a glass tube filled with mercury vapour at a low pressure. The electrodes are located at the ends of the tube. When the lamp is switched on, an arc-discharge excites a barely-visible radiation, the greater part of which consists of ultra-violet radiation. The interior wall of the tube is coated with a fluorescent powder which transforms the ultra-violet radiation into visible radiation or light. The type of light, that is the colour range, is determined by the composition of the fluorescent powder. An important aspect of the gas-discharge lamp is that the discharge has a 'negative resistance characteristic'. This means that when the temperature of the gas or vapour rises, its resistance decreases and will thus tend to draw an ever-increasing current from the supply. The current is limited to a predetermined value by the insertion in the circuit, in series with the lamp, of a limiting resistor or choke (inductor).

There are two types of fluorescent lamp: the hot-cathode and the cold-cathode.

The hot-cathode lamp is the more common type, familiar in tube lengths of 2.5, 1.7, 1.3 m and down to 30 cm. In this type, the electrodes are heated and the voltage of operation is low or medium voltage. To assist starting, the mercury vapour is mixed with a small quantity of argon gas. The light produced varies from 30 to 35 ℓm/W. The colours available from the lamp include a near-daylight and a colour-corrected light for use where colours (of wool, paints, etc.) must be seen correctly. The practical application of the lamp includes the lighting of shops, homes, factories, streets, ships, transport (buses and trains), tunnels, coal-mines and caravans. The auxiliary equipment associated with the hot-cathode lamp includes:

1. The choke, which supplies a high initial voltage on starting (caused by the interruption of the lamp's inductive circuit), and also limits the current in the lamp when it is operating.
2. The starter.
3. The capacitor, which is fitted to correct or improve the power factor of the circuit by neutralising the inductive effect of the choke.

There are a number of methods used to start fluorescent lamp circuits (Figures 12.1–12.6).

The methods fall into two general groups: those which use a switch (sometimes called a 'glow' starter) and those which do not use a switching arrangement but rely on an auto-transformer to produce the high voltage needed to start the lamps. With the glow-starter, it is important to use the correct type for the size of lamp. Although

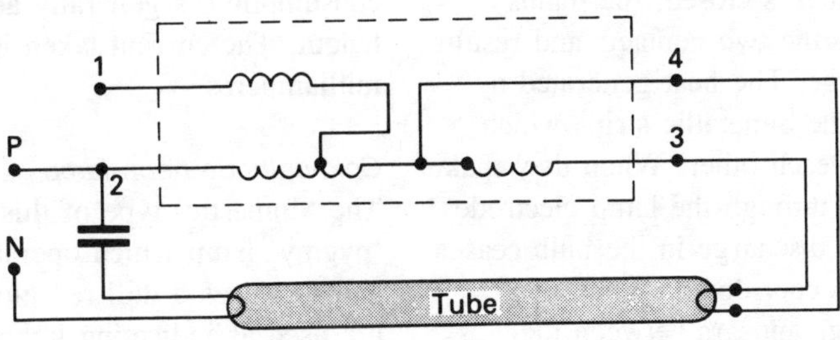

Figure 12.1. Semi-resonant start circuit for a fluorescent lamp.

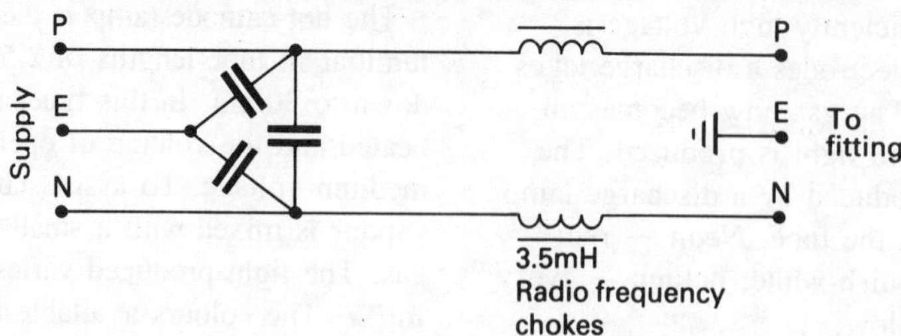

Figure 12.2. 'Circuit to avoid interference with radio reception. Under certain circumstances a fluorescent tube may produce radiation causing interference with normal radio reception, especially in the medium wave band. The above circuit shows a filter network with radio-frequency chokes. For slight mains-borne interference the connection of a 0.01 μF capacitor usually solves the problem.'

'universal' starter switches are available, it must be remembered that they are not in fact suitable for all sizes.

The semi-resonant start circuit has the usual choke or inductor replaced by a specially wound transformer and is used for starting fluorescent lamps in cold temperatures. Current flows through the primary coil to one cathode of the lamp and thence through the secondary coil which is wound in opposition to it. A large capacitor is connected between the secondary and the second cathode of the lamp. The starting current quickly heats up the cathodes and as the circuit is mainly capacitive, this current leads the mains voltage. Because the primary and secondary windings are in opposition, the voltage across the lamp is increased and causes the lamp to strike.

The glow-start switch consists of two separated bimetallic contact strips contained in a small glass bulb filled with helium gas. The contacts are connected in series with the lamp electrodes. When the circuit-control switch is closed, the mains voltage appears across the two contacts and results in a small gas discharge. The heat generated by the discharge affects the bimetallic strips which bend forward to meet each other. When they make contact, current flows through the lamp electrodes to heat them. The gas discharge in the bulb ceases and the strips begin to cool down. When they separate, a high voltage appears between the electrodes and the main gas discharge is started. The voltage which now appears across the contacts in the bulb is, during running conditions, insufficient to cause further discharge in the helium gas, and so the contacts remain open while the lamp is burning.

The instant-start or 'quick-start' method of starting fluorescent lamps consists of an auto-transformer connected across the tube. Two tappings provide a small current for heating each of the electrodes. When the electrodes become hot (usually in a fraction of a second) the tube strikes. The striking or discharge is caused by the very small currents flowing from the cathodes to an external earthed strip which runs down the length of the tube, providing a conducting path. A normal choke is used, but only for current-limiting purposes, since there is no interruption of the current on starting.

The cold-cathode lamp uses a high voltage (about 5kV) for its operation. For general lighting purposes, they are familiar as fluorescent tubes of about 2.5 cm in diameter, either straight, curved or bent to take a certain form. The power consumption is generally about 24W per metre length. The current taken is of the order of milliamperes.

Cold-cathode neon lamp

The 'domestic' type of this lamp is the small 'pygmy' lamp which operates on mains voltage and produces a dull-red glow. Very small lamps are used as indicating lights on wiring accessories (e.g. socket-outlets and switch positions) and on control panels, where space is at a premium and the small filament lamp cannot be accommodated.

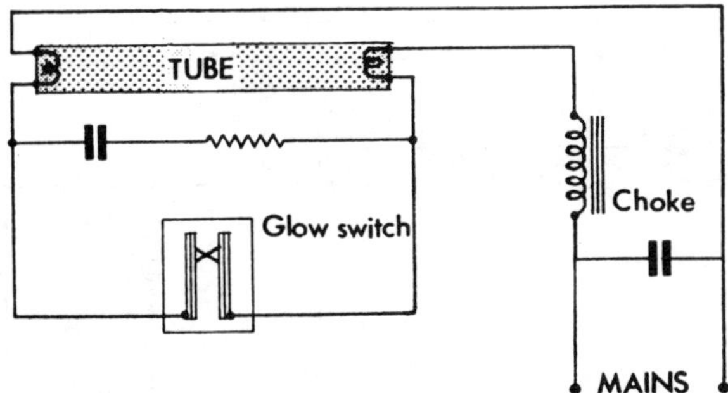

Figure 12.3. Glow-switch start circuit for a fluorescent lamp.

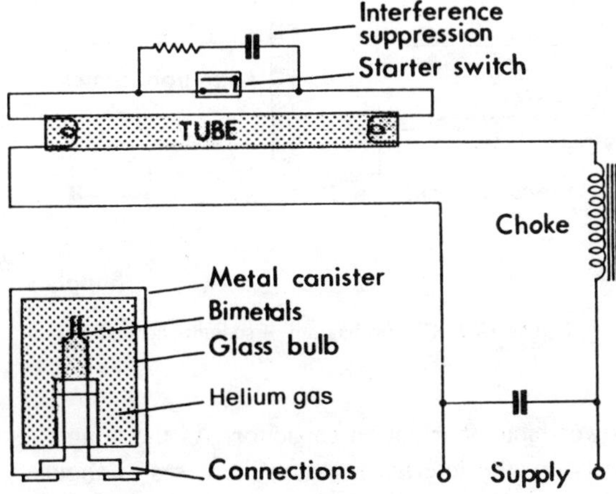

Figure 12.4. Glow-switch starter circuit and details.

The fact that these tiny neons take an insignificant current and do not heat up is another factor in their favour for signalling and indication purposes. Neons are now popular for showing up switch positions in a dark room.

The more familiar lamp of the neon-discharge type is used for sign and display lighting. As the electrodes (or cathodes) are not heated, a high voltage is used for both starting and operation of the lamp. This voltage is obtained from a double-wound transformer, which transforms the mains at 240V to 5000V to earth (this is the maximum voltage to earth allowed for such circuits, though values of 10kV may be applied to tubes from a transformer with an earthed and centre-tapped secondary winding). Most high-voltage neon lamps consist of short lengths of glass tube bent to form a particular shape or letter and connected in series.

Sodium-vapour lamp

This lamp gives an orange light and is used mainly for street and road lighting, and on airfields. The lamp is the most efficient producer of light, but because of its single-colour characteristic it gives many items an inferior colour quality (everything looks yellow or grey to black). The lamp consists of a long glass tube, usually bent into a U-shape. The tube contains a mixture of argon and neon gases, with particles of solid sodium. The lamp is operated from an auto-transformer which raises the mains voltage to about 350–400V. When the circuit-control switch is made, the tube gives off an initial reddish glow, the result of the discharge through the neon-argon gas. The heat of the discharge vaporises the sodium and after about ten minutes or so, the vapour fills the tube. The colour of the light emitted changes from the neon red to orange. Because the sodium is at a very low pressure, it will not vaporise if the tube is cooled in any way. To prevent this, the tube is enclosed in a double-glass jacket, with an evacuated space which conserves the tube's heat. When in operation the running voltage falls to between 100 and 150V, depending on lamp size. The transformer used has a high leakage reactance so that no current-limiting device is needed, such as in other discharge-lamp circuits. Because of the danger of the sodium vapour condensing on the electrodes of the lamp when it is cooling down after being switched off, these lamps are usually designed for operation in a horizontal or near-horizontal position. Lamp sizes vary from 45 to 200W, the latter being a recent development in a corrugated linear form instead of the more familiar U-shape. The lamp circuit has a power-factor correction capacitor to improve its overall power-factor. The lamp will start immediately whether it is hot or cold. Care is necessary in disposing of used sodium lamps, because metallic sodium may burn if it comes into contact with moisture or water.

High-pressure mercury-vapour lamp

This type of lamp is used for street- and road-lighting, floodlighting and lighting industrial premises. The light emitted is bluish-green in colour. There are several types of HPMV lamp.

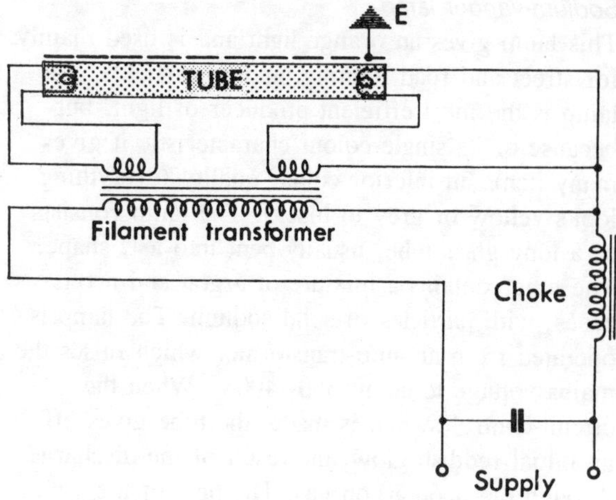

Figure 12.5. 'Instant-start' circuit for a fluorescent lamp (double-wound transformer).

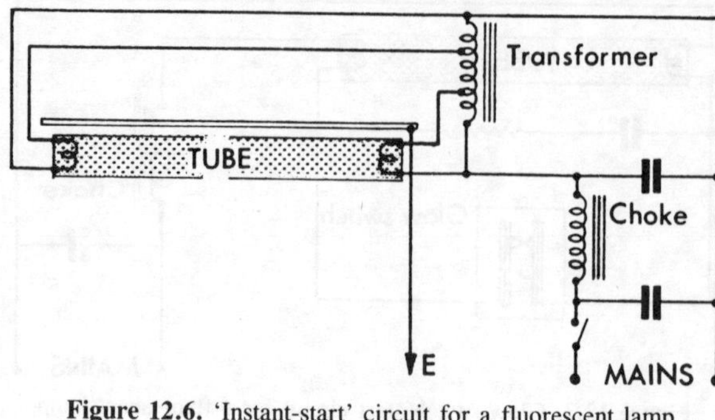

Figure 12.6. 'Instant-start' circuit for a fluorescent lamp (auto-transformer).

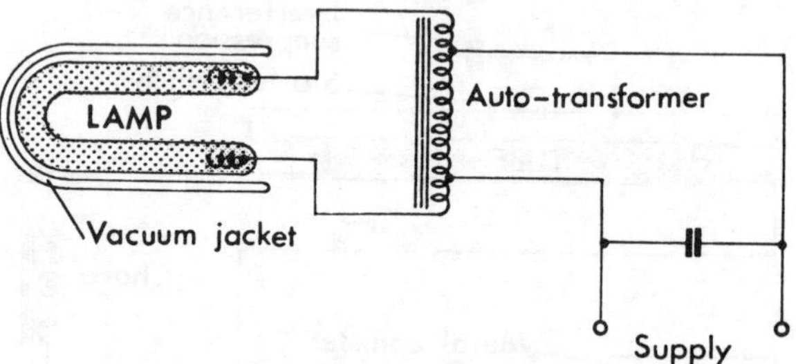

Figure 12.7. Circuit diagram of sodium-vapour lamp.

They are classed according to the loading per centimetre of arc length. The lamp consists of an inner bulb or lamp proper made of special silicate glass to withstand the high temperature of the arc, surrounded by an outer glass bulb. This arrangement prevents the loss of heat from the inner bulb and also the emission of unwanted ultra-violet radiation. The space between the two bulbs is either evacuated or filled with an inert gas. The inner bulb has sealed into it three electrodes, the main electrodes at each end and a third, or starting electrode, adjacent to one of the main electrodes. The lamp contains a tiny globule of liquid mercury and argon gas at low pressure. The starting electrode is connected to the main electrode farthest from it by a high resistance of the order of 50k-ohms. The electrodes are special electron-emitting cathodes, coated with oxide. When the circuit-control switch is made, the mains voltage appears across the tip of the starting electrode and its adjacent main electrode. A discharge takes place through the argon gas. The heat from this discharge gradually vaporises the mercury globules. The vapour carries the discharge along the lamp tube until the main discharge takes place between the main lamp electrodes. The lamp takes about five minutes to reach its full light output. The current taken by the discharge is limited by a choke connected in series with the lamp. The circuit is provided with a power-factor correction capacitor. As the lamp heats up, the internal pressure increases to about 20 atmospheres in the larger sizes of lamp with a loading of 100W/cm of arc length. After switching off, these lamps will not restart until they have cooled down. The lamps are operated in a vertical or horizontal position, depending on type. The suffixes V, H and U (universal) are used to indicate the method of mounting.

Special lamps

There are special lamps available for particular duties. One such is a recent development: the quartz-iodine lamp, in which iodine vapour is used to control the rate of evaporation of the filament material, thus prolonging its life. This type of lamp is smaller than other types of filament lamp, though the problem of heat dissipation is greatly increased. Usually the metal housing of the lamp fitting is of finned construction, and the terminal chamber for cable entry is partially separated from the main housing. The main application of this lamp is for floodlighting. The reflectors used are protected by toughened glass, because there can be

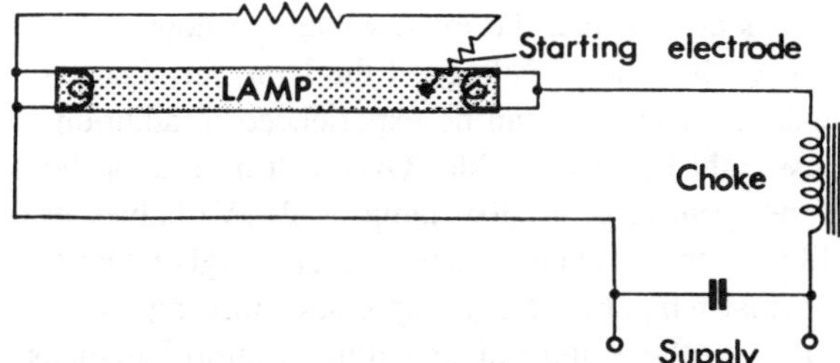

Figure 12.8. Circuit diagram for a high-pressure mercury-vapour lamp.

a considerable difference in temperature between the edge and the centre.

Another lamp is the super high-pressure mercury vapour. It has a very high efficiency and is of very small size. A 70W lamp is less than 5 cm long and has an efficiency of about 40 ℓm/W. The light produced is almost white. The arc tube is of quartz and is cooled by being placed in a jacket containing running water.

Flash lamps of the xenon-gas type are used for photographic work and for the stroboscopic illuminators used for investigation and test purposes. The discharge through the gas is produced by a large capacitor discharging its held charge; the resultant light produced is extremely bright and white.

The mercury/tungsten blended lamp consists of a quartz mercury discharge tube with a series-connected tungsten filament which acts both as a light source and as a ballast-resistance controlling the current in the discharge tube and making it independent of external gear. The combination of blue-green light from the mercury discharge and the reddish-yellow light from the tungsten produces a better colour than the mercury-vapour lamp alone. This lamp has a very long life.

Practical aspects of lighting

Though many aspects of lighting or illumination are the special concern of the qualified lighting engineer, there are some which also affect, either directly or indirectly, the electrician. These aspects are dealt with in the following sections.

Ambient temperature of lamps

The recent development in lamp sizes and the increase in ratings used in domestic, commercial and industrial installations has led to problems resulting from the heat generated by these lamps. If a 1000W lamp is operated in an ambient temperature of 25 °C, the temperature rise can be greater than 60 °C. This means that if the lighting point is a pendant, the flexible cord will be in an ambient temperature of 85 °C. It has always been accepted that, owing to such high temperatures near the lamp-holders, embrittlement of the insulation of the cord will occur, with consequent shortening of the life of the cord. The trend in recent years has been to manufacture lamps smaller in size than that of the equivalent wattage previously made, so that it has become possible to use a higher wattage lamp in an existing type of fitting. For instance, whereas in the past temperatures in enclosed fittings may have been as high as 80 °C or so, it is now possible for temperatures to be as high as 130 °C and even more where the ambient temperature is also high.

The IEE Regulations have recognised this problem of heat from lamps and now recommend that the choice of a flexible cord for a particular lighting duty should be based, not only on current rating, but on the ambient temperature likely to be encountered at a lighting point. Certain new heat-resisting materials are now available.

Conductors for very high temperatures are now nickel-plated copper, instead of the usual tinned-copper; some conductors are natural copper and are associated with thermoplastic insulating materials such as polythene and polyvinyl chloride (PVC). The greatest advances have been made with insulating materials. Natural rubber is now limited to use where the temperatures do not exceed 65 °C. Above this limit the rubber becomes hard and the life of a cord may be as little as a year or so. Inspection of rubber insulation which has become hard during service has shown that it may still function as an insulator provided the cable is not fixed.

Polyethylene (polythene) has many electrical properties. But it is a thermoplastic material and deforms seriously under pressure and excessive heat. At about 110 °C there is a sharp melting point when severe flow may take place with consequential electrical failure. This type of cable is not used in lamp fittings. PVC has excellent age-resisting properties, but has a low maximum operating temperature of 70 °C. This type is also not used for lamp fittings, unless the ventilation is adequate.

Butyl-rubber insulation is suitable for lamp fittings where higher ambient temperatures are prevalent. The maximum permitted operating temperature is 85 °C. At this temperature, the cable has a long life. At higher temperatures the insulation deteriorates rapidly. Around 130 °C it turns to powder. Silicone rubber can be operated continuously at 150 °C, and is used for many of the enclosed lamp fittings installed at the present time. The physical properties of this type of insulation are such that a suitable protection is necessary and a heat-resisting braid is normal for this purpose. Glass braiding with a heat-resisting lacquer is an excellent finish, but makes an expensive cable. An alternative is terylene braiding, which is considered ideally suitable for many lamp fittings. Another good heat-resistant type of finish is an impregnated glass lapping with an impregnated glass braid. The temperature of operation of this type of cable may be as high as 180 °C. For enclosed lamp fittings, where temperatures of this order are obtained, this cable is a suitable answer.

Two sheathing materials which are used widely in installations are chlorosulphonated polyethylene (CPS or 'Hypalon') and PVC/nitrile rubber (NCR/PVC) generally known as HOFR insulants. These materials are both vulcanisable rubbers and besides having good weathering, solvent and oil resistance, are flame retardant. They may be compounded so as to be used over an insulated conductor operating at 85 °C. Another new product which appears suitable, particularly for insulation, is ethylene propylene rubber. The age-resistance of this material is proving excellent and may well prove to be a common material in the near future.

The effect of voltage drop

The voltage applied to a lamp is reduced if the actual voltage at the lamp terminals is lower than the rated lamp voltage. Generally, the reduction in light output is more rapid than the reduction of the wattage. It is therefore not economical to run lamps at less than the rated voltage. Another aspect of reduced voltage at the lamp terminals is that financial loss can be experienced in addition to less light being available. Over-volting a lamp by 5 per cent (e.g. a 230V lamp on 242V) halves its life, as the filament is operated at a higher than normal temperature and vaporises more rapidly. On the other hand, under-volting a lamp lengthens its life but reduces its light output without a corresponding reduction in the wattage consumed. Electricity, in effect, is being run to waste.

Voltage drop can also occur as a result of the lighting cables being too small for the current carried. This situation may arise when old wiring is allowed to supply new lamp fittings which contain lamps with higher wattage ratings. In fact, in many modern commercial and industrial premises it is often found that with high-wattage lamps being used and long circuit runs, cables larger than the usual 1, 1.5 and 2.5 mm^2 are necessary.

Faults in discharge lamps

Because of their associated circuitry, containing components such as starters, chokes and capacitors, and transformers, discharge lamps may fail or fault, to show certain symptoms which can be useful in any diagnosis by the electrician sent to investigate the fault. The following is summarised information on different lamp types.

Mercury lamps. One of the first points to note about these lamps is that they require up to 5 minutes to cool before re-ignition can take place. In factory situations lamps are often extinguished because of voltage 'dips'. If a lamp fails to re-ignite after cooling, the ballast should be checked for over-heating and continuity. If the lamp is nearing the end of its life it will fail to re-strike and should be replaced. If the lamp delivers a poor light output, the choke should be checked for continuity. In some circuits, parallel chokes are used and their currents should be equal. However, one type of 700W circuit uses dissimilar chokes. Some types of lamp may suffer from 'thermal shock' as the result of cold water, e.g. rain, falling onto the hot glass envelopes. Cracked lamps (perhaps the result of damage in transit) will operate until the internal pressure falls to atmospheric when the arc tube will fail. Excessive pressure used when screwing lamps in their holders also produces faults resulting in eventual lamp failure. If the light output is unstable, a possible cause could be poor contact in the lampholder (look for signs or arcing on the cap centre contact).

Low-pressure sodium lamps. The output voltage from the lamp transformer is important and should be in the region of 480V for most types of lamp (650V for the 135W and 150W SOX lamp). An unstable light output indicates the lamp is nearing the end of its life and should be replaced. Starter switches are a source of trouble and should be changed (on the 60W and 200W linear lamps). Voltages should be checked at the lampholders but note that this technique will not apply to switch-start circuits because volts will only appear intermittently as the switch operates and this could generate peak voltages of up to 1.5kV, which will not register on a meter.

Compact-source iodide. If this type of lamp does not light check for the supply voltage appearing at the lampholder terminals. If no volts are indicated this could mean an open-circuit choke or capacitor. The relay should vibrate on closing the starter switch. It should be noted that the starting circuit produces pulses of up to 9kV and cannot be properly tested except with special equipment. Poor light output could indicate the lamp nearing the end of its life. In the case of the 400W lamp, the choke might be short-circuited; in the 1000W lamp circuit, one of the three parallel chokes could be open-circuited.

Linear metal halide (MBIL). If the lamp does not work, the transformer output should be tested (*Note:* the transformer open-circuit volts are well over 1kV). The continuity of the transformer winding and leads should be checked, as also should the lampholder for loose connections.

Metal halide (*MBI and MBIF*). Initial checks for failure of the lamp to operate should be made for open-circuit in the ballast. The open-circuit voltage of the choke is about 570V. The capacitor function is important; in the 400W twin-choke type of circuit, if the voltage at the lampholder is low (it should be just over 400V), the capacitor could be open-circuited. Note that a safety thermal cutout is used in ballast-type lamps; this could be open-circuited with a high ambient temperature condition, and after running with a failed lamp. Nearly half an hour must be allowed for resetting before trying another lamp. In the 400W choke ignitor circuit, the cable length between the choke and the lamp should not exceed 33 m.

Maintenance

Immediately a lighting installation is put into service it begins to deteriorate. A film of dust or dirt begins to reduce the transparency or reflecting power of all the exposed surfaces of lamps, fittings, and the walls and ceiling of a room. This process, if unchecked, may result in the level of illumination falling very low in a comparatively short time. Only thorough and periodic cleaning of lighting equipment and attention to room decorations can maintain the performance of the installation at a reasonably high average value. Generally, a maintenance factor is applied. The general figure is 0.8. This means that in planning the amount of illumination required for a particular installation, the light in lumens must be divided by 0.8 to allow for a decrease in light output caused by dust, etc. Very dirty situations may have a maintenance factor of 0.6 applied to them.

Maintenance of lighting installations also involves the replacement of lamps which have either failed or have suffered reductions in their light output. Labour costs generally determine whether such lamps should be replaced individually as they fail, or by group replacement. In a recent questionnaire, the following average total labour costs were revealed:

Individual lamp replacement – £3.00 per lamp
Group lamp replacement – 50p per lamp
Cleaning of a lamp fitting – £1.50 per lamp

Planning lighting installations

Though the efficient planning of a lighting installation is the job of the lighting engineer, the electrician is sometimes called on to advise in the lighting requirements of small premises. Once the decision for lighting has been made, and the type of lamp and fitting settled, the remainder of the initial planning is largely a matter of simple mathematics in conjunction with the 'lumen' method of design. This is based on theory and the practical results obtained in experimental rooms in which all the factors which affect illumination were variable at will. The mounting height of fittings can be settled within close limits, for they are mounted either directly on the ceiling or suspended from it. Generally, it is usual to adopt a rectangular layout of the light sources, the fittings being spaced at equal distances apart in each direction whenever possible.

The number of lumens required on the working plane is equal to the product of the area of the working plane in square feet and the lumen/ft^2 desired. The lumens provided by the lamps must, however, be greater than this figure to allow for depreciation of the installation owing to dust and dirt on the lamps and their fittings. The following formula is generally used:

$$F = \frac{E \times A}{C \times M}$$

where F = the lumens required per lamp
E = the average ℓm/m^2 required in service
A = area per fitting in square feet
C = coefficient of utilisation
M = maintenance factor.

The coefficient of utilisation represents the proportion of the light emitted by the lamp that actually reaches the working plane, and is dependent on the size of the room, height of the fittings, colour of the walls and ceiling, and the type of fitting used. An average value is about 0.6. The maintenance factor is taken on average as 0.8.

Up to a point, the eyes function better the more light they receive. Beyond that point glare supervenes. At least 150 lm/m^2 should be provided for adequate visual performance on rough or unskilled work. Up to 1,500 lm/m^2 should be provided for difficult or fine work.

Light measurements
The instrument used to measure the amount of light falling on a surface is the photoelectric photometer. This consists of a photoelectric cell made up of a layer of selenium coated onto a steel base-plate. A film of gold is formed over the selenium and is so thin that any light which falls on the cell will penetrate the gold layer to release electrons inside the selenium. These electrons then flow to the gold layer giving it a negative charge. The cell is coupled to a sensitive micro-ammeter whose scale is marked off in ℓm/m^2. The greater the amount of light falling on the cell the greater will be the voltage (ℓm/m^2) recorded.

Economic factors of light sources
Because lamps are consumable devices, both the initial and replacement lamp costs are treated as running costs, and not as overhead charges. For comparative purposes, costs are calculated on a lumen-hour basis:

$$C = \frac{1{,}000}{F}\left(\frac{C_l}{h} + (C_e \times P)\right)$$

where C = total running cost in pence per million lumen-hours

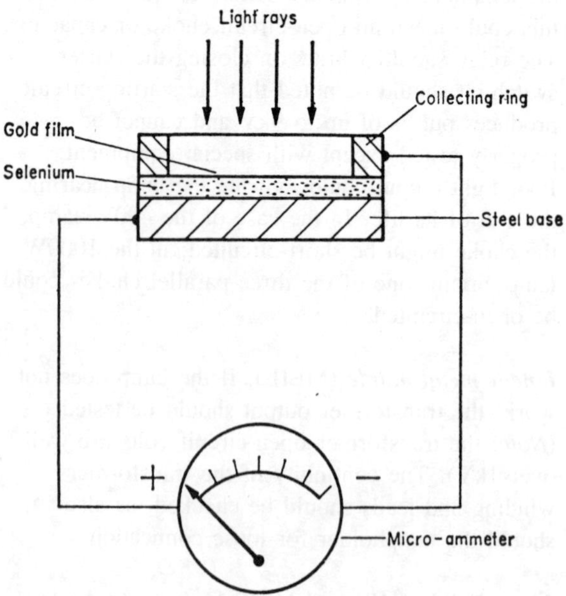

Figure 12.9. The photoelectric photometer or light meter.

C_l = total cost of all lamps in pence
C_e = cost of current in pence per unit (kWh)
F = total lumen output of all lamps
h = lamp life in thousands of hours
P = total lighting wattage.

When calculating C_e, allowance must be made for any kilowatt or maximum demand charges, divided by the estimated annual burning hours.

Light control

Most sources radiate light in all directions, and are too brilliant to be viewed comfortably. The light must therefore be controlled to direct it where it is required and to soften its brilliance. All substances absorb some of the light which strikes or passes through them. All substance also reflect some of the light falling on them, or transmit it, or both. Reflection of light may be of three kinds:

(*a*) *Specular reflection.* When light strikes a mirror-like surface it is reflected at the same angle and in the same plane as it strikes. The type of reflection is much used for the precise control of light, e.g. car head-lamps, silvered shop-window reflectors. Accidental specular reflection is generally unwanted, e.g. lighting fittings reflected in glossy table tops. A mirror-like surface can look dark even though a great deal of light is striking it, and vice versa. Its appearance depends only on what is mirrored in its surface from the particular viewpoint concerned. The streakiness sometimes obtained from specular reflection is avoided by breaking up the reflector surface by ripples, flutes or dimples, by giving it a 'satin' finish, by using a pearl (or otherwise obscured) type of lamp, or by using a moulded or lightly frosted glass cover to the lamp fitting.

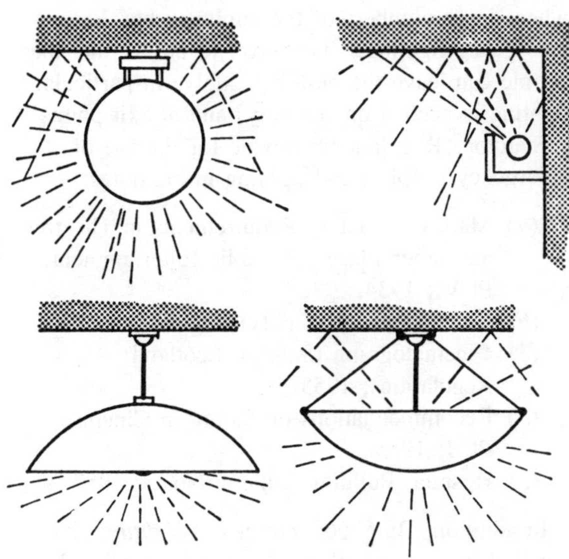

Figure 12.10. Typical lighting arrangements and methods of reflection used to obtain direct and indirect lighting.

(*b*) *Diffuse reflection.* This is the reflection obtained from a perfectly matt surface, the distribution of the reflected light being independent of the direction of the incident light. The distribution of reflected light follows the cosine law, i.e. the intensity in any direction is proportional to the cosine of the angle between that direction and the perpendicular to the surface. A surface having this characteristic appears equally bright whatever the direction of view. White blotting paper and whitewash are nearly perfect diffuse reflectors. Diffuse reflection is useless for the precise control of light, but it can be used to reflect light in a general direction.

(*c*) *Spread reflection.* Depolished metals and satin-finished mirrored surfaces have reflection characteristics between specular and diffuse. Vitreous and synthetic enamels are widely used for the reflecting surfaces of lighting fittings. Vitreous enamel is the more hard-wearing.

Stroboscopic effects. When discharge lamps operate on alternating current systems, their light output varies in each cycle and this produces certain effects. These are rarely very troublesome, but it is sometimes necessary to take certain precautions to minimise them. The cyclic variation in the light output is not normally perceptible with lamps operating on a 50 Hz (cycles per second) supply, since it occurs at twice the frequency of the mains. However, it can give rise to stroboscopic effects where the true speed of rotating machinery or other objects is not immediately apparent and they can appear to be slowed down or even stationary. The means of overcoming this stroboscopic effect are easy to

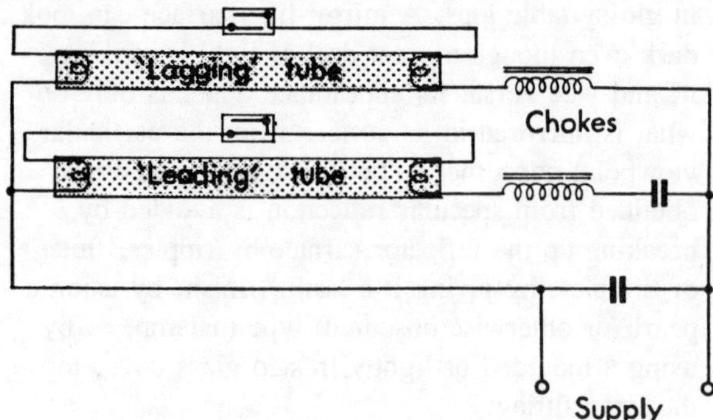

Figure 12.11. Circuit diagram of two fluorescent lamps to reduce stroboscopic effects.

provide in circuitry, and should be used where there is any possibility that accidents may result from misjudgment of machine speed.

Apart from the stroboscopic effect, this flicker from tubular fluorescent lamps may be a source of optical annoyance. This flicker arises from half-wave rectification in the lamps or from the random movement of hot-spots on the lamp electrodes. Flicker is also apparent at the extreme ends of fluorescent lamps and is caused by the fact that a small part of the discharge emits radiation only during one-half of a complete cycle. This fluctuation, which occurs at mains frequency, may be overcome by fitting opaque shields over the lamp ends, or by other methods which screen the ends of the lamp from direct view.

One method used to eliminate or minimise stroboscopic effect is the connection of every second lamp in a pair of fluorescents in series with a capacitor, to change the phase of the second lamp's circuit. The circuit is usually known as a lead/lag circuit and is shown in Figure 12.11. Another method is to use banks of fluorescent lamps supplied from a three-phase, four-wire supply, where each bank of lamps is connected to each phase wire and neutral to give a balanced three-phase lighting load.

Operation of fluorescents on dc supplies. By omitting the power-factor correction capacitor and inserting a suitable current-limiting resistor in the circuit instead of a choke, fluorescent lamps can be operated on dc supplies. A polarity-reversing switch is necessary in the circuit so that the lamp can be operated as required to prevent the tube darkening at one end. For caravans and mobile stores, and buses having 12V dc supplies, there are available transistor circuits for 'mini-lamps'. The most important point to observe in this type of circuit is that the polarity is correct, otherwise damage to the transistor may result. Similarly, for emergency supplies there has been developed a range of invertors, converting 110V or 220V dc supply from an emergency battery to 220V 50/60 Hz ac. These invertors have no moving parts and require no maintenance.

Emergency lighting. Emergency lighting is lighting which is provided as supplementary to the main lighting provisions of a building. This provision is essential in buildings where work is in progress or where large numbers of people are gathered, in, for example, a theatre. Again, an emergency supply is essential in hospitals, particularly for those services (operating theatres, blood banks, etc.) which depend on electricity. The risk of accident is particularly great in industrial premises. Moreover, many industrial processes require that certain precautions, such as closing valves, opening switches or starting standby equipment, be taken whenever the mains supply fails. In buildings where large numbers of the public gather, emergency lighting is necessary to ensure that the people can leave the building safely. In particular, lighting is needed on stairways and at exit points.

Statutory Regulations provide for the use of emergency supplies and lighting in buildings:

(*a*) Manual of Safety Requirements in Theatres and other Places of Public Entertainment, Pt VI; 1934.
(*b*) Cinematograph (Safety) Regulations;1955.
(*c*) Cinematograph (Safety) (Scotland) Regulations; 1955.
(*d*) Recommendations on Safety in Cinemas, Pt. I; 1955.
(*e*) Hospital Building Bulletin No. 1; 1957.

In addition, BS 5266 *Emergency Lighting* gives detailed information about the provision of such circuits in premises.

Lamp characteristics

Lamp type	*Watts*	*Approx. loss in gear (watts)*	*Rated life (hours)*	*Average light output throughout life (lumens)*
Tungsten filament	300	—	1,000	4,300
	500	—	1,000	7,700
	1,000	—	1,000	17,300
Mercury (bulb)	400	25	5,000	20,000
Fluorescent (MBF/U)	1,000	50	5,000	48,000
Mercury (bulb)	250	—	3,000	4,400
Tungsten (MBT/U)	500	—	3,000	9,500
Fluorescent tube (hot-cathode)	80	15	5,000	4,600
			5,000	4,480
			5,000	3,360
			5,000	3,040
Fluorescent tube (cold cathode)	67.5	10	15,000	2,000–3,000
Tungsten-iodine	—	—	—	—
Sodium	140	20	6,000	13,000

Efficiency in lm/W, including gear	*Colour*	*Remarks*
14	Too little blue; too much red; used for normal lighting needs	Low initial cost
15		
17		
44	Improved colour rendering compared with uncorrected mercury lamp	
46		
18	Improved colour rendering	No control gear required
19		
49	White (1)	(1) All applications where colour rendering is not important. (2) Used where a blend with natural daylight is needed. (3) Good all-purpose lamp. (4) Similar to north-sky daylight
47	Daylight (2)	
35	Natural colour (3)	
32	Colour matching (4)	
25-35	Similar to hot-cathode tubes	—
22		
100	Yellow. Inferior colour quality	SON types give a brilliant white with yellow content

13 Cells and batteries

An electric cell is a device in which a chemical is converted into electrical energy. The basic principle is that an electrical pressure (emf) exists whenever a metal is immersed in a chemical solution, that is, there is a source of electrical energy available between the metal plate and the solution (the electrolyte). If two dissimilar pieces of metal (the electrodes) are placed in the same electrolyte and are kept apart, an emf will appear between them. If the metal electrodes are joined outside the electrolyte, the cell emf will drive a current round the completed circuit so formed. The energy driving the current is derived from the chemical action which takes place between one electrode and the electrolyte. In the class of cells known as 'primary' cells, the energy is available from the chemical ingredients. In the class of cells known as 'secondary', the chemical ingredients undergo a chemical change during the passage through them of a direct current. The cell thus becomes 'charged' and will, when an external circuit is completed, deliver a quantity of electrical energy. The secondary cell can be charged and discharged over an indefinite period. To renew a primary cell, the chemical ingredients must be replaced.

Primary cells

The most common primary cell known today is the Leclanché cell, named after its inventor who, in 1868, produced a cell so practical in its elementary form that only recently have scientists been able to devise improved forms to better Leclanché's original cell. The two dissimilar materials used in the Leclanché cell are carbon (the positive or anode) and zinc (the negative or cathode). The electrolyte is sal ammoniac or ammonium chloride. The carbon is in the form of a rod and is surrounded by a mixture of manganese dioxide and carbon. During the continuous discharge of the cell, hydrogen is deposited on the cathode and is oxidised to water by the manganese dioxide until the latter is reduced to a point where the cell virtually ceases to function. If the discharge is discontinued, the depolarising agent in the cell (the manganese dioxide) continues to act until the hydrogen is fully reduced and the emf returns to normal again.

The Leclanché cell is used either 'wet' or 'dry'. In the former category, the cell comprises a positive pole (a manganese dioxide/carbon agglomerate or absorbent charcoal block), and a negative pole of zinc, either in the form of a rod, bent sheet plate or casting. These are contained in a glass jar for the electrolyte (sal ammoniac or caustic soda) in which both electrodes are stood in such a manner that their immersed portions do not come into contact with each other. The 'dry' cell has a zinc case which acts as the negative pole of the cell; the positive pole is a carbon rod mixed with manganese dioxide. The electrolyte consists of a wet paste of starch, sal ammoniac and zinc chloride. The case is surrounded by a cardboard cylinder. The top of the cell is filled with pitch or other sealing material. A vent is provided for the

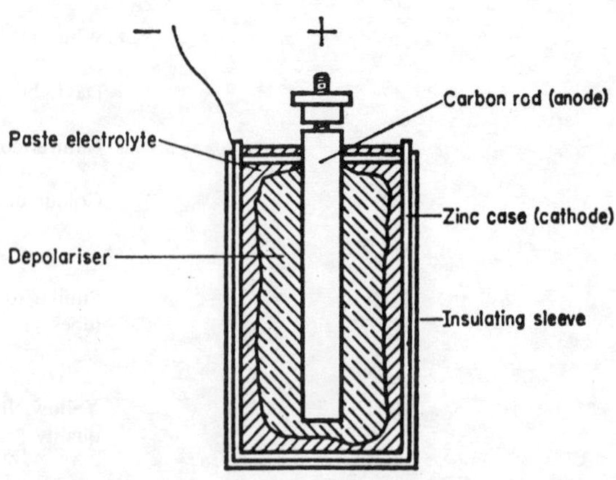

Figure 13.1. Dry Leclanché cell.

escape of hydrogen gas. A modified dry cell is known as the 'inert' cell, because the paste electrolyte is replaced by a dry mixture of sal ammoniac crystals and gum. The cell is rendered active only when required and by the addition of water through vents provided.

The emf available from the wet cell is 1.6 V, though this is reduced by the internal resistance of the cell's components to 1.35 V. The internal resistance is about 1 ohm. The dry-cell emf is 1.5 V when new, but falls quickly to about 1.4 V which is maintained almost to the end of the cell-life. The internal resistance is low, from about 0.1 to 0.3 ohm.

Primary-cell applications

Primary cells, particularly the Leclanché type, find wide use in many fields: telephone and telegraphic circuits, railway signalling, telephone and telegraphic equipment, and in domestic applications for portable torches, tools, and other appliances. The capacity of life obtained from a primary cell depends on the duty it is called on to perform. Generally, the Leclanché is put to intermittent duty, where the discharge currents are no more than 1 A, and then for a short time. Typical discharge currents range from 10 to 500 mA. The cells are most often used as batteries in certain series or parallel connections to deliver a stated voltage. A cell or battery on intermittent service yields a higher ampere-hour capacity than if it were placed on continuous discharge duty. Again, the smaller the current drawn from the cell or battery, be it either on continuous or intermittent service, the greater will be its ampere-hour capacity.

So far as battery economics are concerned, these cells have a relatively low cost per watt-hour. In particular the wet and inert types are free from deterioration in storage. Maintenance attention is increased where the cells are operated in high ambient temperatures, when evaporation of the electrolyte is rapid. This results in the deposition of salts and the eventual creepage of the solution over the top of the jar. With the Leclanché and other types of wet cells, the most important precaution to be observed is to avoid spilling the electrolyte onto the top of the electrodes or near to the top edge of the container. This will cause the salts to 'creep' and result in subsequent trouble by providing a conducting path for leakage currents between adjoining cells. The dry cell is dearer than its wet counterpart.

Some Leclanché cells on the market have air-depolarising carbon units. These cells depend for their polarising properties on the mixing of the depolarising gases with the oxygen in the air within the pores of an absorbent block of specially prepared carbon which acts as the positive pole. The main feature of this type of cell is that, unlike the usual Leclanché cells, the internal resistance does not rise throughout the working life of the cell. This means that the terminal voltage is virtually constant. These cells must work in ambient conditions which allow free access to fresh air. There are two types of cell: the sal ammoniac and the caustic soda. The first type has a carbon block which remains chemically unchanged throughout its life, so that its internal resistance and terminal voltage remain practically constant. The caustic soda cell uses caustic soda as the electrolyte.

Secondary cells

There are two types of secondary cell in use: the lead-acid and the nickel-alkaline. The advantage of the secondary cell is that it has a low internal resistance and can deliver large currents. With care in use, the secondary cell can be discharged and charged over an indefinite period of time.

The lead-acid cell

The cell consists of either a pair or two sets of lead plates immersed in a solution of dilute sulphuric acid. If a direct current is passed through the cell, chemical changes occur at each plate. The plate connected to the positive terminal of the supply becomes coated with lead peroxide. The negative plate becomes spongy lead. Lead sulphate is removed from each plate and dissolves in the acid to increase the strength (or specific gravity) of the acid. On discharge, the chemical energy stored in the cell is delivered to an external circuit as electrical energy. During the discharge, both plates tend to turn into lead sulphate and the acid strength drops. In practice, the cell is assumed to be fully discharged when the terminal voltage falls to about 1.85 V. The charged voltage at the terminals is about 2.2 V, falling to a constant 2 V during discharge. As the cell approaches the end of the discharge period, the voltage falls rapidly to 1.85 V

Lead-acid cell applications

In recent years there has been a rapid increase in the use of the lead-acid cell for a wide range of applications. Motor-car and commercial vehicles account for the larger share of battery uses. The following are an indication of the widespread use of the cell. The first British model of a battery-powered lawn-mower appeared in 1960; over 30,000 mowers are in operation today. The reason for its popularity is the absence of fumes associated with the petrol-driven model of mower and the shock risk and cable nuisance of the mains-operated models. The cost of running the battery mower is about 1p per hour. Other horticultural equipment now operated from lead-acid batteries includes hedge-cutters, spraying equipment and cultivators.

For portable supplies the lead-acid battery is used for film and television camera equipment on location, where generator vans are not a viable proposition or where good mobility is needed. Power tools and appliances are popular in America and are making a significant show on the British market. Since the development of transistor inverters, fluorescent lamps run from a dc source are now in use, particularly in public transport, ambulances, caravans and cabin cruisers. Transistorised bollard lighting units, powered by a 12 V battery, are used by police and highway authorities.

An important application of the lead-acid cell is for miner's lamps. Another is the provision of a standby supply in the event of a mains failure.

The nickel-alkaline cell

About the turn of the nineteenth century the nickel-alkaline cell was developed, quite independently, by Jungner in Sweden and Edison in America. Today, though the cell is widely known, it has not superseded the position of the lead-acid cell, though it has certain characteristics which give it superiority over the latter cell. The main advantages of nickel-alkaline cells include an exceptionally long life; no deterioration during prolonged storage, whatever the state of charge or discharge; minimal maintenance requirements; robust construction with the ability to withstand rough treatment and difficult service conditions; high efficiency of output; and a wide range of operating temperatures.

The two main types of alkaline cell are the nickel-cadmium and the nickel-iron.

The nickel-cadmium cell is the invention of Jungner. The positive mass consists of a mixture of nickel hydroxide and graphite, the latter ingredient being used to increase conductivity. The mixture is compressed into flat pellets and supported in channels made from perforated nickel-plated steel strip. The negative mass is similarly supported cadmium powder, usually with an admixture of iron or nickel.

The nickel-iron cell was invented by Edison. In this cell the positive mass is supported in perforated nickel-plated steel tubes, the nickel hydroxide being interleaved with many transverse layers of very thin nickel flakes produced by a special process. The negative mass is mainly iron and the electrode construction is either that of pocket-plate cells or a pressed and sintered plate incorporating copper powder. The electrolyte is potassium hydrate (caustic potash) in distilled water. The emf of these cells is about 1.2 V.

Battery maintenance

1. *Primary cells*. The maintenance requirements of primary cells are few. The electrolyte tends to creep up the sides of the glass jar and over its top, and that of the porous pot and then to crystallise. To prevent this the upper parts are painted with pitch or paraffin wax. The usual method is to apply a thin coating of petroleum jelly (Vaseline) or other similar grease. Wet cells require at least 24 hours soaking before they are ready for use. At all times the electrolyte should be kept away from the carbon head and terminal assemblies of these cells. This is best done by ensuring that the hands are quite dry and

not contaminated with solution while handling the carbon electrodes. Care must always be taken when making up the electrolyte for caustic soda cells. No electrolyte should be allowed in contact with the inside glass surface within an area 5 cm from the lip.

2. *Lead-acid cells*. This type of cell requires considerable maintenance attention. Charging must be carried out at regular intervals whether the cell has been discharged or not. The electrolyte must also be maintained at the correct level and specific gravity. The electrolyte is 'topped' with distilled water. If the level of the electrolyte falls too low, to expose the plates, air will attack the plates causing hydration. Because of the hydrogen given off, the cell is explosive in certain mixtures of the gas with air, and certain precautions are required to be taken in battery rooms. These include adequate ventilation so that the gas can escape to atmosphere and the prohibition of naked lights, including smoking, in the battery room. The fumes from the cells are corrosive; thus any metal parts in the vicinity of the cells should be painted over with acid-resisting paint. The terminals of the cells should be coated with a thin film of petroleum jelly to prevent their corrosion. The exterior of the cells should be kept clean and dry.

   The state of charge or discharge of the lead-acid cell is determined by either a voltmeter or a hydrometer. The voltmeter should have a high resistance. The reading should be about 2.2 V for a healthy cell. The specific gravity of the electrolyte should be between 1.20 and 1.25. The state of health of the cell can also be seen by the colour of the plates: the positive plate, when the cell is charged, is a dark chocolate brown, while the negative plate is a grey.

   It is important to note that the ambient temperature will affect the specific gravity of the electrolyte. An increase in temperature results in a lowering of the specific gravity. The reduction is about 1° specific gravity for each 2 °C rise. In a similar way the specific gravity will rise for a fall in temperature.

   If a cell or battery is to be taken out of use, the electrolyte must not be removed, after the battery has been fully charged. Periodic charging, by passing a small current through the battery, will keep it in a healthy condition until it is called for duty again.

3. *Nickel-alkaline cells*. In open-type batteries, periodic topping-up with distilled water is needed to replace that lost by evaporation and electrolysis. With nickel-cadmium batteries, the loss is very small, provided there is correct voltage adjustment of the charging equipment. Very occasionally, replacement of the electrolyte may also be required, as the result of carbonation from the atmosphere. Nickel-iron cells should be discharged and short-circuited when they are out of service for long periods. Cells which are completely sealed require no maintenance.

Summary of cell characteristics

(*a*) *Leclanché cell with sal ammoniac electrolyte*. Internal resistance increases as discharge proceeds. EMF: 1.5 V. Terminal volts about 1.35 V. Discharge currents range from 10 to 500 mA; higher currents are available for very short periods. Internal resistance averages about 1.5 ohms.

(*b*) *Leclanché cell with caustic soda electrolyte*. Internal resistance is constant over cell life. EMF is 1.4 V minimum.

(*c*) *Leclanché dry cell*. Internal resistance from 0.1 to 0.3 ohm. EMF is 1.5 V, falling to 1.4 V for the rest of the life of the cell.

(*d*) *Lead-acid cell*. Average emf is 2.2 V. Efficiency (ampere hours) 85–90 per cent. Specific gravity (fully charged): 1.250. Watt-hour efficiency 70–75 per cent. Discharge voltage, 1.85 V minimum. Specific gravity on discharge is 1.100.

(*e*) *Alkaline cell*. Average emf is 1.2 V. Efficiency (ampere hours) is 75–80 per cent. Efficiency (watt hour) is 60–65 per cent. Specific gravity during charge and discharge remains approximately constant at 1.170. EMF during discharge is 1.1 V. The internal resistance is 0.2–0.9 ohm.

Battery-charging

The primary duty of all cells and batteries is discharging. Secondary cells require recharging generally at a rate which exceeds the discharge rate by about 10 per cent. The normal charge rate is chosen so as to restore a fully discharged battery to a state of full charge in ten hours. A rate equal to half-normal is widely used when more time is available.

Lead-acid cell charging when carried out at the 10-hour rate will raise the emf of a cell from 1.8 to 2.2 V in about 6 hours, after which the emf rises rapidly to about 2.7 V. When the cell is nearly fully charged, it gases freely, liberating hydrogen and oxygen at the negative and positive poles respectively. At the same time the specific gravity rises to about 1.350. After disconnecting the charging source, the emf falls to about 2.2 V. The charging voltage must always be above the 2.7 V per cell.

Alkaline cells, though sometimes charged at the ten-hour rate, are more often charged at the 7-hour rate. During the first five hours the emf rises slowly from 1.3 to 1.5 V, then rises rapidly to 1.7 V at which value it remains constant during the remainder of the charging period. The charging voltage is about 1.8 V and above.

Charging methods

There are four methods of charging cells and batteries:

(*a*) constant-current (Figure 13.2);
(*b*) constant-voltage (Figure 13.2);
(*c*) trickle;
(*d*) floating.

(*a*) *Constant-current*. In this method the charging current is held constant by means of a variable resistance in the charging circuit. The current is maintained at the same value irrespective of the rise in emf of the cell.

(*b*) *Constant-voltage*. In this method of charging the voltage is maintained at a value which is slightly in excess of the emf of a fully charged cell. At the beginning of the charging period, the current is large. During the charging process the current falls as the emf of the cell rises to approach the charging voltage (Figure 13.3).

(*c*) *Trickle*. This method uses a very small current (usually of the order of milliamperes) which is passed continuously through a cell or battery to compensate for self-discharge, thus keeping it always healthy and in a fully charged state. The trickle charge current required to do this depends on temperature and other factors, but is always that which will keep a cell voltage at 2.25–2.3 V (lead-acid).

(*d*) *Floating system*. This is a charging method used where a small load is normally supplied by the charging equipment. It is used when the load cannot tolerate the margin between the trickle charge voltage and the discharge voltage. In this case the battery is 'floated' at about its open-

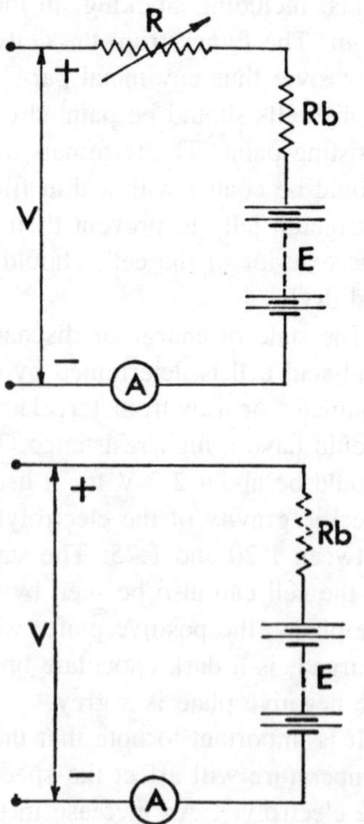

Figure 13.2. Constant-current and constant-voltage charging circuits.

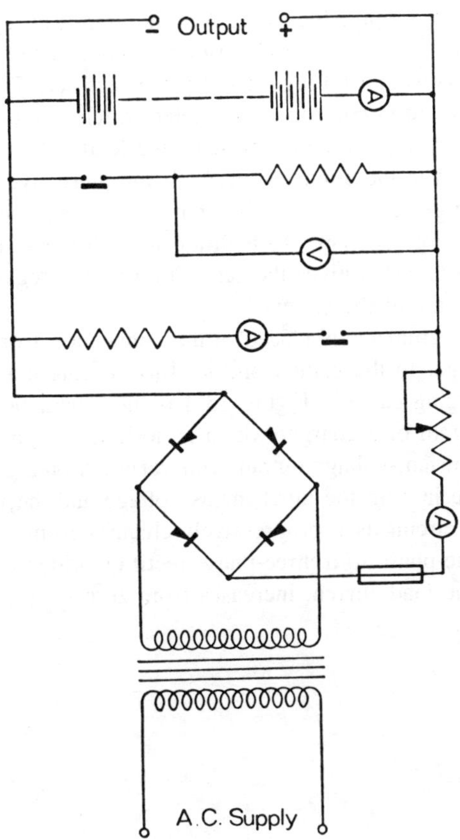

Figure 13.3. Circuit diagram for constant-voltage charging.

circuit (emf) voltage, 2.08 V per cell (lead-acid). There is thus no compensation for standing losses (self-discharge) and the battery must be given freshening charges at intervals.

Charging sources

1. *DC mains*. When charging cells from a dc mains supply, it is possible to connect a large number of cells to the charging source provided that all the cells require the same charging current. Since they are in series connection, the cells will all be charged at the same rate. The main disadvantage of this method is that if there are only one or two cells or batteries to charge, the same voltage is being used, resulting in uneconomical charging costs.

   The voltage of the dc mains can be reduced by inserting a series resistance arrangement, either lamps in parallel or a variable resistor. Generally carbon-filament lamps are used; a 32-cp (candlepower) lamp will pass a current of about 0.5 A on 230 V. The lamps can be inserted or removed to give a current variation in half-ampere steps. The variable resistor is simple in operation requiring only an adjustment to vary the current.
2. *Motor-generator set*. This method comprises a dc generator driven by either a dc or ac motor. The voltage output of the generator is chosen for the charging duty intended. These sets are often found in garages. The plant has an associated switchboard with one or more charging circuits with variable resistors and voltage outputs so that different batteries can be charged at different rates. The board comprises ammeters, voltmeters, and resistor adjustments.
3. *Rectifier*. By far the most popular and common method of charging is by a rectifier which operates from ac mains and gives a dc output. Rectifiers are obtainable with a wide range of output voltages and currents. Two points must be observed when using a rectifier battery-charger. First, it must not be overloaded. Second, care must be taken to see that the highest voltage from the cells or batteries in their fully charged condition does not exceed the rectifier output voltage.

Both lead-acid and alkaline batteries are used extensively for many duties, including emergency lighting in buildings (hospital theatres, cinemas, theatres) and standby supplies in power stations and substations (for operation of switchgear and protective equipment). Because of their long life, the Plante design of acid cells is common in this country. Plante plates are used, in preference to the 'pasted' plates which, although initially cheaper, have a shorter life. Alkaline batteries are sometimes favoured because of their robust construction and their ability to withstand over-charging and heavy discharge. They can also lie idle for long periods without deteriorating. Acid

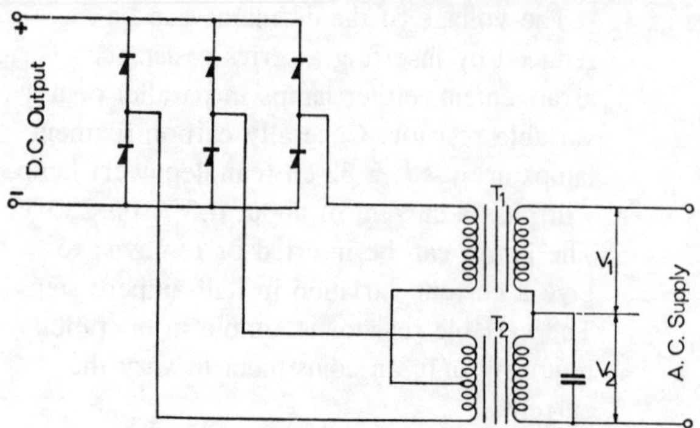

Figure 13.4. Circuit diagram of battery-charging equipment.

batteries are cheaper than their equivalent alkali type.

Both types of battery require maintenance. On-load voltages should be read, that is the voltage available when the full load is placed on the battery supply. Figure 13.4 is the circuit of a typical simple battery-charging equipment fed from ac mains and through a full-wave rectifier. The push-button controls a voltmeter which is shunted by a resistor which represents the load. The push-button in the ammeter circuit is an alternative arrangement in which the ammeter records the discharge current which flows through the series resistor. This gives the same information regarding the state of the battery.

An ammeter is placed in the connection from the charger to the battery and load to indicate the charging current. Figure 13.4 is the schematic diagram of a charger which is designed to provide a constant-voltage output with variation taking place in both the input mains voltage and the load. The circuit used progressively changes from a single-phase to a three-phase rectifier bridge circuit as the load current increases from zero to full load.

14 Extra-low voltage equipment

Though the electrician is mainly concerned with circuits which operate from a public mains supply, electrical work often involves circuitry which operates at extra-low voltage. 'Extra-low voltage' is defined as a voltage which does not exceed 50 V dc or 30 V ac. The circuits which operate at this voltage include bells, telephones, public-address systems, fire and burglar alarm systems, signalling and staff-location systems. Although the IEE Regulations are not specifically concerned with extra-low voltage systems and equipment, there are certain requirements which must be satisfied to ensure safety from fire risk. Because of the low voltages involved, the shock risk is minimal.

Bells and buzzers

These electromagnetic devices are used extensively in a wide range of applications where a sound is required to attract the attention of personnel to a situation or circumstance. There are three types of electric bell: the single-stroke, the trembler and the continuous-ringing.

The single-stroke bell sounds a single note and is used for signalling purposes (e.g. in buses and mines). When the electromagnet becomes energised, the armature and its striker is attracted, causing a movement which brings the striker against the gong. For correct operation of this bell, the bellpush must be pressed ON and released OFF in a quick movement. Otherwise, the sound of the note produced will be muffled by the striker being held against the gong. As soon as the push is released, the armature returns to its original position again.

The trembler bell is the most widely used type. It has the same basic construction as the single-stroke bell, but has an additional terminal which is an adjustable screw contact. The current which energises the electromagnet passes through this contact. As the armature with its striker is attracted away from this contact, the circuit is broken. The electromagnet becomes de-energised and the armature falls back to its original position against the contact to remake the circuit. This movement occurs rapidly and for as long as the bellpush is pressed. The resultant sound is a continuous ring, the tone of which can be altered by changing the setting of the adjustable contact.

The continuous-ringing bell is basically a trembler bell, but with either a mechanical or electrical arrangement to make the bell continue to ring after the bellpush has been released. A small lever is placed below the contact screw. On the first movement or stroke of the armature, this lever drops automatically and, as it drops, it short-circuits the bellpush to cause the bell to ring continuously. The lever can be reset to stop the sound. This type of bell finds wide application in alarm systems.

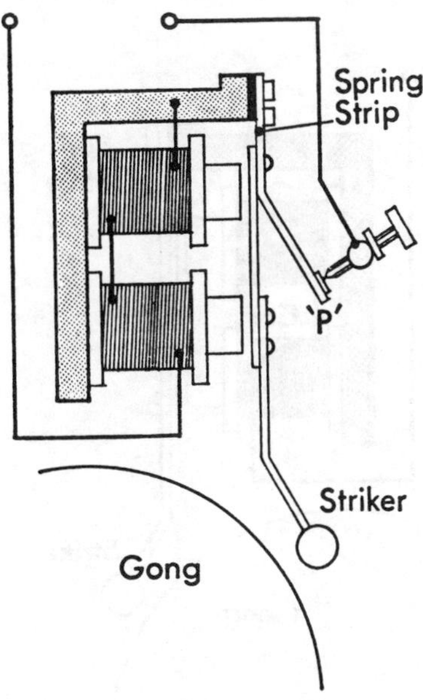

Figure 14.1. Trembler bell.

The electric buzzer is of the same construction as the trembler bell, except there is no gong or striker. The device produces a low-toned buzzing sound and is used where the shrill sound of the trembler bell might be objectionable.

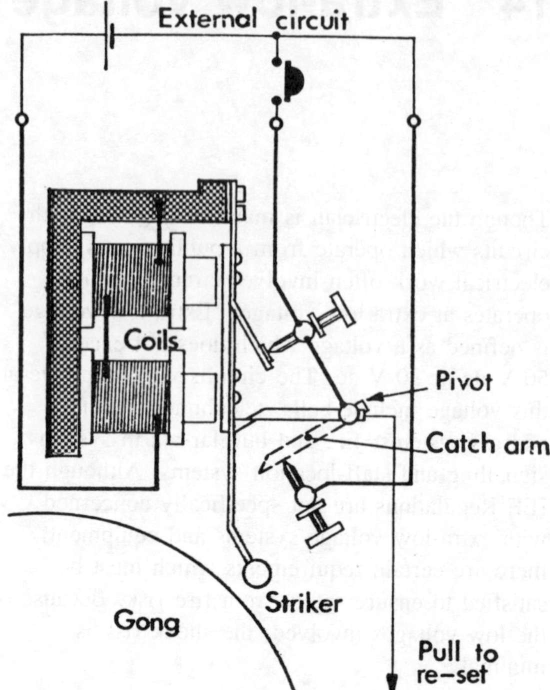

Figure 14.3. Continuous-ringing bell.

Bell indicators

When a bell or buzzer is operated from any one of two or more positions it becomes necessary to install an indicator board to show which bellpush has been operated. There are three main types of indicator: pendulum, mechanical-replacement, and electrical-replacement.

The pendulum type has a movement which is similar to that of the single-stroke bell. A soft-iron armature is pivoted or hinged at one end. The other end carries a flag. The armature is located in front of an electromagnet, the coil of which is connected in series with the trembler bell and its bellpush. When the circuit is made and broken by the action of the adjustable contact on the bell, the armature swings to and fro in pendulum fashion. The movement is seen through a clear circular part of a glass screen. The main disadvantage of this type of indicator is that if the person called happens to be out of the room when the bell rings, the pendulum may have stopped swinging by the time the person returns to look at the indicator.

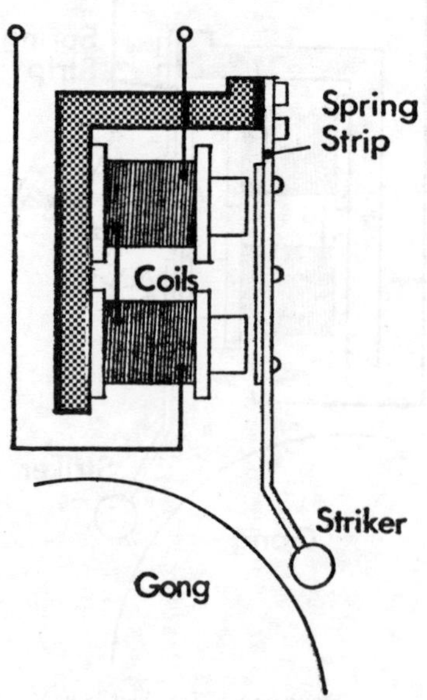

Figure 14.2. Single-stroke bell.

The mechanical-replacement type has an arrangement by which the armature, when it moves towards the electromagnet, is caught and the flag is shown in its appropriate space in the screen or window of the indicator board. The flag remains in this position even though the bellpush is released. To reset the flag, a lever is either pushed or turned round by hand.

The electrical-replacement type has two separate electromagnets. One coil is in series with the appropriate call bellpush as before. The other coil is connected to a 'replacement' circuit with a separate bellpush. When the circuit is energised the flag appears in its window, and remains in this position until the replacement push is operated. The second electromagnet attracts the flag armature to the 'unseen' position.

Bell relays

When the circuit of an electric bell is long in length, it may be found that the volt drop along the circuit wires is so great that the bell will not operate, or else do so inefficiently. Additional cells may be used to raise the circuit voltage to compensate for the lost volts. This, however, may not be a satisfactory solution to the problem. The better solution is the use of a relay. A relay is essentially a pair of electrical contacts operated by an electromagnet. A very small current is sufficient to energise the electromagnet and attract a spring-controlled armature. The movement of the armature causes the two contacts to close and operate the bell. The relay circuit may be energised separately from its own supply, or it may use the bell supply.

Bell supplies

1. The bell transformer is a double-wound transformer whose primary winding is supplied with 240 V ac. The output of the secondary varies with the type of transformer. Class A bell transformers provide a choice of three secondary voltages: 4, 8 or 12 V. Class B transformers provide a single secondary voltage of 6 V. The requirements regarding bell transformers are summarised as follows:

    (*a*) The transformer must be double-wound.
    (*b*) One point of the secondary winding, the iron core of the transformer, and the metal casing (if used) must be earthed.
    (*c*) The transformer should preferably be connected to a separate way in the distribution board. Otherwise, it should have a separate control switch.

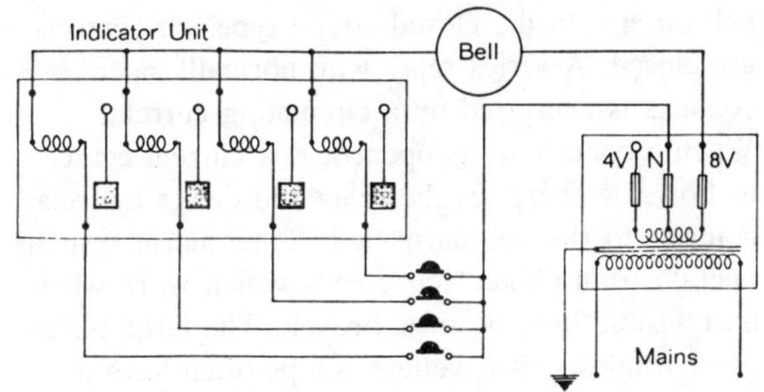

Figure 14.4. Four-way bell indicator and circuit.

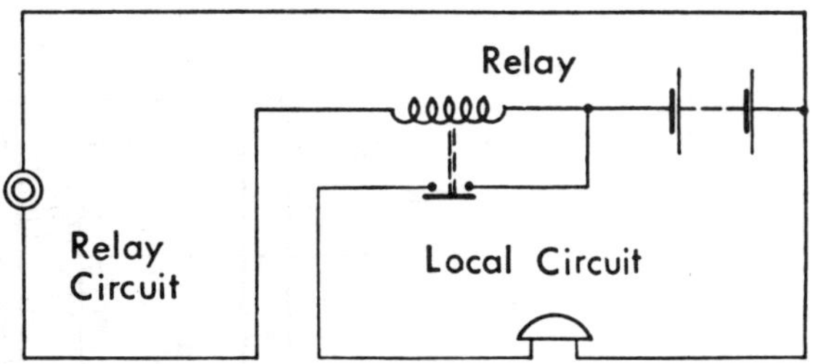

Figure 14.5. Typical relay circuit.

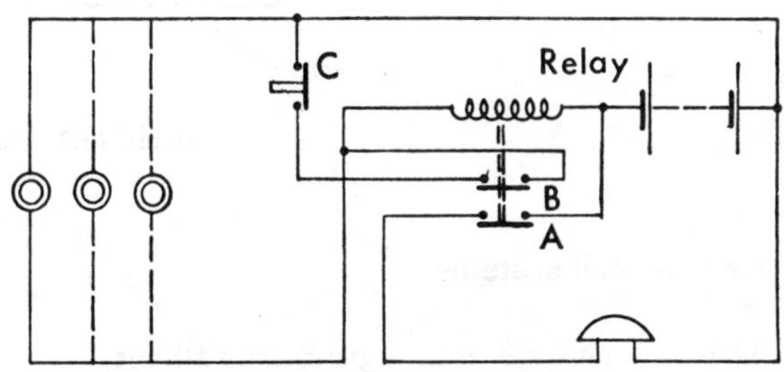

Figure 14.6. Relay circuit for continuous ringing of bell; C is the circuit-resetting contact.

    (*d*) The cables used to supply the transformer should be of an insulation grade suitable for the supply voltage in use.
    (*e*) The secondary wiring need be insulated for extra-low voltage only, provided that it can be completely segregated from mains-voltage power and lighting cables. If the bell-circuit wiring must be run in the same conduit, trunking or duct, as power or lighting cables, then it must be of a grade suitable for the highest voltage present in the power and lighting cables.

2. Primary batteries are suitable only for small installations. Dry batteries are easier to house, install and maintain.
3. Secondary batteries are suitable for a system of any size. Regular maintenance attention is required. They should be of the enclosed type to reduce fumes to a minimum. The location of the batteries should be readily accessible. Where open-type cells are used, adequate ventilation should be provided.

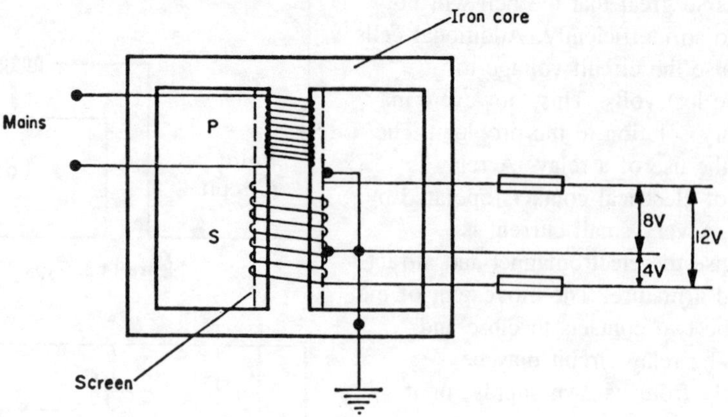

Figure 14.7. Class A bell transformer.

Bell and call systems

These systems are used in private dwellings, hotels, schools, factories and other premises where it is required to attract the attention of individuals to a situation or circumstance. The simplest system is where a person is called to a particular position by a caller. In a private house, the householder is called to the door. A bellpush or similar device is fitted at each call position and an indicator provided to show which push has been operated. A bell or buzzer is used to provide the sound which will attract attention to the call. Bellpushes can be of the wall-mounted, table or pendant type; the contact points are of a metal which gives long service without becoming pitted or corroded. If the bellpush is to be installed outside, protection against the ingress of moisture must be provided.

Indicators are installed in a central position in the building. In large premises, such as hotels and factories, the indicator board is located in a room in which some person is always in attendance, e.g. kitchen or reception office. The use of lamps is necessary where the sound of bells might be either objectionable or useless, e.g. in hospitals at night or in noisy workshops. Hand-setting indicators should be mounted at a height convenient for access and visibility.

Multiple-call systems are used in very large hotels where the call points are too many to be indicated conveniently on a single indicator board or panel. Pushes are fitted at each call point, but the circuits are grouped to serve a corridor or floor. Each group gives the indication in a central service room. In these systems, arrangements must be made to have attendants on duty in corridors or floors to deal with the calls. Multiple-call systems use indicators which have to be reset by the attendant.

Time-bell systems are common in schools and factories to indicate the beginning or end of a time or period (e.g. break, class change). These systems usually have one or two pushes or other switches connected in parallel and a number of bells throughout the building which are also connected in parallel. The bells can be controlled from a clock system, to eliminate the human element required with bellpushes.

The burglar-alarm system is also a call system. The switches in this case are sets of contacts mounted at doors and windows. There are two circuit types; open-circuit and closed-circuit. The first type requires contacts to close to energise the bell circuit. In the closed-circuit type, all contacts are closed. A series relay with normally open contacts is energised by a circulating current. When a contact set is opened, this current ceases to flow, de-energises the relay and closes the relay contacts to ring an alarm bell. Some alarm systems operate from photoelectric cells which work when an invisible light beam is broken. The large plate-glass windows of jewellers' shops often have a series length of very thin wire which, if broken when the window is smashed in, will bring the relay into operation to ring a bell. In certain systems today, no bell rings, but a buzzer and light indication circuit is wired from the protected building and terminated at a nearby police station. Thus the intruder is not warned, and the police have the opportunity of catching the burglar red-handed.

The open-circuit system is seldom used because it can be interfered with. For instance a cut in a wire will render the complete system inoperative, whereas such a break in the series circuit of a circulating-current (closed-circuit) system will immediately set an alarm bell ringing. Supplies are sometimes from the mains, but in this instance a standby-battery supply is provided in the event of a power failure. Alarm bells are often installed in a place inaccessible to unauthorised persons, and outside the building.

Another type of call or alarm system is the watchman's supervisory service. It is designed to provide a recorded indication of the visits of watchmen or guards to different parts of a building in the course of the duty round. The system uses a clock movement of the impulse, synchronous-time controlled ac or 8-day clockwork type installed at each contact station throughout the building. Each station has a box with a bellpush operated by the insertion of a special key. Operation of the contacts energises an electromagnetically operated marker which records the time of the visit on a paper marked off in hours. In some systems, an alarm is given after a predetermined time if the watchman fails to 'clock in' at any contact station.

Luminous call systems are used instead of bells. These systems use coloured lights which summon staff to fulfil a service duty. They are largely used in hospitals and hotels. When the bellpush is pressed in any position in the building, a small lamp lights in a duty room to indicate the general area from which the call has come. Alternatively, a lamp outside the call room lights and remains so until an attendant extinguishes it by operating a reset push located just outside the room. Some systems incorporate a sinle-stroke bell. Call and indicating circuitry is also incorporated in lift systems.

Fire-alarm systems

A fire-alarm system is defined as 'an arrangement of call-points, detectors, sounders and other equipment for the transmission and indication of alarm and supervisory signals, for the testing of circuits, and where required, for the operation of auxiliary services'. Section 36(7) of the Factories Act of 1937 states 'where in any factory ... more than 20 persons are employed ... effective provision shall be made for giving warning in case of fire, which shall be clearly audible throughout the building'.

A fire-alarm system consists of a number of press-buttons or call-points which operate bells, sirens or hooters, generally known as 'sounders'. Manually operated call-points are effective only if there are persons present to give an alarm. But if protection from fire is required when the premises

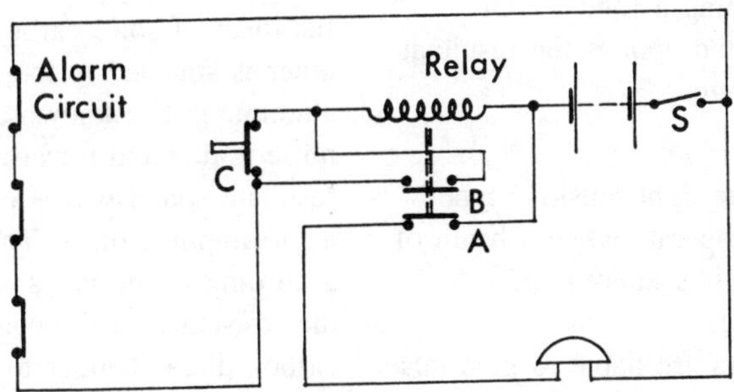

Figure 14.8. Typical closed-circuit alarm system: A — contact to ring bell (normally closed); B — contact to open relay circuit (normally open); S — main switch; C — reset button.

are unoccupied, as at night, during weekends or holidays, then automatic call-points are necessary. On very large premises, additional circuitry is included in fire-alarm systems to give an indication of the location of the fire, so that firemen can go direct to the fire and so that staff can leave the building by safe routes by-passing the fire.

The closed-circuit type of system is used so that circuit failure or breakage will at once be indicated by an audible alarm. Manual call-points consist of a pair of contacts kept together by a thin sheet of glass, which if broken in the event of a fire, will cause the contacts to separate and, through a relay, energise a bell circuit. All call-points are required to be coloured red. The method of operation, (e.g. 'Fire Alarm: in case of fire, break glass') must be clearly indicated either on the point or on a label beside it.

Automatic call-points are known as 'detectors', and are heat-sensitive, which means that they are sensitive to a rise in the ambient temperature of a room. They come into operation at a predetermined temperature (e.g. 66 °C).

There are two types of heat detector. The more common type is the 'point' detector which, as the name suggests, is relatively small. The other type is the 'line' detector which has a long continuous sensitive detecting element extending over a large area of a ceiling. The sensing elements used in heat detectors include:

1. Metal strips, rods, wires or coils which expand when heated.
2. Fusible alloys.
3. Conductors whose electrical resistance changes with a rise in temperature.
4. Hollow tubes containing a fluid which expands on heating and applies the resultant pressure to a diaphragm.
5. Thermocouples.

Some detectors are of the light-sensitive type: photo-electric cells which operate when a beam of light illuminating the cells is scattered and absorbed by smoke particles.

Heat and smoke detectors are liable to give false alarms in certain conditions:

(*a*) *Heat detectors*. False alarms may be caused by abnormal increases in temperature owing to space-heating equipment, industrial processes and sunshine.

(*b*) *Smoke detectors*. False alarms may be caused by smoke and other fumes, dusts, fibres and steam produced by normal processes and activities, or by passing road vehicles. Those detectors using a beam of light illuminating a photo-electric cell may also give false alarms if the beam is accidentally obstructed.

Automatic call-points are sometimes designed to give an alarm and also bring into operation an auxiliary fire service, such as a sprinkler system. Other examples of such services are the closing of windows, and the shutting of the covers of tanks containing inflammable liquids.

Telephone systems

The telephone system converts sound waves into electrical impulses, carries these through wires for long distances and then converts them back to sound waves again. The electrical energy involved in telephone circuits is very small.

The device used to change sound waves into electric currents is the microphone or telephone transmitter (the mouthpiece of the telephone handset). The principle of operation is based on the fact that the resistance of a mass of tiny carbon granules will vary with changes in a pressure applied to it. If the pressure is increased the resistance decreases, and vice versa. Thus, if the mass is connected into a circuit, the current in the circuit will vary as the carbon resistance changes. The modern telephone transmitter consists of two flat discs of solid carbon. One disc is fixed; the other is attached to the reverse side of a thin aluminium disc known as the diaphragm. When a noise is directed towards the diaphragm, the resultant sound waves produced travel through the air to impinge on it. The diaphragm vibrates according to the pressures of the sound waves and the resistance of the contacting surfaces of the carbon discs changes to produce a varying current.

The receiver converts the varying electric current back into sound waves again. It consists of a permanent magnet wound with coils of very fine

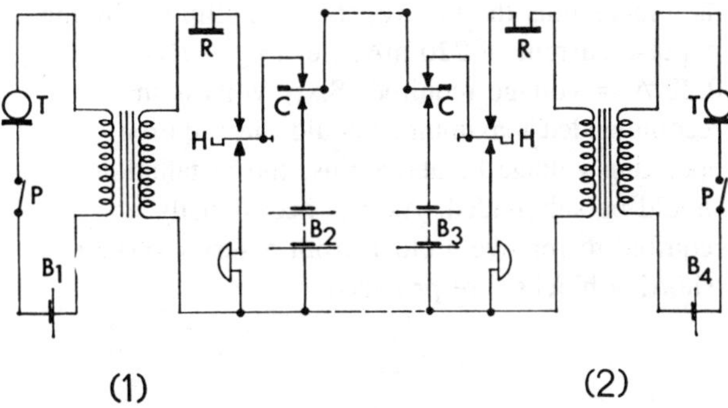

Figure 14.9. Two-way telephone circuit with calling facilities: 1 — first caller; 2 — second caller; T — telephone transmitter; P — 'Pressel' switch in microphone circuit to save current when apparatus is not being used; B — batteries; H — hook switches; C — calling switch; R — receivers.

wire. A thin diaphragm of magnetic material is held in position, very close to the poles of the electromagnet but not touching them. When the current from the transmitter flows through the coils, the resultant magnetic field (that of the permanent magnet plus that of the coils) varies in strength as the current varies. The diaphragm is vibrated and sets up pressure waves in the air to reproduce the sounds at the transmitter.

Though one can describe typical telephone circuits, it should be noted that most telephone circuitry today is very complex, requiring the specialist telephone engineer. The simplest circuit is one which will not only allow speaking between two positions, but also caters for one position calling up the other.

Sound-distribution systems

Sound-distribution systems consist essentially of loudspeakers permanently installed in suitable positions in buildings or in open spaces associated with buildings. They are essentially part of the telecommunications systems of buildings. The currents which operate such systems are derived from a microphone, gramophone, radio receiver or other device, or from a wire broadcasting service. These currents are of a very small order and so require to be amplified to values suitable for the operation of loudspeakers. Sound-distribution systems are found in schools, theatres and cinemas, churches, meeting halls, factories, offices and department stores, hotels and clubs, hospitals, railway stations and sports grounds. Though these systems generally operate from mains supplies, some systems, or parts thereof, operate from batteries or from mains-supplied rectifiers, producing low voltages.

Electric clock systems

These clock systems are used where a number of clocks throughout a building are required to show the same time, or else used to operate time recorders for stamping time-cards which indicate when work has been started or finished.

Most clocks found in small installations are independent units, run by a synchronous motor fed from mains voltage. Impulse-clock systems are independent of mains and operate from extra-low voltage supplies. The master clock is the name given to the primary unit which controls all other clocks in the installation. It is pendulum-operated. It has an impulse transmitter which transmits electrical impulses of alternate polarity at one-minute intervals over a two-wire circuit to the subsidiary or 'slave' clocks. The slave clocks have movements which accept these impulses and alter their clock hands accordingly.

The mechanism of one type of master clock consists of a pendulum of half-seconds beat operated by an electrically-wound spring through a dead-beat escapement. At each one-minute interval, while a small synchronous motor is rewinding the main spring, an impulse is transmitted to the subsidiary clocks. The mains ac supply is transformed to 48 V for operating the synchronous motor and again reduced and rectified to provide 24 V dc for the transmitted impulses. Should the mains supply be interrupted for any reason, the main spring has a sufficient reserve to operate the escapement movement and hands for about 10 hours, though no impulses will be transmitted to the subsidiary clocks. The movement of a subsidiary clock is a one-minute polarised movement with a rotating armature, and incorporates a flywheel to render the hands 'dead-beat'.

The usual master-and-slave installation can cater

for up to 60 clocks. To add clocks to the system, it is only necessary to connect a clock in parallel with the remainder. The clock load and the connecting cables should total a certain value of resistance so that the farthest clock has sufficient voltage at its terminals.

The impulse current is 220 mA. In series-impulse clock systems, the voltage required for the installation is calculated as the total resistance of the clocks plus the line resistance multiplied by the impulse current of 220 mA, i.e. $(R_c + R_1) \times 0.22$ A = voltage required. Sixty volts is the recommended maximum. Should the required operating voltage be above this, the installation should be subdivided. As it is occasionally required to remove a clock from a series system, 'shorting-blocks' are provided.

15 Tariffs and power factor

The scale of charges for electrical energy provided by the supply companies in this country is known as a 'tariff'. At the outset it should be realised that large sums of money must be spent in the provision of generating plant, the buildings and the people to operate it before the consumer can install and use his own electrical machinery and apparatus. The cost of electrical energy is made up of standing charges and running charges. Standing charges include such items as interest on the capital borrowed to buy the plant, salaries and wages of those who are on the engineering, commercial and administrative sides of the supply industry, rents and rates for buildings, premises and areas such as the patch of ground on which an electricity pylon stands, taxes, depreciation of plant, and services such as water and oil. The running charges are those which include the cost of the fuel (coal, oil, nuclear fuel), replacements to plant, maintenance, etc. In addition to the cost per unit generated which these charges require, there is the extra 'profit' margin which is a fraction of a penny per unit. This additional charge covers the purchase of new equipment after the existing equipment has become 'scrap' and also the development costs (e.g. to bring electricity to new housing sites, factories, and to relay cables which have become too small because of increased load demands).

Altogether, these charges add up to a minimum cost per unit. The actual charge to consumers varies, depending on the type of consumer, and this gives rise to the various charges offered by supply companies. The following is a typical range of charges.

Domestic tariff. This tariff applies to premises which are used exclusively as private dwelling-houses. Generally, each of a certain number of primary units (e.g. 60) are charged at 6p. For each of a certain number of secondary units (e.g. 300) is 5.5p. Then for each additional unit the charge is 3.8p. Meters are read quarterly. This tariff induces the consumer to use as much energy as possible so that the average cost per unit is small. In addition, there is a domestic tariff in which there is a standing charge, often based on the floor area of the building, plus a constant charge of, for example, 1p per unit consumed.

Fixed block power tariff. This tariff is applied to small industrial premises and, if separately metered, to motive power and heating in non-residential premises; also to flood-lighting, outside signs and display lighting where the power factor does not fall below 0.9. For each of a certain number of units each quarter, the charge is 4.5p per unit. Thereafter each additional unit per quarter is 2.3p.

Public-lighting tariff. This tariff is applied to energy used for lighting public roads, and public authority communal roads and stairs. It is usually a fixed charge per annum (e.g. £38.00) based on the use of a 1,000 W lamp. The annual hours burning is based on local requirements.

Farm tariff. This tariff applies to farming units which consist of a dwelling-house and farm buildings. Farm houses are assessed as houses under the domestic tariff. Generally the rating of agricultural apparatus is taken into consideration. Units are charged on the primary, secondary and additional units basis.

Industrial power tariff. This tariff is on either a quarterly or a monthly basis. It applies to premises used for the purpose of manufacture, provided that the total electrical requirements of the premises for lighting, heating and power, are supplied by the supply company. The tariff offered depends on the voltage of the supply, either high voltage (in excess of 650V) or medium voltage (less than 650V). The tariff offered is typically as follows:

For each of the first 20 kW of chargeable maximum demand – £2.30.
For each kW of chargeable MD in excess of 20 – £1.37.
For each of the first 600 units each quarter – 2.6p.
For each of the next 600 units each quarter – 2.18p.
In each quarter — 1.56p.

If the voltage taken is medium voltage, the consumer is charged extra. Also, if the average power factor of the installation falls below 0.9 the chargeable maximum demand is usually determined by multiplying the number of kW of maximum demand indicated by 0.9 and dividing by the average power factor.

Off-peak tariff. This tariff is available for approved supplies which are disconnected from the mains at certain times during a 24-hour period. Equipment which is suitable and acceptable to the supply authority for operation on the 'off-peak' tariff includes thermal-storage equipment of various types such as floor-warming installations, thermal-storage block space heaters and hot-water storage systems either for space heating or for hot-water supplies. Also acceptable is space-heating equipment designed to operate predominantly with thermal storage but which includes direct electric heating elements, provided (*a*) that all the heating elements are connected on the 'off-peak' and (*b*) that the equipment is capable of providing continuously (between 'off-peak' periods) the conditions for which it is intended. So that the ON periods can be regulated, the installation is required to have a time switch with a spring reserve. Where the 'off-peak' loading of an installation exceeds 60 A, a suitable contactor (sealed by the supply company) is to be installed by the consumer next to the time switch. Typical times during which the tariff is available (at 2.6p per unit) are 1900 hrs to 0800 and 1200 hrs to 1530.

The two-part tariff. The large consumer of electric energy, as mentioned already, is generally offered a two-part tariff. This is based on a charge made for the maximum demand (integrated over 15 minutes or half an hour) and for the actual energy consumed. In many cases, alternative tariffs are available, in which case the consumer can work out which will be the cheapest to him in the long run. These large consumers install maximum demand indicators. These metering devices register the total kWh taken over a predetermined period divided by the period in hours. The maximum demand is in fact the average demand recorded over a short period, usually thirty minutes. The maximum demand (MD) pointer has also a slipping pointer. When the recording period is ON, the pointer moves over an almost circular scale to register the average demand in kW; it moves the slipping pointer along with it. At the end of the recording period, the pointer is automatically reset to zero and the slipping pointer remains at the highest kW demand during the recording period just ended. The pointer again moves around the scale and if, during this new recording period, the kW demand is higher than in the previous period, the slipping pointer will be moved up to record this new high figure, and stays there. Thus, the reading on the MD meter is always the highest kW demand. When the meter-reader calls to read the meter, he resets the slipping pointer to zero.

The charge for each kilowatt of MD varies throughout the country, from £2 to £4, depending on the type of consumer. It is thus in the interests of the consumer to reduce the amount of this charge as much as possible. For instance, if a factory begins work at 0800 hours and switches on all its electric motors at the precise time, the maximum demand for the rest of the day will be about a tenth of the figure recorded. To reduce the MD, factories generally start in phases, e.g. at 0750 hrs, 0751 hrs, 0752 hrs, 0753 hrs, so that the kilowatt demand involved in starting the motors is reduced to perhaps two or three times the daily average MD figure. Another factor which will affect the maximum demand taken by an installation is the lighting demand, which is high particularly during the dark seasons. The lighting load varies generally from about 20 per cent full-load in summer to 100 per cent full-load in winter, according to the type of building. In contrast, the power demand of industrial premises is fairly constant throughout the year.

Power factor

Most of the machines used in electrical work are inductive (e.g. motors, transformers). The power taken by a motor on ac is not calculated in the same way as that of a dc motor. In dc work, the true watts or power absorbed in the circuit is given by the product of volts × amperes. In an ac circuit which has inductance, the current lags behind the voltage, so reducing the true watts. If, however, both the voltage and current alternating waves are in phase, or in step, the power factor is unity, that is to say, the watts in the circuit are the product of voltage × amperes. When these waves are out of phase, as in the inductive circuit, current is in effect being wasted. The apparent power is the product of $V \times I$. The true watts are $V \times I \times X$ a factor known as the power factor. The power factor is the ratio between true and apparent power and is less than unity in normal circuit conditions. A typical value for an ac motor is 0.7 lagging. This means that the current taken by the motor lags behind the voltage by an angle the cosine of which is 0.7.

As an example, take the case of a single-phase motor with a full-load efficiency of 85 per cent and a power factor of 0.7, and taking a full-load current of 20 A at 240 V. The apparent power is:

$V \times I$, then $20 \times 240 = 4{,}800$ VA.

The true, or useful, current in this case is
$20 \text{ A} \times 0.7 = 14$ A.
The useful or true watts are thus
$= 240 \times 14 = 3{,}360$ W.

Power-factor improvement

Poor power factor results in more current flowing in cables than is necessary. Cables have to be larger in cross-sectional area to carry the heavier currents. Thus, good power factor loads are of great interest to supply companies, to the extent that poor power factor is penalised by charging each consumer for every kVA (kiloVoltAmpere) of maximum demand taken by an installation. The consumer thus has a financial interest in improving the overall power factor of his load. He does this with either synchronous motors, running over-excited, or by using static oil-filled capacitors. The synchronous motor, when its dc field is over-excited, will take a current which leads the voltage by an angle which depends on the amount of over-excitation. When the synchronous motor is used for power-factor improvement purposes, it can either be run idle, or be used to deliver mechanical power at constant speed. It is common practice to have the motor connected to the factory busbars. Two disadvantages associated with the synchronous motor (or condenser) are its cost and the possibility of its falling out of synchronism, with a resulting interruption of the supply.

The static capacitor is made in many sizes and for various voltage systems. They have a low temperature rise and negligible losses. They are widely used in electrical installation work, e.g. discharge-lamp circuits and for motor-starting. Most of the capacitors used in installations are metal-foil, paper-insulated. The capacitance depends on the area of the plates and on the thickness and the insulating qualities of the dielectric. A common method of increasing the area of the plates is to use two metal-foil strips separated by wax- or oil-impregnated paper. The physical size is kept to a minimum by rolling the plates and paper to give a tubular capacitor. The whole assembly is then housed in a plastic container, although higher voltage units and larger sizes are usually housed in a steel casing. In smaller sizes, this is the type used for starting single-phase motors and for power-factor correction in discharge-lamp circuits. Where the power factor of large motors is to be improved, the paper capacitor is again used. In order to give the required capacity, several capacitors are made up in banks. The banks are placed in a steel casing which is then filled with insulating oil in the same way as a transformer. If the motor, or load, is three-phase, three banks are used and connected in delta. The three banks of capacitor normally share the same tank.

When the supply is removed from a capacitor, the capacitor remains charged and, depending on the quality of the insulation, can remain so for a considerable time. To avoid danger of shock when working on a capacitor, discharge resistors are fitted. These resistors are permanently connected across the capacitor terminals and are of a high ohmic value, usually several megohms. They allow any charge on a capacitor to be safely dissipated after the capacitor is switched off. Care must be taken during capacitor maintenance not to remove these resistors. Before working on a power-factor correction capacitor, at least ten minutes should be allowed, after switching off, to enable the capacitor to discharge.

The following case histories (by permission of the Telegraph Condenser Co Ltd.) show how the improvement in power factor results not only in saving but in a return of the money spent in buying and installing the power-factor correction equipment.

Case No.1. A factory had motors ranging from 7 to 25 kW, supplied at 440 V, three-phase. The tariff was two-part: £4 per kVA of maximum demand plus a running charge per kWh. The average MD was 220 kVA and the overall power factor of the installation was 0.76 lagging. It was decided to improve this figure to 0.95 by the provision of individual capacitors to the larger motors and by providing group correction for the smaller machines. The increase of the power factor to 0.95 reduced the kVA demand to about 170. The saving resulting from this reduction was £200 per annum. The cost of the capacitor installation was £300, and was paid for in under two years.

Case No. 2. A large cement factory had two stone-crushers of 140 kW each, three raw mills and three cement mills each of 400 kW, one coal mill at 200 kW and three induced-draught fans of 230 kW each. The total motor load was 4,000 kW. The energy was supplied under a two-part tariff consisting of a charge of £3.40 per annum per kVA of maximum demand plus a running charge per kWh. The annual kVA cost was in the region of £18,000. When tests were carried out it was found that the factory load was 3,675 kW while the maximum demand of kVA was 4,565, a power factor of 0.805 lagging. Though this figure for the power factor was satisfactory, it was decided to raise the figure to 0.95 lagging by the provision of capacitors installed individually to the above-mentioned plant.

The improvement scheme reduced the kVA maximum demand by 687, to 3,868 kVA. The saving per annum, for an expenditure of just over £3,000, was £2,353. The capital outlay was thus returned in 15 months. Later, it was decided to fit an additional power-factor correction capacitor to the switchboard which fed a number of small-kW motors which it was impracticable to correct individually.

White meters

These have been developed by various electricity authorities in order to encourage the increased use of electricity during night hours. The meter, in a white plastic case, has two sets of cyclometer dials. One set relates to the use of the meter during the day, while the other set comes into operation to record the energy used during the night. A real saving on energy costs appears where water is electrically heated during the night-time, together with long-term space-heating. The meter does not really offer advantages by comparison with the standard two-part domestic tariff, unless the consumer has a substantial part of his electrical consumption at night. However, certain types of households could gain advantages by having cheap cooking facilities at night, particularly if they are away from home all day. By the use of the white meter, these households could take advantage of being able to extend household activities such as home laundry and dish-washing, bulk-cooking for deep-freezers, etc. and all for a cheaper rate. The white meter tariff, however, requires a careful analysis of its application before it is considered as a means to gain cheap energy. The meter circuits are operated by a time-switch.

Part B

Electrical workshop technology

16 Portable electric tools

The portable electric tool has found for itself a definite place in workshops and on building sites, particularly to speed up many of the tasks which would otherwise be time-consuming and thus costly. For instance, a man using a powered rotary percussion drill may be able to make 60 holes in the same time that 10 holes could be drilled by using a hand-drill and hammer. So far as sites are concerned, installation work falls into three broad groups:

1. Making fixings to a wide variety of building materials, most of which possess considerable resistance to penetration.
2. Concealing cables and parts of accessories within recesses and channels cut into building structures.
3. Removing and replacing building materials to gain access.

Workshop duties for portable tools include drilling, grinding, polishing, buffing, sawing, and screwdriving.

On sites, the supply is either from a generator or from a step-down transformer. The usual and recommended voltage is 110 V. The transformer is of the double-wound type, with the mid-point of the secondary winding earthed, so that the maximum voltage above earth potential is 55 V. If a generator is used, the supply voltage should be 110 V, ac or dc; as most portable tools are powered by the 'universal' type of motor which works equally well on both types of supply. The motors have rather noisy high-speed drivers with speed-reduction gearboxes for some duties. Tools of this kind require to be fitted with suppressors to eliminate interference with radio and TV services.

Certain tools are now available which meet the double-insulation requirements of the British Standards Institution. The outer metal casing of these tools is not earthed; but they can be operated safely at mains voltage provided that the flexible cords are well maintained and the tools are not abused.

The portable drill

This tool is probably the most common in use today. It consists of an electric motor, usually of the ac/dc 'universal' type coupled to a chuck spindle through one or more trains of gears. The motor is controlled by a switch located in the handle of the tool. The switch has a latch-on catch which enables the tool to be used for long runs without the need for the user to keep the switch depressed. A slight additional pressure on the switch trigger releases the switch to the OFF position.

There are three general-duty classifications for drills: light, normal and heavy. The light-duty drill

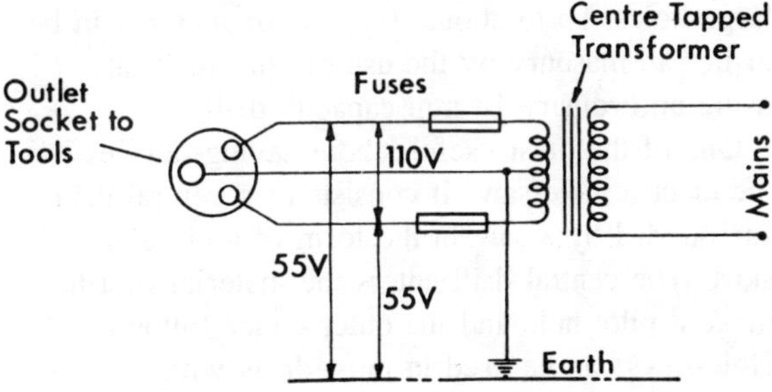

Figure 16.1. Reduction of supply voltage for portable tools using double-wound transformer with centre-tapped secondary.

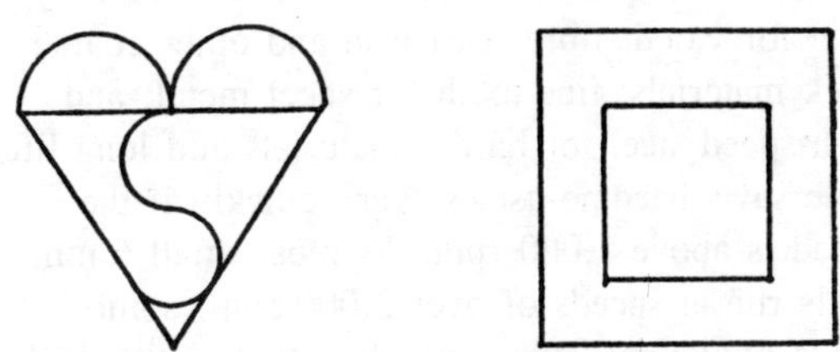

Figure 16.2. The British Standard symbol and symbol for double-insulation.

has a chuck capacity below 8 mm. One inherent characteristic of the universal motor used in the drills is that its speed varies widely with the load it drives. This feature is valuable in electric drills because the best working speed of a drill bit varies inversely as its diameter. That is, the smaller the diameter of the bit, the faster must be the speed. Portable drills are usually rated primarily on their capacity for drilling mild steel. In general they will drill holes in wood twice the diameter of the rated 'steel' size. The drilling of brickwork calls for the use of hard-tipped masonry drills and preferably at slower speeds than is usual for steel, in order to reduce heating. Special slow-speed tools are available. For occasional work, masonry drill bits can be used in ordinary drills, the obvious risk being the overheating and softening of the bonding of the cutting tip. The best results are obtained by using the slowest drill available and/or bearing on the tool itself heavily to keep the speed down.

Drilling holes in concrete requires a combined rotary and hammering action. A number of these hammer-drills are available; in all types the hammer can be thrown out of gear so that the tool can be used as an ordinary slow-speed drill. Very large holes, up to about 10 cm in diameter, can be drilled in masonry by the use of core drill bits using an ordinary 18 mm capacity drill.

One of the most useful labour-saving devices is the electric hole saw. It consists of a central drill surrounded by a saw in the form of a circular skirt. The central drill enters the material first to make a pilot hole and the outer cutter follows. Hole-saws can be used in most drills with 6–18 mm chucks and are available for holes ranging from 18 to 100 mm diameter. The maximum cutting depth is about 18 mm. Hole-saws are made in three types: coarse-tooth alloy-steel for wood, fibre, cast iron and other coarse thick materials; fine-tooth for sheet metal; and high-speed steel for harder materials and long life. Hole saws become useless very quickly if the speed is above 1,000 rpm. As most small 6 mm drills run at speeds of over 2,000 rpm, some speed-reduction device must be fitted to the drill.

In using the electric drill, the exact position of the hole to be drilled should be marked with a centre punch. Ensure that the work is firmly clamped and that sheet metal, in particular, is backed up by a piece of thicker material (e.g. wood) to ensure a clean hole. The drill should be grasped firmly.

Maintenance of portable tools

Because portable electric tools are called on to work in particularly arduous conditions of service, a certain amount of regular maintenance is necessary. The machine must never be allowed to become clogged with dust. Metallic dust in particular can cause serious damage. Most machines can be dismantled by adopting the following procedure, which is generally applicable:

1. Remove the carbon-brush caps and brushes.
2. Unscrew the gear-box, inner gear-plate, brush-holders and armature.
3. Separate the inner gear-plate from the gear-box.
4. Unscrew the brush-holder securing screws and remove the holders.
5. Remove the inner gear-plate from the armature.
6. To examine the switch terminals, remove the switch-cover and the switch screws. The switch can then be withdrawn.

Carbon brushes and the commutator of the armature tend to give most trouble on portable electric tools. One manufacturer has estimated that 75 per cent of all tool troubles are traced to lack of attention to the brushes. The brush consists of a rectangular block of carbon pressed against the commutator by a helical spring. Inside the spring is a flexible copper pigtail which carries the current to the external circuit. The brushes are usually retained in position by an insulated screw-cap. In some tools, the brush-cover is retained by an internally-expanding spring ring.

Brushes should be inspected frequently and kept free from grease and dirt by wiping with a clean rag. Brushes should slide freely in their holders. If brushes are allowed to wear to under about 5 mm in length, the springs will become too weak to keep them on the commutator at the correct tension. Carbon brushes should show a clean, curved polished surface with a correspondingly even brush mark around the commutator. If the brush ends are pitted or burnt, there is usally something wrong with the tool (e.g. short-circuited armature coil). Pigtails should be intact and not frayed. All brushes should run sparklessly in operation. When a brush is to be replaced, the same grade of carbon must be used. If the commutator is dirty or tends to roughness, it should be cleaned lightly with very fine glass-paper. Emery cloth should not be used because of the risk of the cloth's abrasive particles becoming embedded in the copper of the commutator. If the commutator has been worn into a groove, the armature should be removed from the drill and the surface turned in a lathe using a sharp-pointed tool and a high peripheral speed. The surface should then be given a final polish with fine glass-paper moistened with a light machine oil. If the mica insulation between the copper segments was originally undercut (that is, recessed below the level of the adjacent copper) it should be undercut with an undercutting saw before the final polish is given. While the armature is out of the drill, the soldered connections to the commutator should be examined and resoldered if necessary. Quite often, excessive sparking at the brushes causes abnormal heat, sufficient to melt, or at least weaken, the soldered joints. Modern practice in drill construction is to weld the connections from the armature coils to the commutator segments, in which case the need for resoldering does not arise.

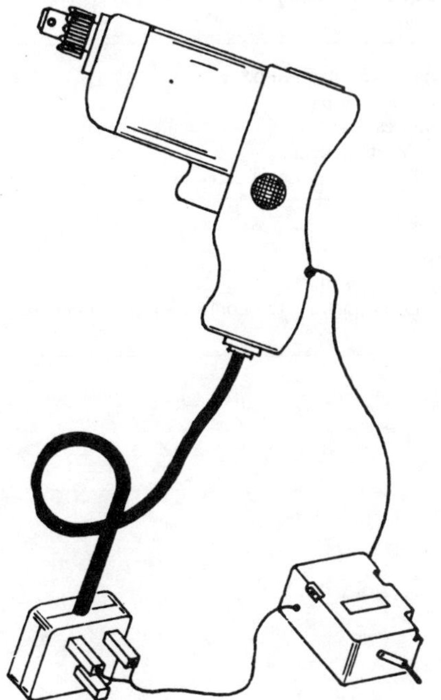

Figure 16.3. Testing portable tool for insulation-resistance to earth.

Portable electric tools need lubrication from time to time, the frequency and extent depending on the type of bearings fitted in the machine. Tools in occasional use should be attended to every three months or so. Tools in more or less continuous use may require lubrication more frequently. Ball-bearings may be of the grease-sealed enclosed type in which both sides of the bearing are sealed either with plates or felts, or a combination of the two. The lubrication thus embodied should last the life of the bearing without replenishment. Care must always be taken not to immerse closed bearings in cleaning solvent as this will dilute, or destroy, the lubricant. Such bearings should be cleaned by wiping with a non-linting rag. Open-type bearings call for cleaning or relubrication with the maker's recommended grade of grease. Sintered brush bearings require lubrication from time to time with a light machine oil. When greasing the bearings and gear-box, first clean out the old grease; bearings and grease-box should be filled only half-full. Grease expands when it is warm and if too much is deposited it will force its way into the motor, block the ventilation holes and damage the windings. Excessive grease also causes overheating. Only high-speed ball-bearing grease should be used.

The most vulnerable part of an electric portable tool is the cable. It should be kept away from oils and greases, and should never be dragged about over rough surfaces. The armature should be examined closely at frequent intervals. This can sometimes be done without the need for dismantling the tool. Excessive heat (which can be felt by the hand) may cause the armature laminations to foul the field core and lead to failure. Thus, the armature should show no signs of rubbing.

When a new tool is being put into use, it should first be examined to see that no damage has occurred in transit. The voltage marked on the rating plate should correspond with the supply voltage. The machine should be properly earthed (unless it is double-insulated) by means of a three-pin plug and the connections to the plug well made.

Faults in portable tools

The following table summarises some of the troubles, and their causes, which occur on portable electric tools:

Symptom	*Probable cause*
1. Lack of power	(a) Carbon brushes badly worn. (b) Breakdown in either armature or field windings. (c) Gears binding (turn by hand to test). (d) Bad electric connections.
2. Flashing at brushes	(a) Open-circuit in armature winding. (b) Commutator out of alignment. (c) Commutator segment lifting. (d) Brushes sticking in holders. (e) Brushes not bedding correctly.
3. Motor casing becomes too hot to touch	(a) Machine being overloaded beyond rated capacity. (b) Blunt twist-drill bits or blunt cutting accessories being used. (c) Excessive voltage at mains. (d) Ventilation ducts blocked (with dirt or grease). (e) Motor winding breakdown. (f) Dirt on electrical parts causing leakage.
4. Smoke emitted from motor	(a) Excessive and continual electrical or material overload. (b) Excessive voltage at mains. (c) Breakdown of armature or field winding. (d) Broken internal connection.
5. Shocks being received from casing	(a) Live connection touching inside of machine. (b) Earth wire of cable touching live part. (c) Short-circuit in connection cable. (d) Breakdown of insulation inside machine. (e) Connection cable burnt through at point of entry to machine.
6. Machine does not start when switched on	(a) Circuit fuse blown. (b) Mains cable disconeted. (c) Internal connection loose or broken. (d) Carbon brush sticking and not making full contact with commutator. (e) Switch faulty.

17 Workshop practice

Workshop machines

The centre lathe

The centre lathe is perhaps the most common of the machine tools used in the workshop. A wide variety of operations can be performed on it. The lathe consists of the following main parts. The *bed* is the foundation on which the lathe is built. A large iron casting, it has its upper surfaces machined to form slideways for the carriage and the tailstock to move along. Some lathes are made with a gap in the bed immediately in front of the headstock. This enables a larger size job to be swung than could normally be accommodated on the lathe. The *headstock* houses the hollow main spindle, the spindle bearings, and the gears for obtaining the various spindle speeds. It takes the form of a casting bolted to the top of the bed. The drive is usually by means of an electric motor, fitted with a pulley and vee-belts. The *tailstock* is mounted on the opposite end of the bed to the headstock. It can be moved along the bed of the lathe or locked to the bed in any desired position. The main casting is bored to accommodate a keyed spindle, called the barrel, which can be advanced by means of a handwheel. The front end of the barrel is provided with an internal taper to take a drill chuck, taper shank drill, reamer, or a centre to support long work.

The *carriage* comprises the saddle and the apron. The saddle is supported and guided by the bed slideways, and carries the cross slide and compound slide. The apron, which contains the feed mechanism, is attached to the front of the saddle. The movement of the carriage can be done manually. However, to ensure a smooth regular feed for metal-cutting operations, arrangement is made for automatic movement. The cross slide is carried on the top surface of the saddle and provides tool movements at right-angles to the spindle axis. A screw engages with a nut attached to the slide and movement is effected by rotating a hand-wheel which is fixed to the end of the screw. A graduated sleeve is attached to the screw. The compound slide is mounted on the cross slide and supports the toolpost and cutting tool. It is provided with angular adjustment which enables conical surfaces to be generated, but its length of traversing movement is limited.

Chucks may be of the four-jaw independent, or three-jaw self-centring, patterns. Each jaw of the four-jaw chuck is operated by a separate square-

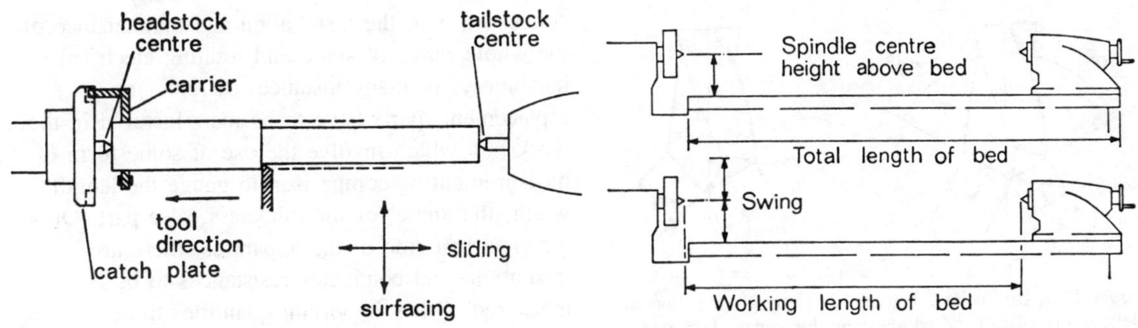

Figure 17.1. Arrangement and movements of the centre lathe and working tool.

Figure 17.2. Arrangement of lathe showing typical working specifications.

headed screw. In the three-jaw type, all the jaws close in together, actuated by the scroll, which is a spiral groove cut on the face of a flat disc.

There are a number of types of lathe tools. The solid type is generally of high-carbon steel. For the smaller sizes of tools, the material is high-speed-steel. Because of the expense of this material, however, tool bits are used. These bits are in effect tool-holders, which accommodate a tool bit of high-speed-steel. Another type of tool is the tipped tool. This is a tool of good-quality steel onto the tip of which a special cutting alloy is brazed. These tips are extremely hard and are able to stand up to a considerable amount of use without the necessity for regrinding. Tungsten carbide is one of the most common materials from which these tool bits are made.

Drilling machine

There are three main types of drilling machine: sensitive, pillar, and radial. Of these, the sensitive machine is the type most often found in the light-engineering workshop concerned with maintenance and repair. It is a light, high-speed machine used for drilling small holes up to about 18 mm. The main drill spindle rotates within a sleeve which is a slide fitted in the body of the machine. The operation of a lever, which is located on the right-hand side of the machine, rotates a pinion which meshes with a rack milled in the sleeve, thus effecting a downward movement of the spindle.

Power is provided by an electric motor, mounted at the rear of the machine, and is transmitted to the drill spindle by a vee-belt drive. The speed of the spindle can be changed by moving the belt onto another pair of pulleys. The drill is held in a self-centring chuck fitted to the end of the spindle and the workpiece is supported on the work table which may be raised or lowered as required. Small drills are easily broken. It is thus important to be able to feel the action of the drill as it is cutting. This is only possible if the drill is fed by hand, and is the reason for the sensitive drill not being provided with automatic feeds.

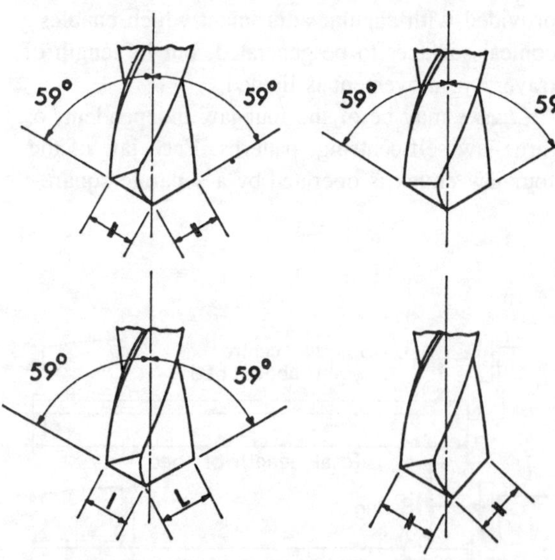

Figure 17.3. Drill points. Top left: correctly ground. Bottom left: incorrectly ground with unequal lip angles. Top right: incorrectly ground with zero clearance. Bottom right: incorrectly ground with unequal lip angles.

Workshop safety

When working on a machine, there are a number of important safety factors which must always be kept in mind. If a machine is belt-driven, guards should be provided, which should be securely fitted and properly adjusted. If a guard has to be removed for maintenance purposes, make sure that moving parts are stationary before doing so. Loose clothing should be avoided when working on machine tools. Goggles should be worn when using grinding wheels.

Workshop measurements

This section deals in summary with the various kinds of measurements which are mainly concerned with the installation and maintenance of the whole range of static and rotating electrical machinery. In many instances of repair or replacement, parts have to be manufactured in the workshop which involve the use of some form of measurement or comparison to gauge the length, width, the angle, or the thickness, of a part. On the electrical side of the apparatus, there are insulation- and conductor-resistances to be measured. Other important quantities to be measured include the temperature, both of machinery and ambient temperature in a room.

Spirit level

This consists essentially of a glass vial containing spirit and filled leaving a small bubble of air. The inside surface of this glass container is curved to a large radius, either by curving the whole tube, or by shaping its inside to the form of a barrel. The vial is set in a base and adjusted so that when the base is horizontal the bubble rests at the centre of a scale which is engraved on the glass. When the base of the level is moved out of the horizontal plane, the bubble, in rising to the top point of the vial radius, also moves along the scale. In the builders' type of level, there is no scale, the level being used as a level gauge with no requirement for the accuracy provided by the workshop spirit level, which is in the region of 0.002 mm.

Micrometer

When work has to be finished to a high degree of accuracy, a micrometer is used. It consists of a main frame which is usually semi-circular in shape. A cylindrical part at the side of the main frame, called the sleeve, and a hardened and precision-finished steel, called the anvil, complete the instrument. Inside the sleeve is a special nut, and through this passes a screwed spindle attached to a graduated and knurled portion called the thimble. The end of the spindle projecting from the thimble passes through the frame and is not screwed. When the micrometer is closed, the end of this spindle, which is also hardened and ground, contacts the anvil. On the metric micrometer, the screwed thread has a pitch of 0.5 mm. Thus two revolutions of the thimble will move the spindle through 1 mm. On the sleeve, the datum line is graduated with two sets of lines – the set below the line reading in millimetres and the set above the line reading in half-millimetres. On older types the millimetres are graduated above the datum line with the half-millimetres below. The thimble is marked in fifty equal divisions, figures in fives, so that each small division on the thimble represents $\frac{1}{50}$ of $\frac{1}{2}$ mm, which equals $\frac{1}{100}$ or 0.01 mm.

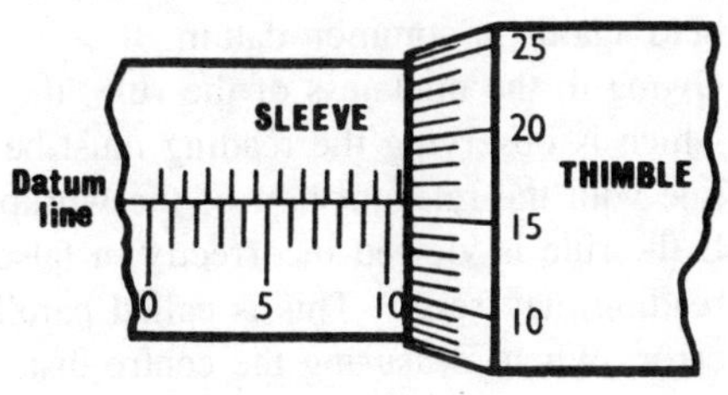

Figure 17.4. A typical micrometer reading.

When the micrometer is being used, it should be opened so that it will pass quite readily over the job. It should then be carefully screwed up until the anvil and the end of the spindle are just contacting the job. In this position the micrometer should pass over the job with just a slight amount of 'feel'. That is, it should be just possible to feel that the anvil and the spindle are contacting the job, and no force is required. Some micrometers have a ratchet stop so that when the right amount of contact is made, the ratchet will come into operation and it will be impossible to screw the spindle up too tightly. A locking ring is often provided so that the instrument can be set to record a particular reading. The instrument must be held squarely to the work whilst the measurement is being taken. The micrometer reading is obtained as follows:

1. First note the whole number of millimetre divisions on the sleeve (known as Major divisions) (see Figure 17.4);
2. Then observe whether there is a half-millimetre visible (Minor divisions);
3. Lastly, read the thimble for hundredths (Thimble divisions), i.e., the line on the thimble coinciding with the datum line. In Figure 17.4:

Major divisions	= 10 × 1.00 mm =	10.00 mm
Minor divisions	= 1 × 0.50 mm =	0.50 mm
Thimble divisions	= 16 × 0.01 mm =	0.16 mm
	Reading is	10.66 mm

Vernier micrometer

The addition of a vernier scale to the micrometer enables measurements within two-thousandths of a millimetre to be made. The vernier micrometer is similar to the standard model except that there is a vernier scale on the sleeve reading in conjunction with the thimble. On the sleeve parallel to the datum line are graduated five divisions which occupy the same space as nine divisions on the thimble, each division on the vernier representing two-thousandths of a millimetre (0.002 mm). To take a reading from the metric vernier micrometer, it is necessary to note which vernier line coincides with a graduated line on the thimble; this gives the number of two-thousandths of a millimetre to be added to the hundredths reading. Where there is no coincidence of the lines, then the intermediate thousandths can be estimated; that is if the reading lies between 4 and 6, then the additional thousandth reading would be 0.005 mm.

Referring to Figure 17.5:

Major divisions	=	10 × 1.00 mm	=	10.00 mm
Minor divisions	=	1 × 0.50 mm	=	0.50 mm
Thimble divisions	=	16 × 0.01 mm	=	0.16 mm
Vernier divisions	=	3 × 0.002 mm	=	0.006 mm
		Reading is		10.666 mm

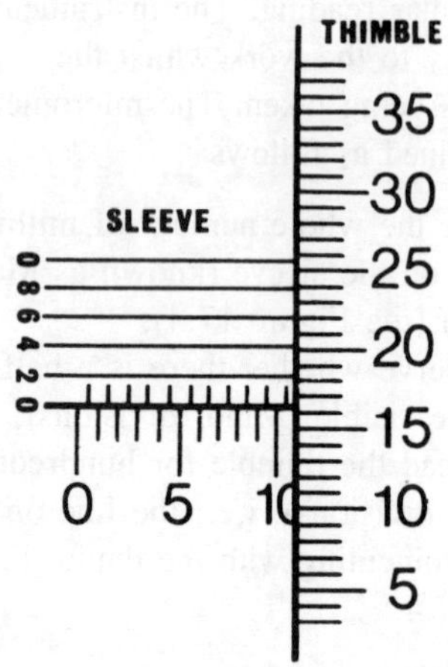

Figure 17.5. Showing application of the vernier scale.

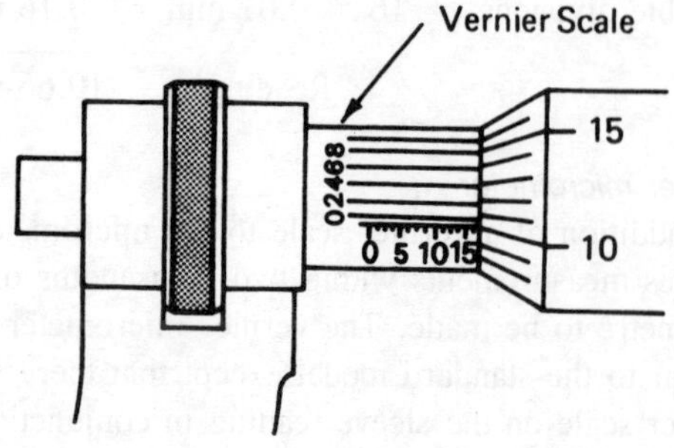

Figure 17.6. Vernier micrometer reading.

Calipers

For less-accurate measurements, calipers are used. Calipers may be 'inside' or 'outside'. The inside calipers are so called because they are used for testing internal work (e.g. the diameter of a hole or bore). The outside calipers are so called because they are used for testing external diameters (e.g. the diameter of a job being turned on a lathe). The calipers are generally set from an engineer's rule. Calipers may be stiff-jointed at the hinge of the legs (opening is maintained by the friction at the joint); or else the joint may be free and spring-controlled (opening is adjusted and maintained by a nut working on a screw). Screw-controlled spring calipers are most easily adjusted. When the calipers are adjusted and indicate the dimension between their legs, the dimension should be read off either a rule or a micrometer.

Vernier caliper

This instrument consists of a main scale with a fixed jaw attached and a sliding vernier scale attached to the adjustable jaw. Provision is made for fine adjustment and the sliding scale can be locked in any position along the main scale.

The rule

The engineer's rule is used for linear or straight line measurement. It is a straight-line standard for comparing other unknown dimensions. To ensure that accurate measurements are made, there are two golden rules to be observed:

1. Ensure that the end of the rule is in line with the face from which the measurement is being taken. This is more easily achieved if both rule and the edge of the component are held against a common datum.
2. Owing to the thickness of the rule, the eye which is observing the reading must be in line with the relevant part of the workpiece. If the rule is viewed incorrectly, a false reading may result. This is called parallax error. When measuring the centre distance between holes of equal diameter, the measurement should be made from the edge of the holes and not from their centres.

Angular testing

When two surfaces are at 90° to each other, their angle is tried by the try-square. It is the most common tool for testing the squareness of a job. When using the square, care should be taken to see that the blade is held perpendicular to the surface being tested, or errors may occur.

When two surfaces are at any angle other than 90° the angle between them must be tested with some form of protractor. Instruments for this purpose may have a scale of degrees, enabling the angle to be read off, or they may consist of a gauge which must be set to the angle before use. The bevel is an example of this second type of gauge, and must be set to the correct angle before use. There are a number of protractors, the most accurate of which is the vernier protractor. This has a 360° scale and the vernier scale enables readings to be taken to 5 minutes or 1/12 degree.

Dial test indicators

The dial test indicator or dial gauge is used where tests for true parallelism are required to be accurate. Rough accuracy is obtained by using the scribing block. The dial gauge is essentially a small clock-like instrument which has a plunger projecting at the bottom. Very slight upward pressure on the plunger moves it upwards and the movement is indicated by the dial finger which is generally arranged to read on 0.025 millimetre of movement. For very accurate work, gauges reading up to 0.0025 mm can be obtained. The dial test indicator is usually mounted on a test stand. The instrument is also used to measure roundness.

Gauges

While instruments are used to measure a dimension, the gauge is used to check the accuracy of a piece of work, without any particular reference to its size. There is an extremely wide range of gauge types available: hole gauges, limit plug gauges and plate gauges. Hole gauges are used to check hole diameters.

Speed measurement

The speed at which machinery rotates is important in some applications where a constant speed is required, or where a speed must be kept within close limits. The revolution counter is the most common workshop instrument for speed measurement though a timing device is necessary, e.g. a stop-watch. Another type of instrument for measuring speed is the stroboscope. This consists of a specially designed neon lamp which produces a flash of light at definite intervals. If the period between the successive flashes is exactly the same as the time of one revolution of the revolving object, or any exact multiple of it, the object will appear to be (*a*) stationary, (*b*) revolving slowly, or (*c*) moving backwards. The neon operates from the secondary side of a special transformer fed through an electronic timing circuit.

Another method used for measuring the speed of a machine is the tachogenerator. This consists of a small generator driven by the machine shaft. The output of the generator is designed at, say, 1 V per 100 rpm. The associated moving-coil instrument has its 210° scale calibrated in rpm. Some speed counters of this type are portable.

Temperature measurement

The most common measurement of temperature is made by using a thermometer, calibrated in degrees C. In many electrical machines it is often not possible to use a thermometer to measure the temperature, particularly of the rotating parts. Measurement of temperature by resistance is a more common method. This compares the resistance of, say, a winding when cold with its resistance when hot. The method gives an indication of the average temperature of the conductors, the temperature of the hottest spot being an estimated 10 °C higher. The formula used is

$$\frac{R_1}{R_2} = \frac{1 + at_1}{1 + at_2}$$

where

R_1 = is the resistance at the lower temperature (t_1)

R_2 = is the resistance at the higher temperature (t_2)

a = the temperature coefficient of resistance of the material.

Thermocouples are also used and are available in very small diameters so that they can be inserted in small spaces between windings where a thermometer would not be suitable. The thermocouple operates on the principle of an emf being generated from a junction which consists of two dissimilar metals being heated. The emf generated is proportional to the differences of temperature between the point to be measured and the ambient temperature.

Phase-sequence testing

In making any connections to three-phase circuits, it is important to determine the order of phase rotation. The accepted phase rotation sequence is RED, YELLOW, BLUE. The portable phase-sequence indicators used consist of a small polyphase motor having a stator with three coils and a metal-disc rotor with an arrow marked on it. Three flexible leads are provided with clips coloured red, yellow and blue respectively. When these clips are connected to the phases of a three-phase system, the disc will rotate. If the rotation is with the marked arrow then the phase sequence is correct. If the rotation is in the opposite direction, the sequence is reversed.

Insulation-resistance

Insulation-resistance is the value of the resistance of insulating materials. Defined, 'insulation-resistance' is the resistance under prescribed conditions between two conducting materials or systems of conductors normally separated by an insulating material. In practical terms, insulation-resistance tests are conducted between two conductors or between a conductor and earth. The generally accepted figure is 1 megohm. Portable appliances and small apparatus should have an insulation-resistance of 0.5 megohm. Motors and other electrical apparatus should have a value corresponding to the following:

$$\text{Insulation-resistance} = \frac{\text{rated voltage}}{1{,}000 + \text{rated kW}} = \text{megohms.}$$

For fractional kilowatt motors the value should be not less than one megohm. When making insulation-resistance tests on machines, it should be remembered that the actual value obtained can be affected by dampness and the amount of humidity in the atmosphere at the time of testing. The testing voltage is twice the working voltage of the machine.

Conductor continuity

The resistance of pure conductors (e.g. copper, aluminium, silver) is low compared with the resistance of resistive conductors (e.g. heating elements) which can be of the order of tens and hundreds of ohms. Testing the resistance of a conductor is used to indicate its electrical continuity. This applies particularly to the electrical continuity of earth-continuity conductors. Certain very-low-resistance testers (e.g. 'Ducter' test sets) are available which will measure the resistance of switch contacts, armature windings, transformer windings, soldered joints, busbars, etc. Values can be obtained as low as 1 microhm.

Electrical quantities

Electrical quantities such as voltage and current, and electrical energy in watts, are measured by various kinds of instruments, including moving-coil, moving-iron, hot-wire, electrostatic, dynamometer and induction apparatus. Commercial instruments are available which offer the measurement of a range of electrical quantities based on one instrument calibrated in a number of scales. For voltage ranges, a number of series multipliers are switched into the instrument circuit. For current ranges, various values of shunt resistances are connected across the meter movement. Voltage- and current-transformers are also used to extend the ranges of basic instruments. A useful portable instrument for measuring current is the tong-ammeter, which operates on the principle of a transformer, the jaws or tong of the instrument surrounding a single-core conductor which acts as the primary winding.

Metalwork practice

Methods of joining metals

Nuts, bolts and screws. The screw-thread is perhaps the most important and commonest method of joining metals found in engineering work. This

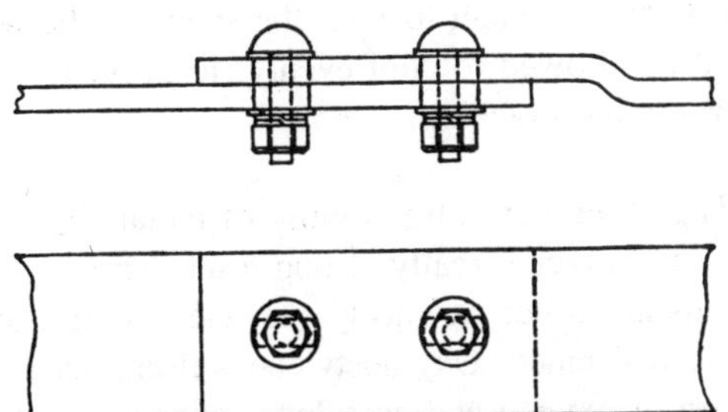

Figure 17.7. Bolted joints with spring lockwashers.

is because the method is cheap and convenient, and at the same time it allows the joined metals to be separated easily. When using a nut and a bolt, it is usual to provide a hole the diameter of which is slightly larger than the diameter of the bolt. If a stud is being used, a tapped hole is made in the main component, and a clearing hole drilled in the part that is to be fixed. The stud is then screwed into the tapped hole. The stud selected for this type of fixing job should be such that the plain part of its length projects immediately above the surface of the job into which it is screwed. A length of threaded portion should not show between the plain portion and this surface. The stud should be long enough to pass through the clearing hole of the part to be joined, and the final threaded portion should project sufficiently to take a nut, or a nut and a locking device if necessary.

Wherever vibration is encountered, locking devices must be used to ensure that nuts do not become loosened. In its most common form, the lock-nut is a nut which is thinner than the associated standard nut. It is usually screwed down on top of the standard nut. Several types of patented self-locking nuts do away with lock-nuts.

If screws are used for holding parts together, one of the parts must be provided with a tapped hole. The other part has a clearing hole. The screw is passed through the clearing hole and screwed into the tapped hole. Screws have a variety of head shapes, each chosen according to the type of work being carried out. They include countersunk, cheese-head, hexagonal, round-head, socket-head and square-head.

Bolting is a common method of joining and connecting conductors in electrical work, though it is confined to conductors of large cross-sectional area. Busbars, in particular, are often joined by bolting. The method has the advantage in that the resulting joint is compact and reliable. But the disadvantage is that the bars have to be drilled to take the bolts. Thus, the effective current-carrying area is reduced. Contact pressure is also less uniformly distributed in a bolted joint than in one held together by clamps.

Riveting. Riveting is used when a permanent method of holding parts together is required. There are a number of rivet types; and the materials from which they are made are also wide in range. Aluminium, duralumin, copper, brass and mild steel are used for light work. For heavy work, mild steel rivets are used. Rivet holes are generally slightly larger than the rivet size. This is to allow for the expansion of the rivet when the riveting process is taking place. When preparing the plates for the joint, they should, if possible, be clamped together with the top plate marked for the holes. The holes are then drilled in all the plates at once, thus ensuring accurate alignment. If well made, a riveted joint is a most efficient method of joining. The riveting process, in the workshop usually performed cold, consists of the closing of the rivet while supporting the rivet head as the plain end is riveted over, using an appropriate cupped punch or the ball-end of a hammer. The rivet end must be spread evenly in all directions, and not bent over one way. Countersunk rivets require finishing with the flat end of a hammer.

For very light work, with aluminium, brass or copper sheet, bifurcated and hollow rivets are used. These do not, however, give such a satisfactory joint as the solid rivet.

Soldering. Soldering is a quick and useful method of making joints in light articles made from steel, brass, copper and aluminium. It is perhaps the most common method of making the conductor joints in electrical work. The two metals are joined by a fusible alloy called solder. A soldered joint is in itself not very strong. If joints are required to be mechanically strong, they should be married (as in stranded conductors), riveted, brazed or welded. Soldering is used in electrical work because of the good conductivity offered. The flux used ensures that the surfaces to be soldered are not affected by

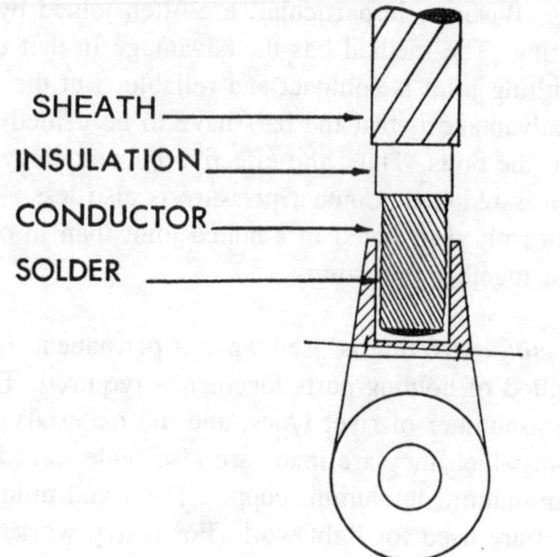

Figure 17.8. Section through a sweated lug termination. Note that after soldering the final insulation is applied.

the fumes and the atmosphere during the process, and it prevents oxidation. Corrosive fluxes must not be used in electrical work. If, however, a corrosive flux is the only kind available, it should be of the type which does not remain corrosive after the soldering has been completed. Silver soldering is a process which gives a stronger joint than that from soft soldering. A good soldered joint is recognised by a small amount of solder and perfect adhesion of the joined surfaces. Unsightly blobs of solder at the joint should make the joint suspect. The soldering iron used should have a bit which has an adequate heat capacity. Iron tinning is made easier by having some blobs of solder in a tin lid with a little spirits, and touching both the spirits and the solder at the same time.

Brazing. Brazing is similar to silver soldering and is used where a stronger joint is needed. The fusible alloy is called spelter, which is obtained in sticks or in a granular state, when it is mixed with borax before being applied to the joint. The heat required for the brazing process is obtained from a flame-torch. In the process, sodium fluoride or sodium silicate is mixed with water and used as a 'stopping off' compound to prevent the spelter from sticking to areas of the work which must be kept free from it. The surfaces to be brazed must be kept clean: and the temperature of the work must be high enough to melt the spelter. The work should be allowed to cool evenly, to prevent distortion and cracking.

Welding. Welding is the joining of metals by fusion and gives a really strong joint. Three methods are used: oxy-acetylene, electric arc, and electric resistance. Oxy-acetylene welding uses a mixture of oxygen and acetylene, mixed in suitable proportions. The mixture of gases gives a flame which reaches a temperature of about 6,000 °C at its hottest part. In the high-pressure system, the acetylene should be adjusted to the working pressure first, and then the oxygen. In the low-pressure system, the acetylene is generated in a low-pressure generator. The gases are carried to the blow pipe by hoses. The heat output of the flame is varied by use of nozzles of different sizes. It is important to use a nozzle of the correct size for the particular job, depending on the thickness of the metal to be welded. A small flame from a large nozzle must never be used. Too much oxygen will cause brittleness and too much acetylene will cause carbonising. Stainless steel is welded by a carburising flame. Brass and bronze are welded by using an oxidising flame and mild steel, copper and aluminium by a neutral flame.

In the electrical resistance method of welding, a heavy current of low voltage is passed through the metal at the point of contact. The temperature at the joint rises rapidly because of the resistance.

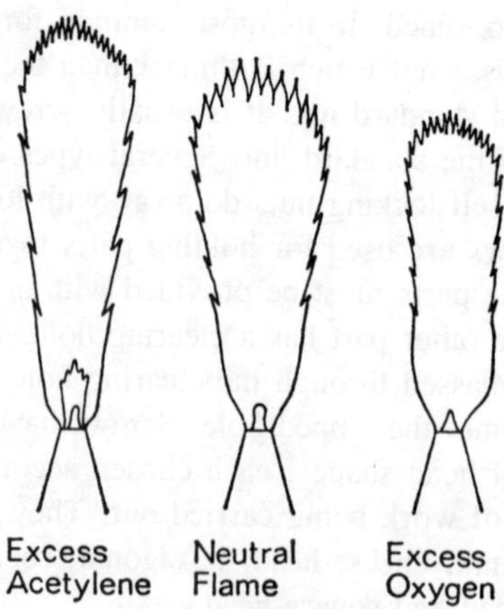

Figure 17.9. Outlines of typical flames from an oxy-acetylene blowtorch.

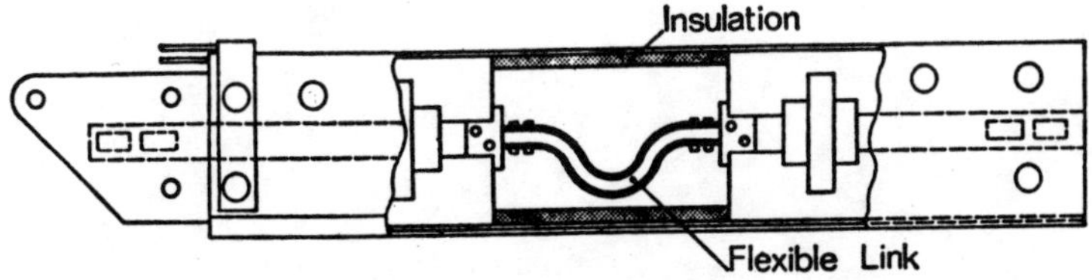

Figure 17.10. Typical flexible joint in a section of busbar trunking. The joint allows for the expansion and contraction of the busbar material as the ambient temperature changes.

When the welding temperature is reached, pressure is applied. Welding using this method is classed as spot, seam, and stitch welding. Electric arc welding involves the production of a prolonged spark between two terminals of an electric circuit: the workpiece and an electrode. The temperature of the spark is in the region of 6,500 °C and intense localised heat is produced. The electrode rod is coated with a suitable flux for cleaning and protection. The electrode itself supplies the filler metal. The ultra-violet and continuous light from the arc can cause damage to the eyes and so face-shields or goggles must be worn at all times.

Index